JUST NEEDS A RECHARGE
The Hack Mechanic™ Guide to
Vintage Air Conditioning

 ROB SIEGEL

HACK MECHANIC PRESS

Just Needs a Recharge: The Hack Mechanic™ Guide to Vintage Air Conditioning

By Rob Siegel

ISBN: 978-0-9989507-1-6

Library of Congress Control Number: 2018904076

The author and publisher recognize that some words, model names, and designations mentioned in this book are the property of the trademark holders. They are used only for identification purposes.

This is not a repair manual. The author is not a professional mechanic. Neither the author nor the publisher are responsible if you injure yourself while working on or driving your car. If you have any doubt as to your ability to do some of the things described in the book, or as to whether your car is safe to drive after doing them, don't do them, and seek the services of a professional mechanic instead.

Front cover photograph by Rob Siegel
Back cover photograph by Aaron Siegel
Interior photographs by Rob Siegel except where noted
Illustrations by Chris Roberts
Design by King+Sons

Printed in the United States

The Hack Mechanic™ is a registered trademark of Rob Siegel

Hack Mechanic Press
19 Mague Place
West Newton, MA 02465

www.hackmechanicpress.com

Acknowledgements

My last book, *Ran When Parked*, was easy. The whole story had just happened; I simply needed to tell it. And the photographs I'd taken on my phone during the trip were easily integrated into the manuscript. In contrast, this book was a bit of a slog. I thought "We'll structure it as a repair manual in narrative form, just incrementally different than *Ran When Parked*. How hard could it be?" Huge thanks to book designer Eric King for never complaining when I threw it over the wall for him to figure out. I'd also like to thank pros Terry Sayther and Anthony Pascarella who edited the book for technical accuracy, Bruce Machon who proofread it, Chris Roberts who did the technical illustrations, and Clyde Gates, Earl Meyers, Chris Roberts, Gary York, Adam Merchant, Steve Jones, and Layne Wyle who supplied photographs. Of course, thanks to my ever-patient and supportive wife Maire Anne Diamond, to the BMW Car Club of America, *Roundel* Magazine, and *Roundel Online* (later *BimmerLife*) for whom I wrote a number of air-conditioning-related pieces, and to the Hack Mechanic faithful who appeared to indicate that there was interest in a book not only on air conditioning, but on *vintage air conditioning*. (Best comment: "When you're done, does it blow old cold?")

Table of Contents

Introduction

"How's that R75/2 workin' for you *now*?"

Let me say right off that I'm not a professional mechanic. I don't fix other people's cars for money. And I'm not a certified air conditioning technician.

Wait a minute. Yes I am. But I only took the online test so I could get my EPA 609 certificate and legally buy Freon, so that doesn't really count.

The point is that I'm a hobbyist, not a pro. Most any professional mechanic who makes his living working on automotive air conditioning has a deeper level of understanding of how it works than I do.

But as those of you who've been reading my *Hack Mechanic* columns for over 30 years know, I do a lot of air conditioning work. In addition to the minor nuts-and-bolts repair-and-recharge stuff, I've resurrected and upgraded long-dead air conditioning systems on numerous vintage BMWs, and have performed from-scratch a/c installations on several cars that never had it. That doesn't make me a pro, but it gives me a lot of insight into the process from the viewpoint of a thrifty do-it-yourselfer who wants cold air in an old car without writing a check for thousands of dollars.

So how did this all start? Pretty simple. Maire Anne and I lived in Austin 1982 through 1984. It was hot; it would reach 90° in May, flirt with three-digit temperatures all summer, and stay at 90° through September. That was where I bought my first BMW 2002. It did not have air conditioning. But when I found another '02 that did have a/c, I jumped at it, which made Maire Anne very happy.

Problem was, it was dead. The a/c, not the car. Actually, the car was dead too, but that's another story. I got it running (the car, not the a/c), and then set myself on the task of reviving the a/c, the prospect of which made Maire Anne very happy. A fellow I knew at work, Tom, was a first-rate backyard mechanic with a good deal of a/c experience. He was the one who hooked up gauges and diagnosed that the 2002 had a bad expansion valve. I ripped out the evaporator assembly, cracked open the tub that the evaporator core sat in, replaced the expansion valve, and buttoned it all back up. Afterward, Tom evacuated and charged the system up for me, literally under a shade tree in his Texas hill country backyard.

I was certainly accustomed to taking cars apart, fixing them, and putting things back together, but it was a revelation that this paradigm extended to air conditioning. The diagnosis part, however, seemed like a black art.

Figure 1: My second newly-acquired BMW 2002 (front). This one had air conditioning, the prospect of which made Maire Anne very happy.

Over the years, I whittled at the edges of a/c work, relying on shops to diagnose the root cause of a problem (e.g., "You have a bad compressor"). I'd replace whatever component they said was bad, then take the car back in for recharge. It was useful, but I knew I could do better.

Then, in the late 1990s, I embarked on a big project: I retrofitted air conditioning into the 1973 BMW 3.0CSi I've owned since 1986. I wrote about this in my first book, *Memoirs of a Hack Mechanic*, passionately explaining how a/c extends the enjoyment of a vintage car, even in relatively temperate New England. While part of the charm of an older car is its simplicity, I never have been an adherent to the tenet that that simplicity necessarily precludes air conditioning. When nearly everyone's daily driver these days has a/c, not having air in an enthusiast car can reduce the amount of time it is driven. After all, if it's ninety degrees out and you're going to dinner with your wife and she's dressed to the nines and you need to buy some milk on the way home, are you really going to take the classic car when it doesn't have a/c but her Honda does? Here in New England, where we keep our beloved classics off the road during the salty months, the driving season becomes awfully short if you also shy away from using the car during the heat of summer. For everything from Maire Anne and I going out for the evening, to pleasure drives, to 1500-mile road trips, my use of and enjoyment of the 3.0CSi has increased dramatically since I installed air. It was one of the smartest automotive projects I've ever done.

In the Retrofit chapter, I summarize the 3.0CSi from-scratch installation. I worked with a vendor who helped me select the parts, but in terms of installation, I was on my own. Once the major components were installed, I took the car to a shop to get the hoses made, then brought it somewhere else to get it evacuated and recharged. It took a couple of tries for me to get everything right. By the end of it, when I had to pay for the *third* evacuation and recharge, it was clear that I needed to invest the time and money to acquire the skills and tools needed to perform pressure-testing, evacuation, recharge, and leak detection myself. I took the plunge, bought what I needed, and never looked back. Ever since, I have gone to what some consider ridiculous lengths to have not just functional a/c but *cold* a/c in my vintage BMWs.

Don't *ever* believe that a car "just needs a recharge"

That having been said, my advice to most folks continues to be this: Unless you do your own work, don't do what I did. If you need a car with working air conditioning, *buy a car with working air conditioning.* Don't buy one with broken air conditioning, and certainly don't buy one without air conditioning and think "how expensive could it really be to install it?" *Any* air conditioning work is expensive. If the a/c doesn't blow cold, the best case is that the system is low on refrigerant. That means it's leaked out, so the source of the leak needs to be found and fixed. If someone selling a car tells you "it just needs a recharge," that's simply *never* true. Cars don't consume refrigerant in the same way that they use oil and brake pads. Air conditioners are sealed systems. You shouldn't need to top them off. It would be more correct to say "it worked last fall. Now it doesn't. This happens every spring. It must have a slow leak

somewhere." At least that would be honest. "Just needs a recharge" is the "ran when parked" of air conditioning.

You have to realize that those "$79 A/C Service" shingles hung out at repair shops are shilling optimism bordering on fraud. If you're incredibly fortunate, there's a single connection that simply needs to be tightened, or a single o-ring that needs to be replaced, and they find it quickly and charge you $200, but that's the exception. It's more likely that a component has failed. Tracking down the problem, replacing bad components, flushing, pressure-testing, evacuating, and recharging an a/c system can easily top a thousand dollars. Rejuvenation of a long-dead system is easily twice that. Multiply by another factor of two for a from-scratch installation into a car that never had it.

That is, *if* you have to pay someone to do it.

But buy it anyway if it's a really good deal :^)

But on the other hand, if you already do other automotive work, a/c work is all learn-able and do-able. Particularly with this book. And I'm here to tell you, when so much automotive repair work consists of stupid things like replacing ripped CV joint boots or figuring out where the "small evap leak" is when the damned check engine light comes on and you pull code P0442, there are few things more satisfying than starting off with a hot car and ending up with a cold one.

You can see, whether your car is a daily driver or a pampered classic, there's the potential to save a boatload of money working on your a/c yourself. A lot of DIY mechanics shy away from air conditioning work, and I've never understood why. In classic car circles, there's even some degree of chest-beating that "I don't need a/c in this car – in fact I took it out to save weight – I just roll down the windows." Some folks refer to using R75/2 refrigerant – 75mph, 2 windows down. I remember driving home from a vintage BMW event in my a/c-retrofitted '73 3.0CSi. I was crossing northern Pennsylvania. It was 90 degrees and humid. I had the windows up, rollin' cool, living the dream, when I passed two friends in their non-a/c-equipped vintage BMW. Rivers of sweat were literally streaming off their faces and being flung out of the car. I thought "How's that R75/2 workin' for you *now*?"

What the hell is "vintage air conditioning" anyway?

When I refer to "Vintage Air Conditioning" as I do in the title and repeatedly throughout this book, what I mean is any or all of the following:

- A system that is separate from the car's heating system—that is, where there's a separate a/c evaporator assembly and a separate heater box, and the outputs of the two aren't combined via a blend door. Although most of what I say in the book applies to *any* air-conditioned car, I've never trouble-shot little motors that move little flaps.

- A system where either the a/c was a factory option or where it's readily available through the aftermarket and installable without having to rip the dashboard out of the car and reprogram the ECU.

- A system that may have originally been charged with R12, or isn't too far removed from the changeover from R12 to R134a in the early 1990s.

- A system that may have flare fittings in it.

- A system where the components are interconnected by hoses that have standard thread-on fittings crimped onto the ends, not the more modern model-specific "block fittings" seen on newer cars.

- A system that is old enough that, when you need to do work on it, you might consider taking advantage of more modern components to improve its performance.

Whether you're repairing an a/c system that recently died or resurrecting a long-dead system, there is a basic sequence of steps. Those steps vary with the scope of the job. If you're simply replacing a single obviously failed component in a system that recently worked, you may need only to fix it, pressure-test it, evacuate it, and recharge it, but if you're dealing with a 45-year-old car whose a/c hasn't worked since Maude was a hit TV show and you want it to blow cold, you should understand that the odds are

you'll need to replace the compressor, condenser, fan, expansion valve, drier, and every hose, and flush out the evaporator, as it's likely the only part you won't be replacing.

Why this book is different

There are many books on air conditioning (often bundled "heat and air conditioning"). This is the only one I'm aware of specifically targeted at resurrecting air conditioning in vintage cars. It's long on hands-on practical information on fittings and refrigerants, and short on equations and graphs (there are literally none).

In this book, I try to capture what I've learned and what I do. Most of that work has been on vintage BMWs, so where I've developed detailed knowledge about things like which bracket you need to mount a Sanden 508 compressor in a 2002 or a car with an M30 motor like a Bavaria, 3.0CSi, or E28 5 Series, or 635CSi, or what the largest parallel flow condenser is that'll fit into the nose of those cars, I go into it in all necessary detail. But the general repair, rejuvenation, retrofit, and diagnosis issues apply to absolutely any a/c-equipped car.

I've structured the book such that there are the usual individual chapters on all of the major a/c components, but there are also detailed chapters on the steps I go through to resurrect a long-dormant system, as well as retrofitting from scratch. As such, in places, there's a fair amount of overlap between chapters, but I think it works well in terms of finding what you need.

Okay? Let's go play in the cold.

Chapter 1

How It All Works
(basic a/c theory)

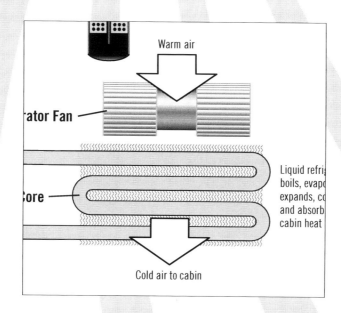

Overview

Let's talk about how air conditioning works.

Read it!

Trust me, you'll be the better for it. (Or, to quote Pink Floyd, "How can you have any pudding if you don't eat your meat?") While you can get surprisingly far with automotive a/c by simply buying those cans of R134a that come with an attached hose and hooking them up to the low side and shooting the refrigerant in, you'll get a lot further by developing a basic understanding of the theory (for example, at a minimum, understanding what "the low side" means).

The image most people have of an air conditioner is a rectangular box sticking out the window of a house. You plug it into household electricity, turn it on, and cold air blows out the front. To many, it's magic, little different than a picture appearing on the screen of a television set. But really, in both theory and in practice, air conditioning is not terribly complicated. It's certainly way less complicated than television. Although at times, it's equally entertaining. And way more frustrating. And certainly more expensive.

The very basics

You probably know the very fundamentals. All matter can exist as a solid, liquid, or gas. For example, H2O can exist in all three states (as ice, water, or steam) at specific temperatures. The refrigerant in an air conditioning system exists as a liquid or a gas. It never gets cold enough to exist as a solid.

But you may not know the role that heat plays in changing matter between those states:

- A liquid absorbs heat when it changes state from a liquid to a gas.

- A gas rejects (gives off) heat when it changes state from a gas to a liquid.

- Heat always travels from a warm object to a cooler object.

And, with that, we can explain how a/c works.

How we "make cold"—A gas cools when it expands

All conventional refrigeration and air conditioning systems work on the principle that a gas cools when it expands. If that sounds like an exotic piece of physics that you should've learned in college but were instead sucking beers at The Blue Wall, it's not. Well, it is, but you don't need to be intimidated by it because you've experienced it yourself when you've sprayed paint or deodorant and found that the can became cold in your hand. Many people have also experienced this cooling effect when cooking with a propane-powered barbeque grill, feeling the propane tank, and finding that it's cold.

So there's no magic. When a liquid turns to a gas and expands, it cools. Air conditioning is built around that lovely and useful bit of physics. An a/c system is designed to let a liquid turn into a gas and expand, which "generates cold." This cold is then blown at you. That's really all it is. At the conceptual level, it's pretty simple.

Now, clearly, it's impractical to have an a/c system that cools by endlessly releasing gas so it can expand and cool in the same way as spraying from a deodorant can. Thus, for efficiency's sake, you need a closed system that allows liquid to turn into a gas and expand in one section and make that section cold while also turning the gas back into a liquid in another section. In order for this to happen, the gas must be compressed. That's why you're always hearing about the "compressor." It's there to compress the gas so it can condense back into a liquid so it can repeat the cycle and turn back into a gas and expand and "generate cold," which I keep putting in quotes because it's technically not true (more on this below). All of the references you've probably seen to the high and low pressure sides of an a/c system have to do with this compressing and expanding of the gas. Where the gas is being compressed, it's under high pressure; where it's expanding, it's under low pressure. As you read about a/c, you'll see the terms "high pressure" or "high side" (color-coded as red) and "low pressure" or "low side" (color-coded as blue). Now you can identify them as the areas where the gas is compressed and where it is expanding and, ahem, "generating cold."

(As an aside, note that the propane-powered refrigerators that are in RVs and used for off-the-grid living don't function by endlessly releasing propane so it can expand and cool. These are called ammonia-absorption refrigerators. They still work on the principle of a liquid—ammonia and water—evaporating and cooling as it expands. They use the propane to heat the ammonia and water mixture.)

I must now add to this description a wonderful bit of thermodynamics, the concept that there is no free lunch—that if you are making part of a system cold, you must also be making another part of that system warm. Therefore, in the process of compressing the gas so it can condense back into a liquid, you are creating heat elsewhere that needs to be removed. The other major parts of the system—the evaporator, condenser, and expansion valve—are there to play their roles in this compression and expansion and transfer of heat. In a square home air conditioning window unit, the evaporator (the part that gets cold) is in the front of the unit, inside the window, and the condenser (the part that gets hot) is in the back of the unit, outside the window. In a car, it's analogous—the evaporator is inside the car, under the dashboard in the passenger compartment, where it can cool the interior, and the condenser is outside the car, in front of the radiator, where it can dump heat.

The shortest a/c diagnosis primer to be found anywhere

Now that you have that level of understanding, I can say this: If an air conditioning system isn't functioning at all, and you've checked simple stuff like the fuses, the belt, the compressor clutch, and the pressure switches, it's likely either because the gas isn't being compressed, or it isn't expanding, or most likely of all, because the gas has leaked out and there's not enough gas there to compress and expand in the first place. There really aren't too many other things it can be. That's 90% of a/c diagnosis right there. You're welcome.

A quick tour of the components

Having deconstructed the basic theory behind a/c, let's reconstruct it component-by-component in the physical context of the car. We'll do it in an ungodly level of detail in the book, but here, this will be like the real estate agent giving you the power walk-through of the house.

The beating heart of the a/c is **the compressor**. In a home a/c unit, the compressor is powered by an electric motor, but in a car, the compressor is bolted to the engine block and driven by the crankshaft pulley via a belt that's engaged via a magnetic clutch. Original compressors in vintage cars are upright piston-style units that look similar to lawnmower engines. In about the late 1970s, these gave way to what are commonly called "rotary compressors," even though most of them actually have pistons inside. For clarity's sake, I use the term "rotary-style" to refer to any small, modern, compact compressor with a cylindrical form factor.

Figure 2: A modern, compact, rotary-style compressor retrofitted into a vintage car.

The **evaporator core**—the part that gets cold—lives under the dash, along with the **expansion valve** that the gas expands through, and the **blower fan** that blows the cold air at you. In a vintage car, these three components usually live together in an **evaporator assembly**. Some cars have no expansion valve and use an **orifice tube** instead.

The **condenser**, the component that dumps the heat—essentially a radiator for the a/c system—lives

Figure 3: **Basic Layout of A/C System with an Expansion Valve and Drier**

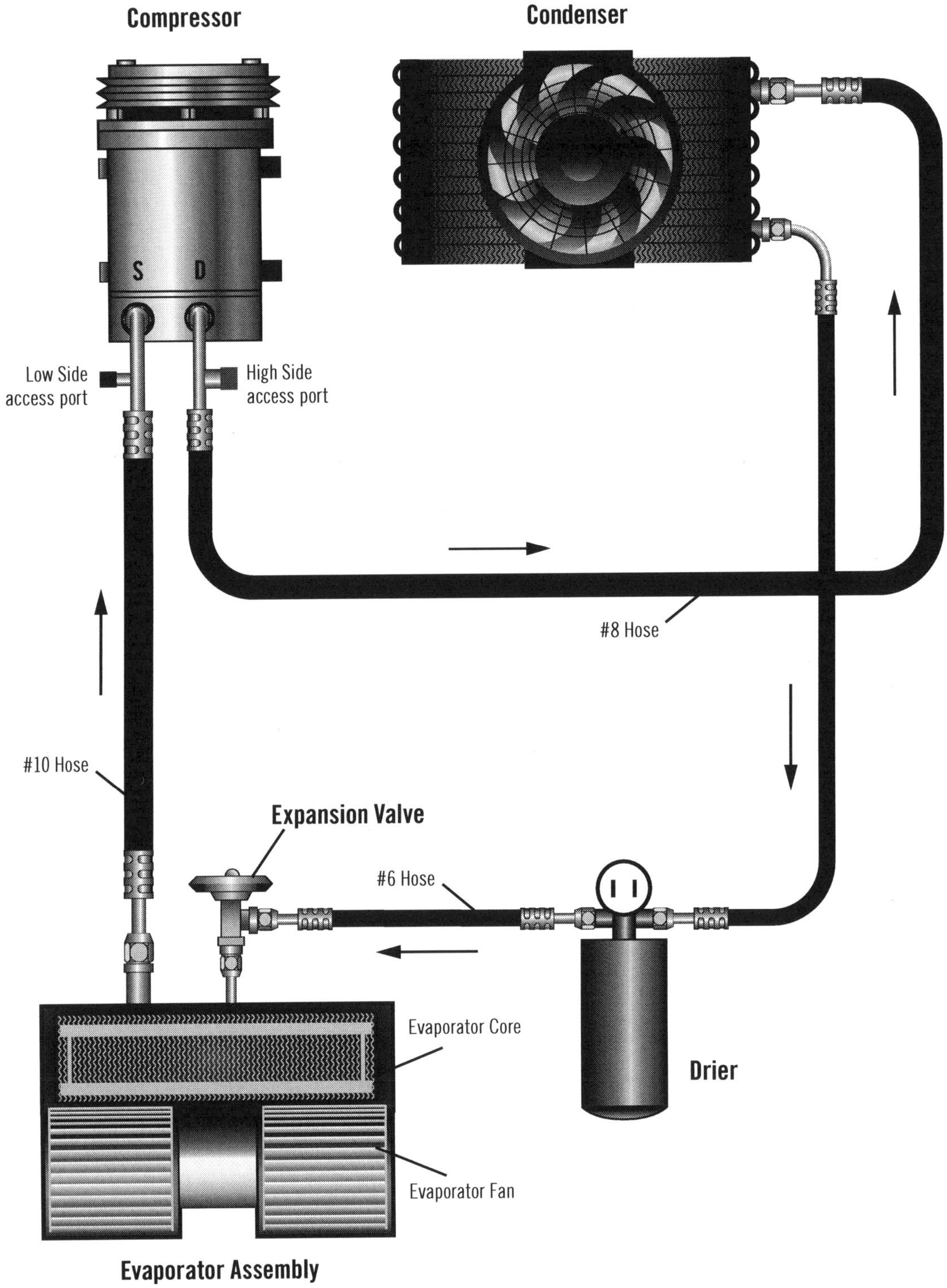

Compressor

Condenser

S D

Low Side
access port

High Side
access port

#8 Hose

#10 Hose

Expansion Valve

#6 Hose

Evaporator Core

Drier

Evaporator Fan

Evaporator Assembly

in the nose of the car, in front of the radiator, with an **auxiliary electric fan** in front of it to help cool it off. This is usually the same auxiliary fan that helps cool the radiator.

Figure 4: Evaporator assembly with evaporator core, expansion valve, and blower motor.

Figure 5: A newly-installed condenser and electric fan in the nose of a vintage car.

Lastly, there is a **receiver-drier**, a beer can-sized bottle of desiccant that removes moisture from the system. The drier is in the engine compartment, located between the condenser and the evaporator. If a car has an orifice tube instead of an expansion valve, it has an **accumulator** between the evaporator and compressor instead of a receiver-drier.

Figure 6: An old-style receiver-drier. Note that the third hose doesn't actually go into the bottom of the drier; it passes beneath it.

Although it isn't a single physical component, there is also a **mechanism to cycle the compressor** (to turn it off and on). For the moment, you can think of the compressor cycling mechanism like a thermostat in your house, turning on the a/c when it gets too warm, and turning it off when it's cool enough.

For systems with an expansion valve and a drier, the basic topology is shown at left on page 16.

For systems with an orifice tube instead of an expansion valve and an accumulator instead of a drier, the layout is shown on page 18.

As you can see, in an automotive a/c system, the components are distributed throughout the car. Contrast this with a home window air conditioning unit where everything is packed into one neat box. A combination of aesthetic, aerodynamic, space, and power requirements makes this impractical on a car, but if you look at a refrigerated tractor/trailer (a/c mounted on the front) or an RV (a/c mounted on the roof), you'll see exactly these sorts of standalone units. If they break, you can simply unbolt them and install another one. On the one hand, it would be sweet if you could do that in a car, but on the other hand, you'd need 120 VAC (household electricity) to power it.

Figure 7: **Basic Layout of A/C System with an Orifice Tube and Accumulator**

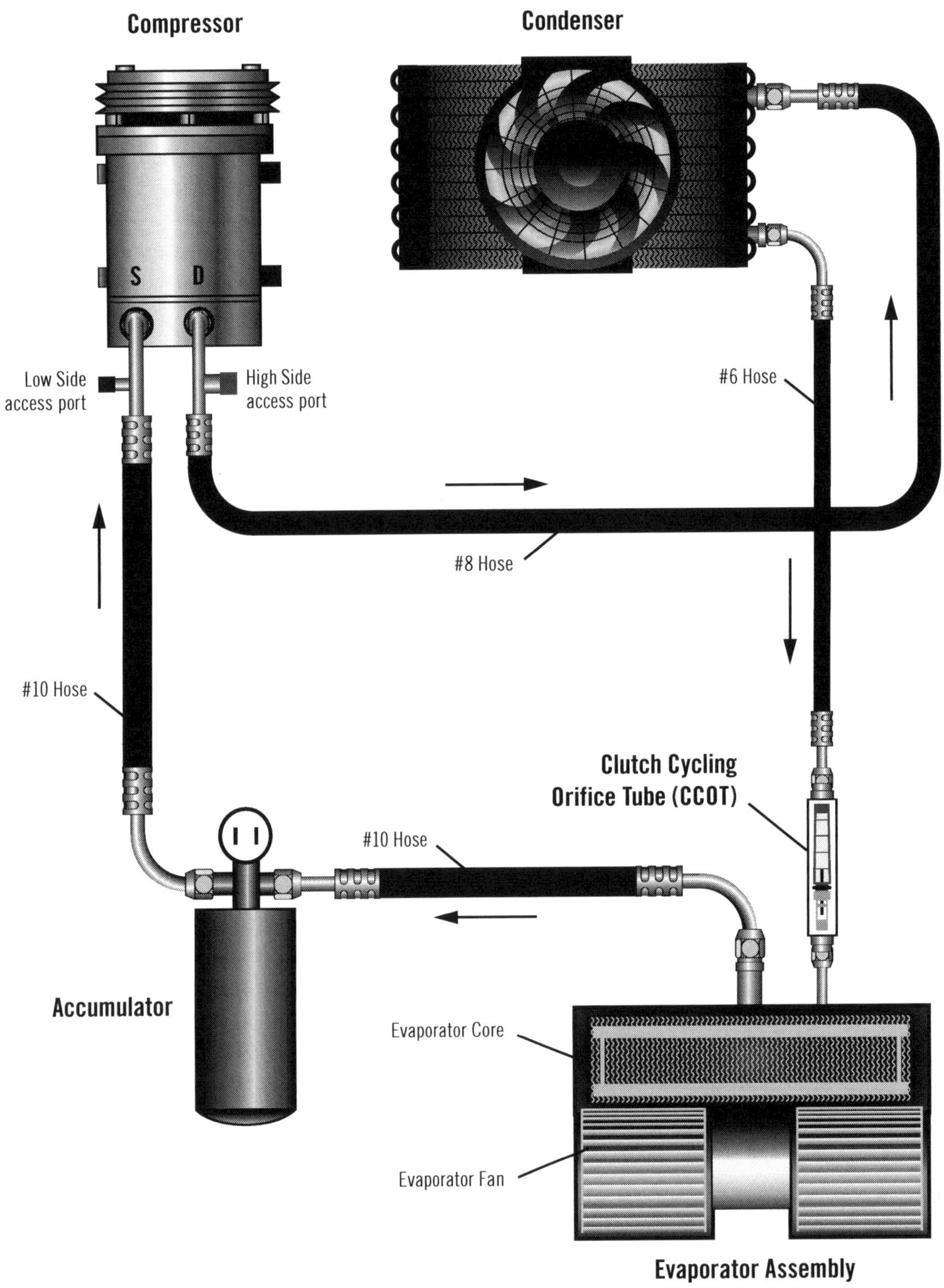

Compressor

Condenser

S D

Low Side
access port

High Side
access port

#6 Hose

#8 Hose

#10 Hose

**Clutch Cycling
Orifice Tube (CCOT)**

#10 Hose

Accumulator

Evaporator Core

Evaporator Fan

Evaporator Assembly

Or you can do this. I mean, I'm "The Hack Mechanic," but this is over the line, even for me.

Figure 8: One enterprising person's MacGyvered a/c solution.

A very short history of automotive a/c

It appears that, other than odd one-offs, the first factory-available automotive air conditioning systems were installed in about 1939 by General Motors and Packard. Both of these early systems were large, trunk-mounted, and always on, with the compressor continuously driven by the crankshaft belt and no clutch to disengage it. To turn them off, the belt had to be removed. As such, they were largely a short-lived expensive trinket for the well-heeled.

Factory-installed automotive a/c went away, then reappeared to stay in 1953, initially still using a trunk-mounted evaporator. But the next year, a/c systems with all under-hood and under-dash components configured as they are now began appearing. The number of American car models with factory air steadily increased through the 50s and 60s. By the late 1960s, a/c was standard equipment on luxury lines like Lincoln and Cadillac. It rapidly went from luxury to perceived necessity. By 1980, 72% of new American cars had a/c. That increased to 92% by 1990.

The amazing thing is that, technologically, little in automotive air conditioning has changed since the 1950s. There was the switch from flare fittings to o-rings, from R12 refrigerant to R134a, from upright compressors to smaller more efficient ones, and from serpentine condensers to parallel flow units. And the changeover to electronic climate control and dual zones made the integrated heater boxes / evaporators

more complicated. But that's about it. It's actually rather remarkable. You can say the same thing about home refrigeration and air conditioning—sure, we have digital controls, frost-free freezers, ice makers, through-the-door water dispensers and such, but the underlying technology of a gas cooling as it expands is identical.

A more correct explanation—a liquid cools when it boils, evaporates, and expands

Having just explained how air conditioning works in this wonderful easy-to-understand way, I now need to admit that it's wrong. Well, maybe not wrong, but there are two things that I've over-simplified to the point where they're technically incorrect.

First, the "gas cools when it expands" part. Think about my examples—the can of spray paint or the propane tank on your gas grill. How do you know when the spray paint or the propane tank is empty? *It no longer sloshes.* So why is the explanation wrong? Gas doesn't slosh. *Liquid does.* That means that what's inside these cans is a substance—deodorant, paint, propane, whatever—that is under pressure so it exists in a liquid form at room temperature. When you discharge it, it boils into gaseous form, expands, and cools.

It's the same with air conditioning refrigerant. When you buy a can of R134a, it's pressurized so it's in liquid form at room temperature. And more to the point, some of it is pressurized and in liquid form when your car's a/c is running. So when I say that "a gas cools when it expands," that's true, but we've left out the complication that when your a/c is working, the refrigerant is a liquid that is evaporating and turning into a gas, *then* expanding, and *then* cooling.

Thus, an air conditioning system doesn't merely compress gas so it can expand and cool. *It compresses gas so it can become a liquid, and so the liquid can boil, turn back into a gas, and in the process, evaporate, expand, and cool.* This is an important distinction, as we'll see in a moment.

My second gross oversimplification is this issue of "generating cold." Technically, nothing actually generates cold. Instead, heat always flows from a warmer body to a cooler one, thus cooling off the warmer body. Refrigeration and air conditioning work because refrigerant in a portion of the system (the evaporator) absorbs heat from the passenger compartment and carries it away. It's a little counterintuitive. The evaporator is where the liquid refrigerant is evaporating, expanding, and cooling, so it is at a lower temperature than the air in the passenger compartment. The refrigerant runs through tubes in the evaporator. These tubes are surrounded by thin metal fins to help facilitate heat transfer. Since the surrounding air is hotter than the refrigerant in the evaporator, the air gives up some of its heat to the refrigerant. This causes the air to cool. The cooler air is then blown at you by the evaporator fan. In the process, the refrigerant in the evaporator is warmed, and that heat is carried away and exchanged with the outside when the refrigerant passes through the condenser. So an a/c system doesn't actually "generate cold." It removes heat and transfers it to another location.

The four tiers of understanding

1) Black boxes

I tend to view air conditioning knowledge as four tiers of understanding. In the first tier, you're like me back in Austin with my first air-conditioned BMW 2002. You don't really understand anything, and instead just treat the system as a series of black box components—a compressor, a condenser, an evaporator assembly with an expansion valve in it, a receiver/drier, and a couple of fans and switches. You can actually get pretty far without having any real system understanding. As I've said, you can take the car in to get the a/c recharged, they can tell you it needs a component such as a compressor, you can replace it and take it back in to them for charging. But without understanding, you can't diagnose much on your own.

2) Black boxes with functional names

The second level of understanding comes from having some basic familiarity with how an air conditioning system works. You become comfortable with the idea that a gas cools when it expands. You assume that the words "compressor," "condenser," "evaporator," and "expansion valve" accurately portray the functions of the components carrying their names, but you don't really understand the details of how they do it. You know enough about the low (blue) and high (red) sides to be able to hook up a gauge set and evacuate and recharge the system, so long as nothing weird happens, but you still need to keep consulting the diagram to remember which components are on the high and low sides, and which hose on the compressor is suction and which is discharge.

3) Understanding the flow

A step increase in your knowledge occurs when you look at the flow diagrams that show not only the high and low sides of the system, but where the refrigerant is liquid and where it's gaseous, and begin to understand the role each component has in changing the refrigerant from gas to liquid and back to gas, and how that actually causes the system to cool. That flow is depicted in figure 9 on page 24. The illustration shows a system with an expansion valve and a drier, but it's the same for a system with an orifice tube and an accumulator instead, except that the accumulator is on the outlet side of the evaporator rather than the inlet side.

Below I talk about the flow diagram in detail.

- When we talk about an a/c system having refrigerant in it, it's a mixture of liquid and gaseous refrigerant, just like the state propane is in in a barbeque tank. The refrigerant is brought in under pressure when the system is charged, and kept under pressure even when the engine is off. Atmospheric pressure is 14.7 psi. In comparison, when an a/c system is off, the so-called static pressure is typically about equal to the ambient temperature in °F. So if it's 80° outside, the static pressure is about 80 psi. When the system is running, typically the high side is about 225 psi and the low side is about 30 psi. With these numbers, you can see that, as I said, the refrigerant is always under pressure, even when the a/c isn't running.

- Low pressure induces expansion (boiling), which, when followed by evaporation, absorbs heat from the surroundings, thereby making things cold. So refrigerant that is evaporating is cold. Conversely, high pressure induces condensation, which gives off heat. So refrigerant that is condensing is hot.

- The compressor and the expansion valve form the dividing line between the low pressure and the high pressure sides of the system. The high side consists of the discharge side of the compressor, the condenser, the receiver/drier (if there is one), and the inlet of the expansion valve or orifice tube. The low side runs from the outlet of the expansion valve, through the evaporator, to the accumulator (if there is one), and back to the suction side of the compressor. You can look at your blue (low side) and red (high side) charging fittings and verify with your own eyes that this is true.

- The suction side of the compressor is on the low (blue) side. It's sucking in the low-pressure gaseous refrigerant that's coming out of the evaporator, compressing it to create high-pressure gaseous refrigerant, and sending it out the discharge side, which is the high-pressure (red) side. This causes the discharge pipe to get very hot. (By the way, a fluid can't be compressed. You ever try squeezing a gallon of liquid? Nothing happens. The compressor can only compress gas. So the refrigerant is always in a low-pressure gaseous state when it enters the compressor, and in a high-pressure gaseous state when it leaves. Remember that fact, and you'll never need to consult a diagram again to remember which side is the low/suction side and which is the high/discharge side.)

- The compressor compresses the gaseous refrigerant. The high-pressure gaseous refrigerant leaves the compressor and enters the top of the condenser. As it passes through the condenser, the air blowing on it by the cooling fan causes it to cool and become liquid—to condense. In doing so, it dumps heat to the ambient air. By the time the refrigerant exits the bottom of the condenser, it should be 100% liquid.

- The high-pressure liquid refrigerant then flows through the receiver/drier and into the expansion valve or orifice tube at the inlet to the evaporator. The expansion valve, as its name implies, allows the liquid to turn into a gas and expand. It's a metering device, imposing a restriction in the flow path, like a spray nozzle at the end of a garden hose. As liquid refrigerant passes through the expansion valve, the restriction causes the refrigerant pressure to drop. The expansion valve and evaporator are designed so that there is enough space inside the evaporator that the liquid refrigerant can turn gaseous, and the gas can expand. That is, not all of the expansion actually occurs at the expansion valve. Some expansion occurs inside the evaporator itself. By the time the refrigerant exits the evaporator, it's 100% gaseous.

- A fan blows over the evaporator to move air around the evaporator's fins, which allow the heat to be transferred from the air into the refrigerant, which in turn cools the air, allowing it to be blown in your face. As part of this heat exchange, the gaseous refrigerant in the evaporator is warmed.

- The low-pressure gas is now returned to the suction side of the compressor. The compressor does its thing and compresses the gas. The high-pressure gaseous refrigerant then enters the top of the condenser. The air blowing on it by the cooling fan causes it to cool and become liquid—to condense. In doing so, it dumps its heat to the ambient air.

Technical literature will sometimes talk about the refrigerant "boiling" inside the evaporator. This is technically accurate, and is another way of saying "changing state from liquid to gaseous," but it usually does not help a novice's understanding. This is because the experience most of us have with boiling is when we boil water. Water does not spontaneously boil at atmospheric pressure, so boiling it requires adding heat (putting the water on the stove and turning on the burner). However, unlike water on a stove, when R12, R134a, or any other refrigerant is at atmospheric pressure, it boils (changes state from liquid to gas) at about -15 °F. So in the air conditioning context, "boiling" doesn't mean "turning on a source of heat to make it boil." It means "absorbing heat from the cabin air, causing it to undergo a phase transition from liquid to gas, causing the gas to expand and

Figure 9: **Refrigerant Flow and Heat Transfer**

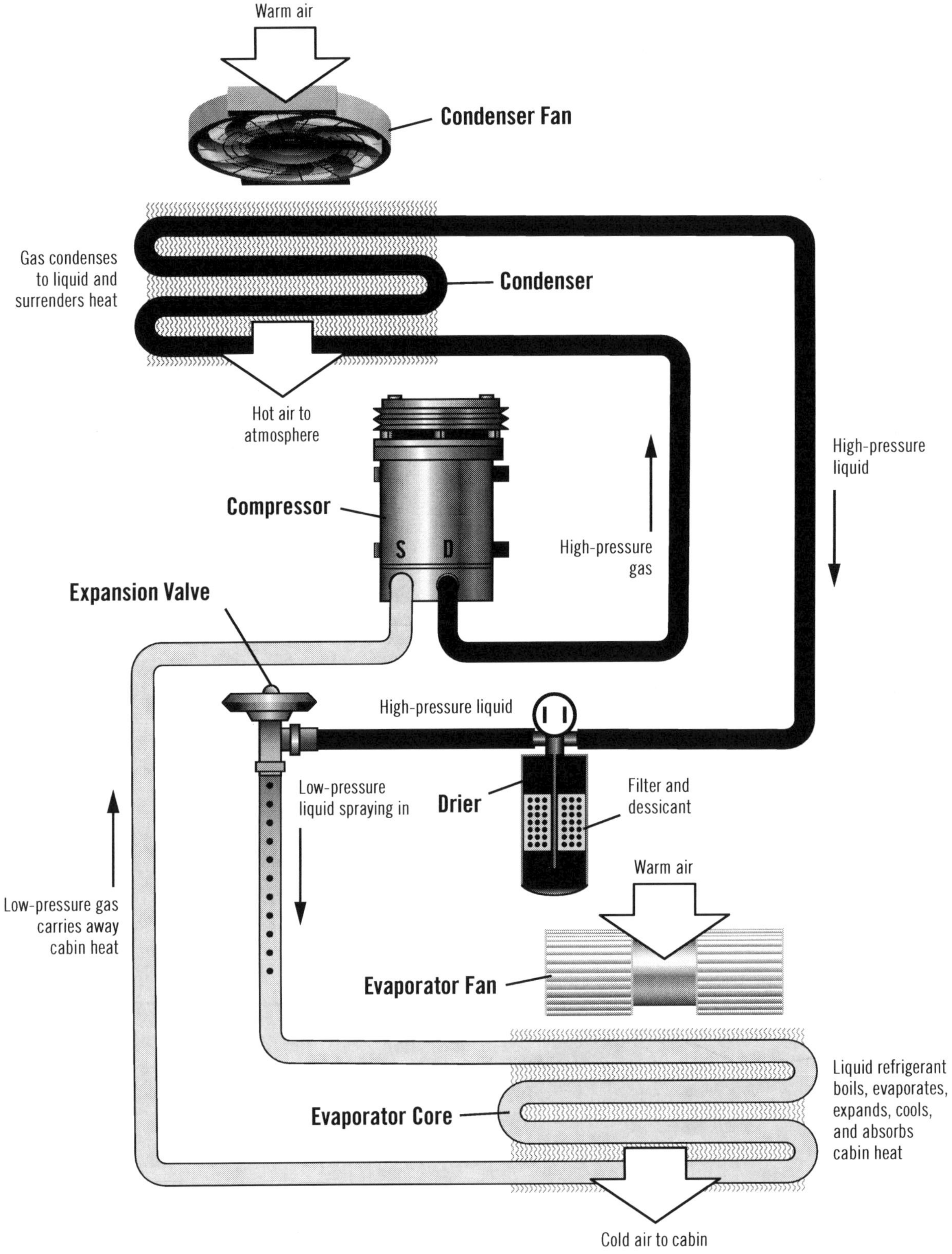

Warm air

Condenser Fan

Gas condenses
to liquid and
surrenders heat

Condenser

Hot air to
atmosphere

High-pressure
liquid

Compressor

S D

High-pressure
gas

Expansion Valve

High-pressure liquid

Low-pressure
liquid spraying in

Drier

Filter and
dessicant

Low-pressure gas
carries away
cabin heat

Warm air

Evaporator Fan

Liquid refrigerant
boils, evaporates,
expands, cools,
and absorbs
cabin heat

Evaporator Core

Cold air to cabin

cool, the cumulative effect of which is to cool the cabin." It's a subtle but important difference.

4) The reversed Carnot cycle and all that

A fourth level of understanding requires both a deeper knowledge of the physics of the Carnot cycle and heat transfer as well as a lot of experience. For several reasons, I'm not going to go into it in detail. Understanding the details of the Carnot cycle is not necessary to work on an a/c system; my physics background is now 40 years in the rear view mirror so it's a stretch for me to claim that I understand the details myself, and you can read about it in many places online. But some tidbits you'll find in the fourth level are:

- Phase transitions between liquid and gas (and vice versa) don't happen instantaneously. A lot of energy is absorbed (or given off) without any change in temperature.

- Superheat is the heat that is added to a gas after it has already turned from a liquid into a gas. Superheating is important on the low side because you want to be certain that the compressor is sucking in vapor and not liquid.

- Subcooling is the opposite of superheating—continuing to cool a liquid after it has condensed from a gas. Subcooling is important on the high side because you want to make sure the evaporator has an adequate supply of liquid refrigerant.

- Refrigeration obeys the reversed Carnot cycle, which contains the following four elements:
  - Isentropic compression
  - Condensation (superheating, actual condensation, and subcooling)
  - Adiabatic expansion
  - Evaporation (including superheating)

- In the compression phase, superheated vapor is drawn into the compressor at relatively low temperature and pressure, and is compressed to high temperature and pressure in an isentropic (constant entropy) process.

- In the condensation phase, the high-pressure superheated gas enters the condenser and releases heat to the ambient air. In doing so, it undergoes three separate phase transitions:
  - The top part of the condenser removes the superheat from the gas so it can reach the condensing point (de-superheating).
  - The gas is condensed into a liquid (actual condensation). This doesn't change its temperature, but releases latent heat.
  - When the refrigerant reaches the bottom of the condenser, it's all liquid, and is subcooled to ensure that there's plenty of liquid refrigerant for the evaporator.

- In the expansion phase, the subcooled liquid expands adiabatically (without heat transfer) through an expansion valve or an orifice tube, changing phase to a low-temperature and low-pressure mixture of liquid and gas.

- In the evaporation phase, when this mixture enters the evaporator, the surrounding air causes it to boil and evaporate. The vapor expands and cools, and in doing so, absorbs heat from the surrounding air. Some amount of superheating also occurs in the evaporator to ensure that the refrigerant is in a fully vaporized state before it reaches the compressor (since fluid is incompressible).

- The lightly-superheated refrigerant vapor, heated by the cabin air, is then drawn back into the compressor, completing the process. Since R12 boils at –21 degrees, R134a at –14.9, refrigerant can take on heat and still seem cold, so the "superheated" low pressure refrigerant line can still seem cold to the touch.

You can go full geek and study phase transition diagrams for different refrigerants, but in terms of this book, that's where I draw the line :^)

Enough theory for now? Probably.

Theory summary

The a/c system compresses low-pressure gaseous refrigerant into high-pressure gaseous refrigerant. It passes through the condenser and condenses into liquid form. When it hits the expansion valve, it sprays into the evaporator, boils (evaporates into a gas), expands, and cools. Because the evaporator is cooler than the air immediately surrounding it, heat from the cabin air is drawn into the refrigerant. This cools the air immediately surrounding the evaporator, which is then blown into the cabin. The heated gaseous refrigerant is then sucked into the compressor, where it is compressed, repeating the cycle.

Let's tear it up. And then put it back together.

Chapter 2

The Choice of Refrigerant

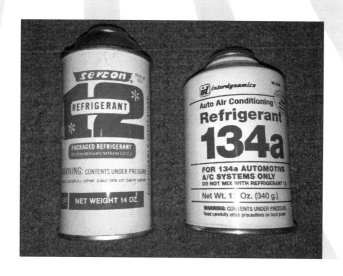

There are several factors that affect a/c performance. Among them are condenser type (serpentine versus parallel), condenser size, amount of air moved by the condenser fan, replacement of the old upright piston compressor with a modern rotary-style unit, compressor size, amount of air moved by the evaporator fan, and reducing hot ambient air entering the cabin. But when dealing with a/c in a vintage car, the choice of refrigerant may be as important as any of these.

Now, I am neither a chemist nor a professional air conditioning technician, and the topic of refrigerant can fill far more than this one chapter, so you should take all of the following with a bright flashing "The Hack Mechanic's opinions on this matter may be a load of do-it-yourself non-professional malarkey" sign attached, but this is a nutshell of the refrigerant issue, or at least my understanding of it.

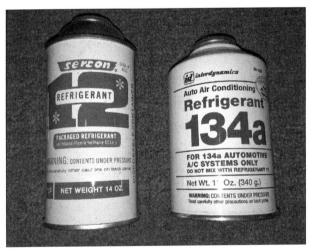

Figure 10: Old-school can of R12 (left) and new can of R134a (right).

A very short history of refrigerant

As we discussed in the Theory chapter, all conventional refrigeration and air conditioning systems function on the principle that a gas cools when it expands (more specifically, when the refrigerant in its liquid state boils, turns into a gas, and then expands, cools, and absorbs heat from the surrounding air). There are many substances whose low boiling point makes them applicable for consideration as refrigerants,

but some are either toxic (ammonia) or flammable (propane).

In the early 1930s, a new refrigerant was developed. It was a chlorofluorocarbon (CFC), specifically dichlorodifluoromethane, known as R12 or Freon. Its lack of flammability and toxicity resulted in it being widely used in many refrigerant, air conditioning, propellant, and fire retardant applications until it was discovered that the widespread use of it and other similar chemicals appeared to be significantly degrading the Earth's ozone layer and potentially causing a world-wide public health crisis.

By international agreement in 1987 (the Montreal Protocol), use and production of CFCs such as R12 began to be phased out. Automotive manufacturers were required to stop using R12 by the end of the 1994 model year, but the exact transition point varies not only by manufacturer but by model. International manufacturing of new R12 ceased in 1996, though existing R12 can still be reclaimed, purified, and resold. In addition, small cans of new old stock R12 are still widely available on eBay and Craigslist.

While I am not a climate scientist, I regard the issue of CFCs depleting the ozone layer as settled science. However, in certain corners of the internet such as air conditioning forums, you'll find the often-repeated conspiracy theory that the ozone layer issue was a smokescreen for DuPont wanting to introduce another refrigerant as its patent for R12 was about to expire. This is demonstrably untrue. Four companies produced CFC-based refrigerants equivalent to R12, and their patents ran out in the 1950s[1]. That having been said, I have little doubt that once the CFC repeal gathered steam, DuPont, like any major corporation, lobbied hard to influence the process to its advantage (there's no doubt that they became the largest manufacturer of R12's replacement, R134a). I also believe that the potential fines levied by the EPA for anyone caught venting refrigerant (see the following chapter on Legality) colored them in the eyes of many refrigeration technicians as heartless government bureaucrats and provided ammunition to give the whole thing an anti-government slant.

1. http://www.imcool.com/articles/aircondition/refrigerant_history.htm

But, as Tom Petty said, you believe what you want to believe.

Note that there are other refrigerants—R22 and R410, for example—that are or were intended for use in residential and commercial refrigeration and air conditioning applications, not for automotive applications. I don't cover them in this book.

The confusion over converting to R134a

In the automotive world, the replacement for R12 was R134a. You can spend multiple evenings reading about the differences between the two refrigerants. The molecule size of R134a is smaller than that of R12, so there was/is concern that R134a can leak out through a car's original non-barrier hoses and through the metal-on-metal flare fittings often employed on old R12 systems. R134a systems run at higher discharge-side pressures than R12 systems. The two refrigerants use different oils (more on that below). Somewhat counterintuitively, you use less R134a than you would R12. And, most important, bottom line, R134a simply doesn't cool as well as R12, especially in a car with a small a/c system designed to use R12.

As R12 was being phased out in the early 1990s, there was a lot of conflicting information on the issue of whether you needed to convert a working R12 system to R134a, and if so, how to do it. Initially, the cost of R12 spiked to $100 a pound and higher, and with R134a then costing just two bucks a can, conversion seemed to be the thing to do, but there was not agreement on the steps necessary for successful conversation. At one end of the spectrum was the intimidating and expensive recipe that said that the compressor and the expansion valve needed to be replaced with R134a-specific versions, the old hoses all needed to be changed to newer "barrier hoses" to forestall leaks from 134a's smaller refrigerant molecules, any flare fittings or black o-rings needed to be replaced with R134a-compliant green o-rings or they'd leak, and the evaporator and condenser needed to be flushed to remove any traces of the old oil prior to adding the correct R134a-specific oil. Of course, the receiver/drier also needed to be replaced,

as it does any time you open the a/c system up. At the other extreme were the inexpensive kits sold at auto parts stores containing just R134a charging fittings and a bottle of oil you were supposed to dump in without any flushing. These were derisively called "death kits" by refrigeration professionals, as they had a reputation for causing the compressor to seize a few months later.

Over time, a credible middle ground emerged. Compressors, as long as they were working properly, could be drained and re-used. Refrigerant-specific expansion valves were preferred, but not absolutely necessary. The concern that original R12 hoses would leak R134a like spaghetti strainers appeared to be somewhat overblown. Using R134a-specific barrier hose was best, but it seemed that the insides of the original hoses often became impregnated with a combination of old refrigerant and oil that acted like a barrier. So *as long as the system had been operating correctly and wasn't leaking refrigerant*, you could drain the compressor of its old oil, flush the system, refill it with new R134a-compatible oil (see below), change only the o-rings and the receiver-drier, evacuate it, and recharge it with R134a.

Of course, the magic words there are "as long as the system had been operating and wasn't leaking refrigerant." Who in their right mind would go to the time and expense to convert a tight, functioning R12 system to lesser-performing R134a? And thus you probably see the problem: R134a conversion became something that was often done to a car whose a/c was working marginally, if at all. Add into this the fact that, particularly with European cars, the a/c, even when new and properly charged with R12, wasn't great to begin with, and you can see why R134a conversions were about as well-regarded as leprosy.

The recipe for R134a conversion

Everyone hates a long explanation and wants a straightforward recipe for R134a conversion, so here it is:

- Make sure your air conditioning functions perfectly.

  - If it does, why on earth would you convert it?

  - If it doesn't, fix it so it does, in which case, why on earth would you convert it?

  - (Okay. I'll stop. But I really want to make sure you get the point.)

- Read up on enthusiast forums that are specific to your car whether an R134a conversion will cool your car sufficiently, or will make you hate your air conditioning. If it's the latter, either don't do it, or couple it with updating the compressor to a modern rotary-style compressor, and the serpentine-flow condenser to a modern parallel-flow condenser. But realize that, if you're updating the compressor and condenser, you'll probably need to make new hoses, as the old ones may not fit or reach (see the chapter on Rejuvenation).

- If you're re-using the compressor, drain all the oil from it, refill it with a little oil suitable for R134a (PAG or Ester oil; I'd recommend Ester), rotate the compressor, drain it again, do this two or three times, then refill the compressor with the correct amount of oil (typically about 6oz).

- Flush the condenser and any original hoses and hard lines, and pop-flush the evaporator as best as you can (see the chapter on Flushing).

- Install a new receiver-drier.

- If the system has o-ring fittings, replace the old black o-rings with new R134a-compliant green ones. O-rings can be found at the hose connections to all the major components (compressor, condenser, receiver-drier, evaporator).

- Recharge with the correct amount of R134a, which is typically about 20% less than the original amount of R12.

But really, the issues of conversion and performance need to be cleanly separated. If an a/c system isn't working, the root cause needs to be diagnosed. The overwhelming amount of the time, the cause is that most or all of the refrigerant has leaked out, in which case the source of the leak must be located and fixed. If you're lucky, it's a leaking connection; you tighten it or replace one bad o-ring, and bam, it's repaired and it can be evacuated and recharged with whatever refrigerant it had in it. But you're rarely that lucky. Most of the time, there's a major failure in some component.

As I said, there's also the issue of how well the a/c worked even when the car was new. Since the southern and western United States experience hotter weather than many other industrialized nations, 1960s and 1970s American cars probably had the best, most overbuilt automotive air conditioning systems ever installed, with very large condensers in front of the radiator, and thus many of them reacted fairly well to R134a retrofit. In contrast, it doesn't routinely get as hot in Europe as it does in the southern United States, and the air conditioning systems in European cars, even when new and pumped full of R12, weren't all that great (as my colleague Mike Miller says, the original air conditioning on a BMW 2002 is like "a hamster blowing on a snow cone").

There's a wonderful story, possibly apocryphal, about representatives of BMW of North America relaying complaints about the poor performance of BMW air conditioning systems to BMW headquarters in Munich. This was as BMW was establishing a foothold in the United States in the 1970s, and as their larger 5 and 7 Series cars were beginning to compete in the market against Mercedes. BMW reportedly didn't understand what the fuss was about, as the a/c worked fine in Germany. According to the story, two BMW engineers flew into Texas in August, and were picked up in a black 530i with the air conditioning on full. And the rear power window switches disconnected. By the time the car reached the dealership, 30 miles away, in the hundred-degree Texas heat, the sweating BMW engineers knew there was, indeed, a problem.

The story notwithstanding, considering the mediocre performance of the car's a/c in a hot climate *even when new and charged with R12,* retrofitting such a car in such a climate with R134a would be a recipe for disappointment unless additional improvements were made, and even still, might not be adequate.

Sticking with Freon (R12)

With the changeover to R134a in the early 1990s rapidly vanishing in the rearview mirror, there aren't a lot of cars still running around with R12 in them, so demand for R12, and thus price, is lower than in the early panicked sky-is-falling days. As of this writing, new old stock cans of R12 sell on eBay in the $25 to $30 range. However, note that bare cans of R134a are no longer two bucks; they're selling at Autozone for about $15 (more for the ones with the integrated valve, hose, and gauge). Thus, as long as you do your own work, the price difference between R134a and R12 isn't that big of a deal. If you have a vintage car with a small a/c system, live in a hot climate, and want to be absolutely certain that, at the end of a long and expensive a/c rejuvenation or retrofit process, you have a cold car, you might want to consider sticking with R12. R12, however, can still can be very pricey if you have to find a shop and pay them a premium, both for the refrigerant and for working with it.

I've read reports of counterfeit cans of R12, possibly charged with dirty reclaimed refrigerant, being sold on eBay. I don't know the veracity of the reports. But, to me, nothing verifies New Old Stock (NOS) like a dirty, slightly rusty can with an original price sticker from Checker Auto Parts for $1.69. I would say that if you find R12 being sold in a can that has a 1/2"-16 ACME top thread like a can of R134a, be very suspicious. NOS cans of R12 should not have any threaded fitting on them.

To legally buy R12, even from a private party, they need to ask you for an EPA 609 certification, but a) from a practical standpoint, really, no one cares, and b) the EPA 609 certification is easily available by taking an online exam, as I did. For much more information, see the following chapter on Legality.

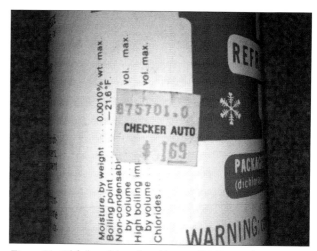

Figure 11: I'd feel confident that this can of R12 is authentic.

In terms of environmental hazard, let me be very clear about this. I believe that the evidence is overwhelming that R12 is an ozone-depleting agent. In contrast, R134a is *not* an ozone-depleting agent, but it *is* a greenhouse gas. In either case, whether you're a professional or a do-it-yourselfer, it's illegal to discharge either R12 or R134a into the atmosphere. If a system has refrigerant in it and is leaking, you need to open it up, find and fix the leak, and then recharge it. But if you need to open the system up, you must either use recovery equipment to capture the refrigerant, or take the car to a service station that has recovery equipment. There are potential five-figure penalties if you are caught venting refrigerant. Because separate recovery equipment is necessary for R12 and R134a to prevent cross-contamination, and because no new car has had R12 since 1994, fewer and fewer service stations maintain R12 recovery equipment, and thus it's harder to find places who will work on R12 systems, even if all you want them to do is capture yours so you can work on the car's a/c with a clear conscience.

That having been said, in my opinion, when choosing which refrigerant to use for an a/c retrofit or rejuvenation, the primary factor that should be considered is the desired performance in the environment you plan to drive. While new a/c systems designed for use with R134a perform very well (my 2003 BMW 530i's a/c is great), on cars like 1970s-era BMWs whose a/c was marginal at best even when they were new, there is the real possibility that one can go to the time and expense of R134a conversion and, even with a rotary-style compressor, a parallel-flow condenser, and a big cooling fan, not be wholly happy with the results. For this reason, if you are considering an R134a conversion, I strongly recommend posting the question to web forums specific to your car. ("Hey, anyone in Phoenix convert a BMW E30 to R134a? Did you install a parallel flow condenser? Are you happy with the performance?").

Having done six retrofits and rejuvenations on 1970s BMWs, half of them using R12 and half using R134a, I can say this: R12 is some seriously great shit. When you turn on an R12 system (I'm talking about a system that I've also updated with a rotary compressor, a parallel flow condenser, and a big fan), it blows cold almost instantly, and gets so cold that the biggest problem is that your right knee is in danger of frostbite. Seriously. In contrast, on the R134a systems I've done, even with the compressor/condenser updates, once they've run for a while, they get adequately cold but not freezing, as long as the temperature and humidity don't hit the upper 90s. When the heat and humidity are in the upper 90s, however, they struggle. If you're going to be daily-driving an old car in a wicked hot (or worse, wicked hot and disgustingly humid) climate, and if you can either deal with the a/c service yourself or find one of the shrinking number of places that service R12, you might consider being a holdout and sticking with R12.

That having been said, personally, as time goes by, I'm less and less sanguine about the continued use of R12 in my cars. Part of this is environmental; I think that anyone using it has a responsibility to ensure that they're only introducing it into a system that is as leak-free as humanly possible. Part is a flammability issue (see below). But part is that, even with its superior cooling capability, R12 is beginning to be seen as a black mark, especially in climates where there aren't a lot of a/c specialty shops. I had a very nice, very original 1987 BMW E30 325is that was still running R12. A gentleman from Quebec was close to buying it until he heard about the R12. "I'd have to have it converted first," he said. "There's no one up here

who will work on cars with R12."

Alternative refrigerants

Not only are R12 and R134a by far the most commonly-used automotive refrigerants, up until about the 2015 model year, they were pretty much the *only* refrigerants used by manufacturers since a/c first went into cars. Think of them as the Coke and Pepsi, the Democrat and Republican, the Mercedes and BMW, the Fender and Gibson, the McDonald's and Burger King, the moose and squirrel of refrigerants (clearly I could go on). But they are not the only choices for the do-it-yourselfer. I find it best to break up refrigerants this way:

1. The big two EPA-approved refrigerants that have been used in the most cars for the longest (R12 and R134a).

2. The other three EPA-approved "New Climate Friendly Alternative Refrigerants" that are jockeying to replace R134a. These are R1234yf which is being installed into certain new cars right now, R152a (also known as "duster") which people do retrofit (see below), and R744, which is CO2.

3. Other EPA-approved refrigerants, of which there are more than you'd think, which people do retrofit but weren't adopted by any manufacturer.

4. Other non-EPA approved refrigerants such as flammable hydrocarbon-based refrigerants (e.g., propane and its blends).

So, if you want, you can have the RC Cola Libertarian Porsche Rickenbacker Wendy's Boris of refrigerants, or the Moxie Green Party Studebaker Alembic Five Guys Natasha of refrigerants, or… clearly I could go on here as well. It's probably best that I don't.

I think we've beaten the R12 and R134a to death. So let's move on to…

EPA-approved "New Climate Friendly Alternative Refrigerants"

Because R134a is a greenhouse gas, there is a planned phase-out of its use in vehicle a/c applications. The current target for phase-out in the US appears to be

2020 (the 2021 model year). Its use is already banned in new cars manufactured in the European Union (EU). Three new EPA-approved refrigerants—R1234yf, R152a, and R744, are under consideration.

The EPA rates refrigerant gases by their Global Warming Potential (GWP), a measurement of the gases heat-trapping capacity. Carbon dioxide is used as a baseline, and thus has a GWP of 1. The following table, comparing the environmental impacts of past, current, and future refrigerants, is taken from the EPA's website[2].

Environmental Impacts of MVAC Refrigerants		
Refrigerant	Global Warming Potential (GWP)	Ozone Depleting?
CFC-12 (R12, Freon)	10,900	Yes
HFC-134a (R134a)	1,430	No
HFC-152a (R152a)	124	No
HFC-1234yf (R1234yf)	4	No
CO2 (R744)	1	No

From here, you can see that, in going from R12 to R134a, in addition to eliminating R12's use of an ozone-depleting agent, the GWP dropped nearly 87%. The switch to R152a (discussed below) would be a 91% GWP reduction relative to R134a, and to R1234yf would be a 99.7% GWP reduction.

R1234yf

In Europe, where use of R134a in new cars is already prohibited, the most common replacement refrigerant is R–1234yf (2,3,3,3-tetrafluoropropene). Since the 2015 model-year, some US-spec cars have already been shipping with R1234yf as well. As of this writing, the cost of R1234yf is about $70/lb. It is also, somewhat surprisingly, classified as "mildly flammable." I have not read about anyone using it in retrofit applications, which, considering the high cost, is not surprising.

R744 (CO_2)

BMW and Mercedes have announced that, reportedly due to concerns over R1234yf's mild flammability, they are adopting another refrigerant, CO_2. System pressures with CO_2 are reportedly four times what they are for other refrigerants. As such, it does not look like CO_2 is something that can be retrofitted into a vintage car.

Wait. CO_2 is under consideration as a refrigerant? When R134a is being discontinued because *it's a greenhouse gas*? Yes, and yes it's kind of funny. But it actually makes sense because CO_2 is *less* of a greenhouse gas than anything else proposed.

R152a

R152a (1,1-difluoroethane) is the ingredient in canned compressed air used to blow out computer keyboards and other electronics, and is sold commercially with names like "Duster" and "Dust-Off (ironically, R134a and R12 used to be sold for the same applications) for as low as three bucks a can. You can find many intriguing posts on R152a, including claims that it is a "drop-in replacement" for R134a (e.g., that it works with the same oils), as well as articles claiming that it cools better than R134a though not as well as R12. Because of these factors, people are already using R152a in retrofit applications, so I'm going to talk about it at some length below.

While neither R1234yf nor R152a are hydrocarbon-based like propane, they are both somewhat flammable; we'll get to how flammable in a moment. You'd think that would automatically rule R152a out for mobile a/c use. But then again, you can find articles about how, although R12 itself is not flammable (indeed, CFCs similar to R12 were also used in Halon fire extinguishers), R12 with mineral oil—the a/c lubricant most commonly used with it—dissolved and aerosolized in it, *is* flammable, and how, when that mixture burns, it produces phosgene gas, a deadly nerve agent used in WWI. So the labels "not flammable" and "flammable" are not quite as black-and-white as they appear.

2   https://www.epa.gov/mvac/refrigerant-transition-environmental-impacts

Figure 12: R152a, sold as keyboard duster. Note the flammability warning at the bottom of the can.

While I stress that I am not an expert, I spent a few evenings researching R152a. I found academic papers showing that R152a's thermodynamic properties are such that its performance is expected to be superior to R134a but not to R12. I found any number of videos where folks used it to charge up their cars and claim that it works very well, with lower head pressures than R134a. And I found the widely-repeated statement that the EPA has "approved" R152a for automotive air conditioning.

But when searching for actual EPA documents, here's what I found[3]:

- All flammable refrigerants were prohibited in 1995.
- R152a was exempted in 2008.
- "R152a is acceptable for *new* mobile air conditioning (MAC) systems, with *use conditions* [see below] to mitigate risk."
- Refrigerant concentrations of R152a in the passenger cabin free space cannot exceed 3.7% for more than 15 seconds.
- Proponents of R152a are "not selling or suggesting that R152a should be used as a retrofit gas."

And yet, people *are* using R152a as a retrofit gas.

In an EPA presentation[4], I found the following: "While some tests have shown that HFC-R152a has limited flammability and is difficult to ignite when released into the engine compartment, *it still requires risk mitigation* such as a secondary loop (chiller system) or active detection and safe discharge if used as a refrigerant in vehicle a/c systems. *HFC-152a is therefore not suitable for use in vehicles not designed for flammable refrigerants.* Current CFC-12 or HFC-134a direct expansion systems cannot be safely retrofitted for flammable refrigerants."

What follows are what the EPA document lists as the *use conditions* that must be designed into a new car to mitigate the risks of R152a's flammability:

"Direct expansion HFC-152a systems with refrigerant-containing components within the passenger compartment would require active safety systems that can detect and respond with high reliability to any leakage of refrigerant into the passenger compartment and require additional safety mitigation for risk of leakage into the engine compartment from collision damage or component failure. Secondary loop HFC-152a systems eliminate the risk of refrigerant leakage to the passenger compartment and explicitly satisfy the EPA-proposed criteria that refrigerant concentrations in the

3. https://www.scribd.com/document/336943936/U-S-Environmental-Protection-Agency-Mobile-Air-Conditioning-MAC-Regulatory-Landscape

4. https://www.arb.ca.gov/cc/hfc-mac/mvac-gwp/references/hfc-152a_secondary_loop_usepa_2007_workshop_report.pdf

passenger cabin free space not exceed 3.7% for more than 15 seconds."

Note that, above, when they talk about "direct expansion systems," they are referring to the vast majority of automotive air conditioning system ever made, where expansion valve and an evaporator located in the passenger compartment provide the cooling. When they reference a "secondary loop" (chiller) system, here's what they mean. In large ammonia-based refrigeration systems such as skating rinks, because ammonia is poisonous and could cause fatalities if it leaks indoors, the refrigeration equipment is sometimes kept in an outbuilding, and is used to "chill" a saltwater brine that is then pumped under the ice. That's an example of a secondary loop (chiller) system. They're talking about needing to do the same thing to safely use R152a in a car.

R152a has a flammability classification of A2, which is "moderately flammable," a step up in flammability rating from R1234yf's rating of "mildly flammable." It is apparently not very flammable while in gaseous form, but if liquid R152a is aerosolized, it is easily ignitable, and when burned, produces the highly toxic gases hydrogen fluoride and carbonyl fluoride. Thus, the myriad of videos on youtube where people test the flammability of R152a by spraying it into a candle or cigarette lighter are highly dangerous and should not be imitated by anyone under any circumstances. These R152a flame-test videos appear to show a range of flammability, from supporting combustion to blowing the flame out. None of them appear to show the blowtorch-like tongue of flame one reportedly gets from, say, lighting brake cleaner on fire (don't do that either).

To add another complication, most R152a that's packaged as a "duster" product is manufactured with a bittering agent added to prevent inhalant abuse. You can find many online comments referring to the residue that the bittering agent leaves when sprayed. Since a/c systems are supposed to be hyper-clean, the idea of a residue coursing through the system is troubling. And yet, finding R152a "duster" products without the bittering agent is difficult precisely because manufacturers don't want to advertise a "bitterant-

free" product for fear of promoting inhalant abuse. Out of curiosity, I searched and did find some firearm cleaning products that appeared to be R152a without the bitterant. I also found the one pictured above, branded, unbelievably, as "Stoner" (the manufacturer also appears to sell a line of car care products under that brand, so I think it's accidental). However, with shipping, its cost approaches that of R134a, so the $3/can cost advantage of R152a vanishes.

The conundrum of R152a is highlighted by the fact that cans of keyboard duster—which is marketed and sold to be sprayed around electronics (I repeat—*sprayed around electronics!*)—bear the warning "highly flammable" right on the outside of the can. If you look up the Material Safety Data Sheet (MSDS) for R152a, it says, among other things, "In accordance with aerosol flammability definitions, this product is non-flammable. However, the pressurized liquefied gas is extremely flammable." Since, when used in an a/c application, it does in fact exist in liquid form in half of the system, one must admit that it gives one pause.

In short, while there are any number of videos and posts on forums from folks who claim to have successfully used R152a, it is incorrect to say that the EPA has "approved" R152a as a drop-in retrofit refrigerant. They haven't. It has some degree of flammability, and no one disputes that, if ignited in aerosolized liquid form, it produces highly poisonous gases. It is only approved for new-car applications if coupled with use conditions such as a real-time leak detection and purging, or with a chiller system that eliminates R152a from running into the passenger compartment.

Part of the knee-jerk response to an analysis like mine is that we shouldn't worry about having a pound or two of flammable refrigerants because we don't worry about having 20 gallons of gasoline in a car. I find this disingenuous. We *do* worry about having 20 gallons of gasoline in a car. There is zero tolerance for a car leaking gas. If you smell gasoline, you stop *immediately* and have it fixed. In contrast, ten-year-old cars not only routinely leak refrigerant, but for decades we've expect them to be topped up without bothering to fix the leak. The idea of refrigerant with any level of flammability leaking, especially into an enclosed passenger compartment, is troubling.

But I do admit that, with any of these flammable refrigerants, there is more gray area than you'd initially think. I felt this palpably when I learned that, in two of my cars, the perfectly legal combination of R12 and mineral oil could phosgene gas me like a WWI doughboy in France if a line ruptures and the mixture burns. I'm not certain that R152a poses a real-world hazard that's any more dangerous than this. I do think there is a big difference between charging with propane (see the section below), which is so flammable that its most common application is heating, is prohibited by the EPA for use in mobile air conditioning systems under any circumstances, and has caused fatalities, versus using R152a, which is not burned in heating applications and which is an EPA-approved refrigerant, albeit not for retrofit applications. But that doesn't mean I think you should ignore EPA's advice and retrofit a car with 152a either.

Other EPA-approved refrigerants

In addition to R12, R134a, R1234yf, R152a (duster), and R744 (CO_2), the EPA lists a surprisingly long list of approved MVAC refrigerants for which there are standardized service fittings or plans to develop specifications for such fittings[5]. As of May 21, 2012, there are ten other approved refrigerants. These are Freeze 12, Free Zone / HCFC Blend Delta, R-414B/HCFC Blend Omicron/Hot Shot, R-414A/GHG-X4/HCFC Blend Xi/McCool Chill It, GHG-X5/Autofrost X5, R-406A/GHG-12/GHG-X3/McCool, R-416A/FRIGC FR-12/HCFC Blend Beta, SP34E, R-426A (RS-24, new formulation), R-420A, GHG-HP/HCFC Blend Lambda, and Ikon-12/Ikon A/Blend Zeta. As the "blend" modifier in many of the above refrigerants implies, some of these appear to be blends of R134a and other refrigerants.

To be clear, I have not used any of these refrigerants. Some, such as Freeze 12, Autofrost, Hot Shot, and

FR12, have been around for years, claim to be drop-in replacements for R12 (e.g., they claim to work with the mineral oil originally used by nearly all R12 systems), and have enthusiastic followings.

Back 15 or 20 years ago, when we were still on the decay curve of cars with slowly-leaking R12 systems being daily-driven, and owners desperately wishing to find a solution less costly and invasive than what many were telling them they needed to do to convert to R134a, there was great interest in the siren song of drop-in replacement refrigerants, even the possibility of simply topping up with a different refrigerant (we'll get to that below). These days, if you have a garaged well-cared-for vintage car that originally had R12, unless it has had an a/c rejuvenation, the odds are huge that it is going to have a bad hose or a leaky seal somewhere, and the chances that you'll be able to simply shoot in a can or two of a different refrigerant and have it blow cold are pretty slim. Thus, I think that the R12 drop-in replacement issue is important to fewer and fewer owners, and thus that interest in the topic of alternative non-EPA-approved refrigerants has generally waned.

In addition, even though the above are EPA-approved refrigerants with standard service fittings, the odds that you'll be able to pull into an a/c shop and have your system serviced with, say, Autofrost, aren't great. Remember, if you do this, you're RC Cola Libertarian Porsche Rickenbacker Wendy's Boris. Or something.

That having been said, you might read up on a particular refrigerant, understand it, like what you see, decide it's for you, and say that you'll be the only one servicing the system, so what they hell. I can't stop you, but realize that if the system needs service, and it's full of refrigerant, it's *still* illegal to vent it. You as a DYI-er aren't going to reclaim it, and the odds of your finding a shop to reclaim it are slim. You've backed yourself into a corner.

I wouldn't do it.

Non-EPA-approved refrigerants (Flammable hydrocarbon-based refrigerants: Propane and

5. https://www.epa.gov/mvac/unique-fittings-label-colors-mvac-refrigerants

its blends)

What? *Propane?* Are you fucking *crazy?* Do you *want* to die? That's the usual response. Let me be absolutely clear here: I agree. *Don't use propane.* But it is helpful to understand why some folks do, and why it's perhaps not the boogieman it's made out to be.

First, **no flammable hydrocarbon-based refrigerant is EPA-approved for MVAC applications**. On the EPA website[6], it lists "All flammable refrigerants, including OZ-12® (Hydrocarbon Blend A), HC-12a® (Hydrocarbon Blend B), and Duracool 12a except HFC-152a and HFO-1234yf in new MVACs" as "unacceptable."

That having been said, you can read extensively online about the use of propane—either straight as it is in R290 or Duracool 12a, or blended with isobutene, as it is in HC-12—as an alternative refrigerant. I've read pro-propane posts that are serious expositions by licensed a/c technicians explaining how propane, straight or mixed, has been used for many years in commercial refrigeration applications, how you need to use refrigeration-grade and not fuel-grade propane, how you need to make sure it's moisture-free, how you only use about a pound of it, how, just like natural gas, it's fine as long as it doesn't leak, how it's used in "chiller" systems as I described above in the section on R152a, how, just like natural gas, it should be mixed with mercaptan to provide that Sulphur smell in case it *does* leak, and how, even if it does, it is only flammable in a narrow range of concentrations.

I've also read less credible missives where posters decry any suggestion that propane might be unsafe for use as a refrigerant (common knee-jerk response: "You *do* know that you carry 20 gallons of highly flammable gasoline in your car, right?").

As I went down the propane rabbit hole, I stumbled upon posts where people sidestep the toxicity and flammability issues of propane altogether and allege that the only reason R12 and R134a were the only EPA-approved refrigerants was the influence of Big Chemical (e.g., DuPont) in Congress. From there, it's

a small step to posts that deny any and all possibility of human-caused ozone depletion or climate change whatsoever. The final stage of the journey occurred when I was perusing one lengthy thread about the pros and cons of propane-based refrigerants and looked at a poster's signature. I saw that it said blatantly anti-Semitic things, and realized that I was on a white supremacist website. Entertaining the use of a flammable refrigerant shouldn't inherently have to carry with it political affiliation, but such things do seem to ride in on its off-the-grid coattails.

Personally, I think the fundamental issue with propane or other flammable alternative refrigerants is that, while they may cool the car fine, an automotive a/c system simply isn't designed to use them safely. A car isn't stationary like a home refrigeration unit or a stove. Automotive systems are subject to much higher levels of vibration than stationary systems, and vibration can cause leaks. If you charge your car's a/c up with propane, the propane isn't stored in a tank subject to inspection like it is with even a barbecue grill. The propane doesn't have a manual shut-off valve like a grill or a heater, or an automatic shut-off like a propane refrigerator in an RV that senses if the flame is lit and shuts the system down if it's not. There is also the possibility of an accident causing a rupture, and the a/c condenser is in the nose of the car, directly in harm's way. In contrast with gasoline, yes your car has flammable gasoline in it, but the gas is stored in a tank that's in the back of the car, not in the nose, the gas lines aren't usually routed through the passenger compartment like the a/c lines, and the moment you smell gas, you stop and get it fixed. And the idea of a firefighter not knowing that your car's a/c is full of propane, and cutting the wrong line, is troubling to me.

Plus, there are the service and resale issues. My understanding is that you as a DIY owner can, I believe, pump the a/c system full of whatever refrigerant you want—no black helicopters will show up at your house—but if you're a professional, you can't be legally charging customers' cars with hydrocarbon-based refrigerants like propane. This means that cars charged with propane are do-it-yourself jobs, which adds to propane's redneck image. In addition,

6. www.epa.gov/snap/unacceptable-substitute-refrigerants

if someone needs to take the car in to be repaired, there's a problem. Since propane and its blends are not EPA-approved, there are no standard service fittings for them. Thus, if you tell a shop the car's a/c has propane in it, they won't work on it, and if you *don't* tell them, there's the chance that their charging and storage equipment will be contaminated, which can get *them* in trouble and will make you their least favorite customer. In the general marketplace, use of a non-standard refrigerant, particularly a flammable one, is a black mark on the car's resale value.

One final thing about propane and its blends. You might think that at least it lets you off the hook in terms of venting, but that's apparently not true. I believe that, once you use *anything* as a refrigerant, venting it is illegal. On the faq page of Duracool's web site[7], they state that "Refrigerant disposal must be carried out by certified personnel. It is illegal to vent refrigerants to the atmosphere."

Enough on refrigerants? Probably.

Okay, one more thing.

Mixing refrigerants—DON'T!

Don't. Ever. Mix. Refrigerants. Why would you? Well, if you follow some of the links for the weird EPA-approved and non-EPA-approved refrigerants, you may read posts that claim that, in addition to their drop-in capabilities, some refrigerants can be used to top off old R12 systems—that cooling can be restored by doing nothing except shooting in the new refrigerant without first evacuating the old. Even if this is true (and I don't know if it is or it isn't, but from my lengthy diatribes about no system ever "just needing a recharge," you know where I stand), *don't ever do this. If you do, you've created a contaminated stew in your car that will contaminate the recovery equipment of a shop that works on it!* Remember, you *can't* legally vent refrigerant, so if you do this, you've backed yourself into a corner. So don't do it. Ever.

In addition, if you are considering using one of the non-EPA-approved propane blends to top an old R12 system that is low on refrigerant, for the love of god, stop and think for a moment that you would be introducing something flammable into a system that is demonstrably leaky. I'm no lawyer, but this sounds like gross negligence to me. ***Don't do it!***

Refrigerant oil

The companion to refrigerant, the jelly to its peanut butter, is refrigerant oil. Any a/c system needs oil to keep the compressor's moving parts lubricated. Unfortunately, the oil won't simply stay in the compressor; it winds up circulating around the system along with the refrigerant. Thus, the oil needs to be compatible with the refrigerant, dissolving in it and being carried as a fine mist in the gaseous refrigerant.

R12 systems use mineral oil because R12 is a CFC and mineral oil attaches to the chlorine atoms and is thus carried through the system. When the new refrigerant, R134a, was introduced, mineral oil wasn't compatible with it—it wouldn't dissolve in it and be carried along by it. Thus, with R134a came a new oil—Polyalkylene Glycol, or PAG oil. This is the type of oil that is in the a/c system in most new cars, and that is shipped inside most replacement compressors.

The problem is that PAG oil is hygroscopic—it absorbs water—and R134a reacts with water to form hydrofluoric acid, which, needless to say, has a damaging effect on the compressor and other components. Any contamination of the system with moisture, either through use of an open container of hygroscopic oil or a bad seal on an a/c component, can cause the system to self-destruct. Jumping ahead to a later installment, this is why it is imperative that an a/c system be evacuated (pumped down) so any moisture in the system is boiled off prior to charging. It is also why a compressor, when filled with oil, must be stored with its fittings securely capped, and why, if an a/c component is removed from the system, it should be replaced and the system sealed back up quickly. You really don't want to, for example, remove the compressor and just leave the hoses dangling for more than a short amount of time. Once the system is closed back up, it should be evacuated again in short order.

There is another commonly-used type of a/c oil—Polyol Ester Oil (POE). Ester oil has the advantage that it binds with both R134a and R12, so its use was advised in retrofit applications where there may be some trace amounts of R12 left in the system. Ester oil compatibility with both R12 and R134a gives another big advantage in that you can build a system using it, charge it with R134a, and if it doesn't blow cold enough, you can evacuate the R134a and re-charge the system with R12—in other words, it makes R12 and R134a drop-in replacements for one another. However, like PAG oil, ester oil is hygroscopic, so, when used in an R134a system, you have the same problem with acid forming if the oil has been left open to the air.

Figure 13: A small can of pressurized mineral oil for R12, PAG oil for R134a, and Ester oil for both.

Because some of my cars have R12 and some have R134a, I'm trying to standardize on using ester oil in everything.

Refrigerant summary

While there are quite a few choices of refrigerant, for most people, R134a, combined with an upgraded compressor, parallel-flow condenser, and a big fan, is a good choice. R134a is safe, moderately priced, and doesn't harm the ozone layer. It is a greenhouse gas, however, and it is being phased out, but small consumer-grade cans should be around for a good long while. Those who live in very hot climates and have cars with large interiors and very small-capacity a/c systems may want to consider sticking with R12. I still use it in two of my cars, but am not sure I'd use it again. If you use Ester oil, you can charge the system with 134a, and if cooling isn't sufficient, evacuate it and drop back to using R12. R152a is interesting, but it is "moderately flammable" and not EPA-approved for retrofit applications. Regarding other oddball EPA-approved refrigerants and non–EPA-approved hydrocarbon (propane) mixes, you can make up your own mind, but they largely lock you (and the next owner) into forever servicing the system yourself, and, for those that claim to be "drop-in replacements," I think that much of their appeal goes away if you take the "do it once, do it right" approach of rejuvenating the system so it's clean and tight.

Wow. That was a lot.

Chapter 3

Legality

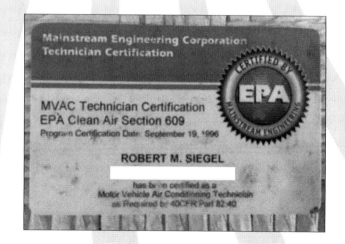

Overview

Here's the executive summary: **Don't vent refrigerant**. It's illegal. Even if you're a do-it-yourselfer, if someone rats you out, you can get fined tens of thousands of dollars. Legal questions notwithstanding for a moment, under no circumstances should you *ever* vent R12, as it is a nasty ozone-depleting agent. R134a is *not* an ozone-depleting agent, but it is a greenhouse gas, and it's illegal to vent it as well. Other gases, when used as refrigerants, are also illegal to vent. DIY-ers rarely own recovery equipment, so if you need to work on your car's a/c system and there's refrigerant in it, take it to a shop and have the refrigerant recovered. That'll keep your nose clean and your conscience clear. More detail is below.

What the EPA says

The following bullets are verbatim from the page on the EPA's website on Mobile Vehicle Air Conditioning (MVAC) systems[8]:

> **Refrigerant**: Must be EPA-approved and cannot be intentionally released (vented) into the environment.

> **Servicing**: When payment of any kind is involved (including non-monetary), any person working on an MVAC system must be certified under section 609 of the Clean Air Act (CAA) and they must use approved refrigerant handling equipment.

> **Reusing Refrigerant**: Refrigerant must be properly recycled or reclaimed before it can be reused, even if it is being returned to the vehicle from which it was removed.

There is also a requirement that the charging fittings on the car and the manifold gauge set hoses be correct for the refrigerant being used, and that adapters not be attached to hoses and then removed for fear of refrigerant cross-contamination.

But it's the venting part that's of most interest to DIY-ers. In 40 CFR part 82, subpart F of section 608

of the Clean Air Act, it prohibits individuals from "intentionally venting ozone-depleting substances *or their substitutes* while maintaining, servicing, repairing, or disposing of air-conditioning or refrigeration equipment."

The "or their substitutes" part is crucial. To be clear, R12 is an ozone-depleting agent. R134a (the substitute for R12 introduced in the early 1990s and used in all cars until, well, right about now) is *not* an ozone-depleting agent, but it *is* a potent greenhouse gas. The other EPA-approved proposed substitutes for R134a that I discussed in the Refrigerants chapter (R152a, R1234YFC, and CO_2) are lesser greenhouse gases.

However, if you follow the links on the EPA website, you'll find that even R152a and R1234YFC are currently considered to be environmental risks, and are thus prohibited from intentional release. Considering that R152a is what's used in keyboard duster cans *and is designed and packaged to be sprayed into the atmosphere*, this flirts with absurdity, but it *is* the law. When these chemicals are used in the context of refrigeration, their venting is prohibited.

When the deleterious effects of R12 on the ozone layer became known and R12 was superseded by R134a in the early 1990s, there were large fines threatened against professionals *and DIYers* caught venting R12. The EPA website states[9]:

> "EPA performs random inspections, responds to tips, and pursues potential cases against violators of the Section 608 regulations. EPA is authorized to assess fines of up to $37,500 per day for any violation of these regulations."

There is also the carrot of the same $10,000 "rat-out" reward that applies to those providing information leading to the prosecution of other environmental violations. I think these large fines were counterproductive, and had the main effect of fostering animosity toward Federal bureaucrats, but what do I know.

Regarding venting, it doesn't matter if you're a DIY-

---

8. https://www.epa.gov/mvac

9. https://www.epa.gov/sites/production/files/2015-08/documents/section_608_of_the_clean_air_act.pdf

er or a professional. It's still illegal. The distinctions between pros and DIY-ers appear to be that professionals (those who receive remuneration for their services) must receive training and certification, must use only EPA-approved refrigerants, and must use the correct charging fittings. But as near as I can tell, it is only in the area of venting refrigerant that a DIY-er can be fined. Note that "de minimus" (the minimum) releases of refrigerant while connecting and disconnecting hoses *are* allowed under the EPA rules, but that's all.

Do you need an EPA certificate to buy Freon (R12)? Yes, but…

Although in this book I talk somewhat glowingly about using R12, the more time goes by, the more circumspect I am about its continued use. While there's no question that nothing else works as well in old cars whose a/c was marginal to begin with, particularly when used in hot climates, I do believe that R12 is a nasty ozone-depleting chemical, that its replacement with R134a was a good thing for the planet and its human inhabitants, that for most people there are good alternatives, and that it is beginning to be a resale black mark; people don't want R12 in cars that they buy.

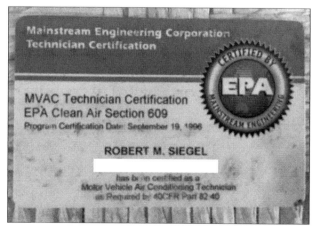

Figure 14: My not-nearly-as-big-of-a-deal-as-you'd-think EPA 609 card.

But that having been said, let me explain the law as I understand it.

First, we're talking about R12—dichlorodifluoromethane, CCl2F2. It's often called "Freon," but you have to be careful because the term "Freon" is also used to refer to R134a, even by the manufacturer Chemours (formerly DuPont).

It's frequently stated that R12 is no longer available. That's not true. Production of new R12 ceased on January 1st, 1996, but it can still be reclaimed, purified, and resold in 30lb canisters. And small (12oz and 14oz) cans of New Old Stock (NOS) R12 are still widely available on eBay and Craigslist.

It's frequently said that it's illegal to buy or sell R12. That's not true either. 40 CFR part 82 subpart F of section 608 of the Clean Air Act states that EPA-certified technicians are allowed to purchase ozone-depleting substances, meaning R12. Sections 608 and 609 are very similar, but Section 609 is specific to Motor Vehicle Air Conditioning (MVAC). To receive an "EPA section 609 technician certification," you can step through a simple, short, low-cost online training program. If you successfully complete the quiz at the end, they'll send you an EPA 609 certificate (it's like a AAA card).

Any vendor selling R12 is required to ask you for the certificate. Those vendors in the refrigerant business will certainly ask for it. When NOS cans of R12 are sold on eBay, eBay policy is that the seller must require the buyer to present an EPA 609 certificate, but eBay can't really enforce whether this happens or not. And those folks who are cleaning out their garage and selling NOS cans of R12 on Craigslist certainly don't know or care about an EPA 609 card.

Note that I am not advocating that you get an EPA 609 certificate simply so you can click on cans of R12 on eBay and legally buy them, nor advising that you can look on Craigslist and buy R12 without a certificate. I'm simply stating what the legality and reality both appear to be. Again, personally, for environmental, resale, and flammability reasons, I'm less and less sanguine about the continued use of R12 in my cars, and I think that anyone using it has a responsibility to ensure that they're only introducing it into a system that is as leak-free as humanly possible.

Do you need an EPA certificate to buy R134a? No, but…

If you look on the EPA website[10], you'll find the following alarming statement:

> "Starting on January 1, 2018, the requirements discussed on this page will also apply to most substitute refrigerants, including HFCs [which includes R134a]."

However, deeper on the site, you'll find that this applies to cylinders, cans, drums, and totes, but does not apply to the DIY-targeted cans that are two pounds or less.

So, for now, a DIY-er will still be able to walk into an auto parts store and buy R134a, the refrigerant most commonly found in cars.

Is it illegal to "top off" a system? No, but…

There is a commonly-repeated belief that section 609 of the Clean Air Act prohibits the "topping off" of an air conditioning system (adding a small to moderate amount of refrigerant to what's already there in order to replace what's leaked out and restore performance). I myself believed that topping off was prohibited. However, that is apparently untrue. The EPA's own website[11] says:

> "Vehicle owners generally have three options for addressing leaks and recharging refrigerant in their MVACS. These include:
>
> • Topping off the system with refrigerant.
>
> • Evacuating remaining refrigerant and recharging the system.
>
> • Repairing or replacing leaky MVAC components and recharging the system.
>
> Topping off or recharging a system should improve cooling the passenger compartment, but neither service permanently fixes refrigerant leaks. If done properly, repairing or replacing leaking MVAC components will provide longer lasting benefits.

Topping off versus evacuation and recharge

A top-off involves adding refrigerant to your MVAC. There is no way for technicians to determine how much refrigerant is in your MVAC system when you arrive at the shop, so they must guess how much refrigerant to charge into the system. They may undercharge or overcharge the system—both of which impair system performance.

Evacuation and recharge service involves removing the MVAC refrigerant, cleaning it using recycling equipment (to remove impurities), recharging it into the system, and adding new refrigerant to replace the amounts that have leaked out. Evacuation and recharge service allows technicians to add the precise amount of refrigerant recommended by the MVAC manufacturer.

Some technicians believe that evacuation and recharge is better for MVACs because the refrigerant is cleaned before being recharged. However, there is no reason to clean the refrigerant unless technicians open the system. Opening a system means any service, maintenance, or repair that could release ozone-depleting refrigerant. When technicians repair or replace system components, they should recycle the refrigerant.

EPA does not require leak repair before refrigerant is charged into a vehicle, but some states or localities may require the practice. EPA regulations also do not dictate any particular service, as long as the technicians are certified and use recycling equipment that meets EPA standards. For example, EPA does not require that MVACs be evacuated and recharged instead of topped off."

So, EPA guidance expresses a marked preference that you repair a leaky system, but does not expressly forbid topping off. Indeed, if topping off was prohibited, EPA representatives could simply park outside

---

10. https://www.epa.gov/section608/refrigerant-sales-restriction
11. https://www.epa.gov/mvac/options-recharging-your-air-conditioner

any Autozone in the summer and arrest everyone buying a can of R134a with an integrated gauge and charging hose, as these are expressly designed to top off systems. Certain repair shops may have their own policy and guidelines. But if they tell you that "the EPA" or "the feds" won't let them top it off or require that the refrigerant in it be removed if it is leaking, that is, apparently, untrue.

Reuse equipment

As said above, if a car is leaking refrigerant, the preferred path is to recover the refrigerant, weigh it to determine how much has been recovered, find the leak, repair it, and then recycle, refine, and restore the correct amount of refrigerant to the car. However, very few do-it-yourselfers have recovery equipment. I certainly don't. You aren't breaking any law if you work on your own air conditioning system without recovery equipment, provided that you don't vent refrigerant. The majority of my work is in resurrecting dead a/c systems that don't have any refrigerant in them, or in performing from-scratch retrofits. The handful of times I've had full-up systems that needed service, I've taken them into local shops to have the refrigerant recovered, then fixed them, pressure-tested them, and recharged them myself.

For example, many years back, I had a Suburban with rear air that took a whopping 84 ounces of good old-fashioned R12. The compressor seized while I was driving the car. Replacing the compressor required opening up the system. I could not, legally or in all good conscience, let all that ozone-depleting refrigerant out, so I took it to a shop and paid them to recover the R12, then replaced the compressor and recharged it myself. I asked the gentleman at the shop if, after I replaced the compressor, I could bring him the truck and he could put my Freon back in and not charge me for it, since it was mine. "Yeah, that's not really how it works," he said. But my conscience was clear. Interestingly, the EPA website says "Technicians occasionally tell customers that any refrigerant that was in the vehicle cannot be returned due to federal regulations. No such federal regulation exists." The tech didn't say the Freon couldn't be reintroduced,

only that he couldn't put it back in and not charge me for it.

Legality summary

Don't vent refrigerant. Don't vent refrigerant. Did I mention that you shouldn't vent refrigerant? R12 in particular is atmospheric poison, but don't vent any refrigerant. Stay legal, stay clean. If the system needs to be evacuated, take it in and have it done.

And don't vent refrigerant.

Chapter 4

Tools for A/C Work

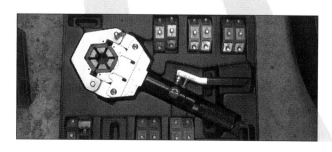

Overview

Air conditioning is specialty work that requires some specialty tools. You're a car person. You dig tools. Just buy them. You won't be sorry.

Manifold gauges

If all you're going to do is replace components that a repair shop tells you are bad, you can get away without gauges. But if you're planning on diagnosing, pressure-testing, evacuating, and recharging your air conditioning, it all starts with a manifold gauge set. The gauges provide the window into what's happening inside the system, a kind of air conditioning EKG. They also are essentially the adapter that allows you to connect cans of refrigerant for recharge, a vacuum pump for evacuation, and a bottle of nitrogen for pressure testing. While you *can* take advantage of the cans of R134a sold at the auto parts store that have an integrated hose, a low-side quick-release fitting, and a gauge, and use them to recharge or top-up your system, they're not really the best idea, as you don't know what the high side is doing. Also, for the $25 you need to pay for a gauge-equipped can of R134a, you can be well on your way to buying a manifold gauge set, which you need anyway in order to diagnose and service your cars.

A manifold gauge set consists of two gauges, one blue for the low pressure side, the other red for the high pressure side, with both gauges connected to a "manifold"—a pipe with three ¼" 7/16-20 SAE fittings on it. The fittings near the ends of the manifold are for the blue and red gauges, respectively. Red and blue charging hoses connect these to the low and high-pressure charging fittings on the car, allowing the system pressures to be displayed on the gauges.

Although manifold gauges are basically the same for R12 and R134a, the fittings on the far ends of the hoses are different to accommodate the unique charging fittings used for the two different refrigerants. Hoses for R12 gauge sets have standard ¼" 7/16-20 SAE threaded fittings with posts in the middle to depress the pin in the valve of the R12's charging fitting (like tire valves) when they're threaded on. In contrast,

R134a manifold gauge hose fittings are physically larger and snap in place rather than screwing on. Two unequal-sized R134a charging fittings (13mm and 16mm) on the car's a/c components have ridges on them, and the fittings on the hoses have a collar that you lift up on as you press it onto the charging fitting. The collar then snaps over the ridge as you press the fitting on. Like R12 hose fittings, R134a hose fittings have a post in the center that depresses the pin in the valve core when you snap the hose fitting onto the charging fitting.

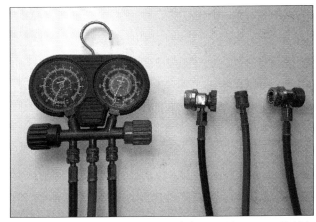

Figure 15: A manifold gauge set with hoses with snap-on R134a fittings.

Figure 16: R12 (left two) and R134a (right two) fittings on the ends of the gauge charging hoses. The R134a fittings are the high-quality kind with knobs that extend the valve depressors.

However, in addition to the pin, high-quality charging hoses for R134a fittings have twist knobs on the end of the hose fittings that move the pin to depress the valve core. In this way, you can turn the fitting knobs to the left to retract the pins, snap the hoses on, then turn the fitting knobs to the right to extend the pins, depress the valves, and not have any refrigerant escape. If you're using R134a charging fittings, I strongly recommend that you buy a manifold gauge set that has the twist-knobs on the hose ends.

The blue and red hoses connect to the car, but the third hose, the yellow one, allows a bottle of nitrogen, or a vacuum pump, or a can of refrigerant, to be connected to the center of the manifold. Thus, the manifold gauge set and the yellow hose provide the path by which the system is pressure-tested, evacuated, and recharged.

The free end of the yellow hose usually has a ½"-16 ACME thread, allowing it to be threaded directly onto a can tap which, in turn, threads onto the top of a can of R134a. There are also yellow hoses with a ¼" 7/16-20 SAE threaded fitting on the end, which may be needed to connect the gauge set to other can taps such as side-piercing taps. There are adapters that convert the ½"-16 ACME fitting to ¼" 7/16-20 SAE, but I find it easier to have two yellow hoses, one with each fitting. For much more information about the fittings, see the Fittings chapter.

Note that there are automotive and residential heating ventilation and air conditioning (HVAC) versions of manifold gauge sets. The gauges themselves are nearly identical, but HVAC gauge sets will typically have pressure/temperature scales for R22, R410a, and R404a (the refrigerants used for residential HVAC applications), and will typically have hoses with 5/16" SAE connectors. When shopping, be sure to buy an automotive manifold gauge set.

A quick look on Amazon shows automotive manifold gauge sets for as low as $20. Name-brand sets from Mastercool or Yellow Jacket obviously cost considerably more. As with the purchase of any tool, set a budget that reflects how often you intend to use the gauge set. If you're a DIY-er who may use the gauges only once, you don't need to pay for professional quality, but you don't want junk either. Look at the reviews and buy accordingly.

Leak detection tools

There will be two entire chapters on leak detection, but from the tools standpoint, the four main tools are a nitrogen bottle to pressurize the system, soap solution, a hydrocarbon sniffer, and fluorescent dye. For more information, see the chapter on Leak Detection.

Nitrogen bottle

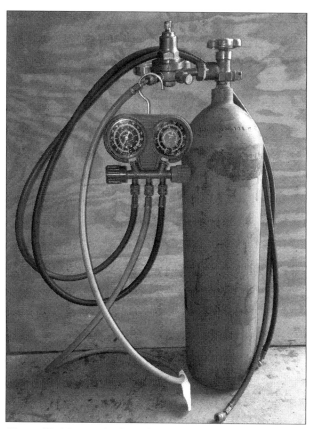

Figure 17: Nitrogen bottle with regulator and gauge set attached. Photo is for reference only; any pressurized bottle should be chained to the wall or in a tip-resistant cart.

Years back, a friend turned me onto leak-testing by pressurizing the system with nitrogen. Unlike compressed air, nitrogen is dry, so it doesn't introduce any moisture into the system. You can buy a small (20 cubic foot) nitrogen bottle and get it filled at a welding or food supply shop. You'll also need a ¼" 7/16-20 SAE flare to ½"-16 ACME adapter, depending on the fitting on the end of your yellow hose.

Set the pressure regulator to about 120 psi and open the valve on the tank to introduce the nitrogen through the yellow hose. Then slowly open up the knobs on the gauge set, let the nitrogen flow in until the pressure stabilizes, close the knobs, shut off the pressure in the tank, and watch the pressure. Note that for the purpose of taking the photo below, the bottle is free-standing, but in general, any pressurized gas bottle should always be kept chained to the wall or in a tip-resistant cart. Pressured gas bottles are extremely dangerous if they fall and the regulator breaks off. They launch themselves like missles.

Soap solution

Figure 18: Purpose-built leak-finding solutions like Big Blu work much better than home-made dishwasher soap and water.

Home-rolled soapy water sprayed on a/c fittings will expose large and medium-sized leaks, but dedicated soap solutions like Big Blu work way better, particularly on very small leaks. Pressurize the system, spray the solution first at the connections, and if you don't find a leak there, spray it on all hoses and components.

Sniffer

Sniffers directly detect the hydrocarbons in the refrigerant, and can be extremely effective in finding leaks that elude soapy water. I have an ancient Yokogawa unit that you plug into the wall, but there are small battery-powered wand units on Amazon in the $25 range.

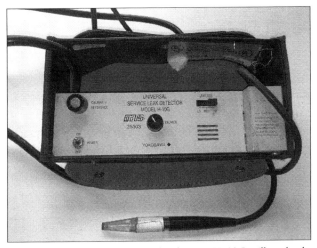

Figure 19: My 120VAC-powered Yokogawa H-10G still works the balls, but there are now inexpensive handheld battery-operated units.

Fluorescent dye

Fluorescent dye is very useful in leak detection because it can be added to the system prior to charging and can then be searched for if the system develops a leak at some point down the road. During system assembly, concentrated dye can be added directly into any component by unthreading a hose and pouring it in. Many folks instead elect to buy refrigerant oil that already has dye pre-mixed into it and using that to fill the compressor prior to installation. If the system has already been charged with refrigerant, dye mixed with refrigerant oil can be injected through the low pressure side using an oil injector tool. If you're taking this route, be certain to select dye mixed with the same kind of oil (e.g., mineral oil for R12-only systems, PAG oil for R134a-only systems, and ester oil for either) that's already in the system. An ultraviolet (UV) light and glasses are used to increase the visibility of the dye. The downside is that, as with anything involving dye as a leak detection aid, old dye will throw you off the trail.

Figure 20: Two kinds of fluorescent dye (right, pre-mixed with PAG oil for R134a, and left, to be added to mineral oil for R12), UV light, and glasses.

Flush canister

If the system has been left open, or if you're changing refrigerants and/or oil, or if there's any visible contamination when any hoses are disconnected, you're going to need to flush the system. Flush canisters into which you pour flush chemicals, then hook the canister to an air compressor to pressurize it, are available. Ones with quick-disconnect fittings and a shut-off valve such as the one pictured are preferred. See the chapter on Flushing the System for more detail.

Figure 21: An a/c flush canister, hose, and nozzle. Photo courtesy Oemtools.

Vacuum pump

Figure 22: My old battle axe Robinair vacuum pump.

After you've pressure-tested the system with nitrogen to check it for leaks, you need to pull a deep vacuum for at least 90 minutes to boil off any moisture. To do this, you need a vacuum pump. You connect it to the manifold gauge set via the yellow center hose. The fitting on the pump can be either ¼" 7/16–20 SAE or ½"-16 ACME. There are adapters to convert between them. DIY-quality pumps are available from a variety of sources for about $100. As with the gauges, the occasional DIY needs are not the same as a pro who would rely on it every day.

For more information, see the chapter on Evacuating the System.

Hose crimping tool

In a modern car, if a hose has a leak, either on the rubber part or at one of the fitting ends, you generally replace it with the factory hose or aftermarket equivalent. In fact, you may have little choice, as the fittings on the ends may be "block" fittings that make the hose unique to the car.

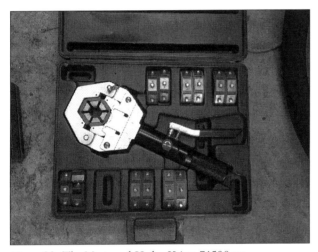

Figure 23: The Mastercool Hydra-Krimp 71500 set.

But on a vintage car, replacement a/c hoses may not be available, or even if they are, might not be applicable if you're upgrading the a/c with a rotary compressor and parallel flow condenser (the original components likely had flare fittings whereas the new ones almost certainly have o-ring fittings). Thus, it's likely you'll need custom hoses. There's a whole chapter on this later in the book, but long story short, there are shops that will build you custom hoses provided you tell them the size, length, and the fittings on the end, but these things can be difficult to judge. The process really works best if you decide on the connector for one end, crimp it on, test-fit that end, trim the hose

to length, and crimp on the other end. On certain cars where the hose passes through a narrow passage in a bulkhead, you may have little choice but to put the hose through and then crimp on the connector. To do these things, you need to have a hose crimping tool that crimps on beadlock fittings.

The Cadillac of handheld hydraulic hose crimpers was and is the Mastercool Hydra-Krimp 71500. As the list price is north of $600, few do-it-yourselfers own them. When I found a lightly used one on eBay for about half that a few years back, I pounced. It's been a joy to own and use. Now, with the double-edged sword of Chinese manufacturing offering up just about anything that has demand for half the price, an Asian knock-off is available for about $200.

You can also buy just the crimping jaws, but you need to hold them still in a bench vise. This is better than nothing, but it precludes the possibility of being able to crimp the fittings right there in the car.

For more information, see the chapter on Making and Installing Hoses.

Can taps

Cans of R134a typically have a threaded boss at the top onto which you thread a standard can tap, and then twist a valve that drives a punch into the top of the can to tap it. The fitting on the tap is almost always a ½"-16 male ACME fitting for a yellow R134a hose to thread directly onto.

On legacy R12 cans, there's usually a raised flange at the top that an awful old-school leak-prone R12 top tap mates with. The simpler way to do it is to use a side-piercing can tap. The fitting on the side-piercing can tap is usually ¼" 7/16-20 SAE, but sometimes taps will have both this and ½"-16 ACME fittings. For more information, see the chapters on Fittings and Charging.

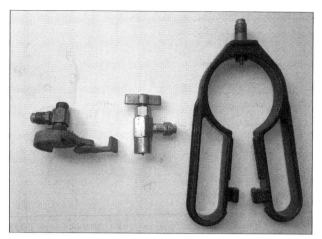

Figure 24: (left to right) Old R12 top tap missing its T-handle, R134a top tap, and side tap.

Vent temperature thermometer

Less than ten bucks will buy you a dedicated easy-to-read mechanical vent temperature thermometer that is indispensable during charging. It looks like an old-school meat thermometer. You just stick it in the vent as if you're cooking a turkey.

Figure 25: An inexpensive vent temperature thermometer. Yes it was cold when I took the picture.

Infrared thermometer

For measuring the actual temperature of the air-conditioned air, a vent temperature thermometer as shown above is best, but an inexpensive infrared thermometer is invaluable for quickly and easily measuring the temperature at places like the evaporator and condenser inlet and outlet. This is particularly useful if you need to calculate subcooling and superheat (see the Troubleshooting chapter). These days they're less than twenty bucks.

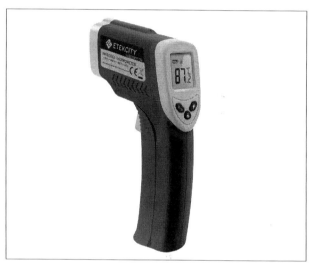

Figure 26: An inexpensive infrared thermometer is useful for measuring temperatures other than at the vent. Photo courtesy Etekcity.

Recovery equipment

Whether a system has R12 or R134a in it, if a system isn't cooling well, the way that a professional is expected to work is to recover the refrigerant in the system, weigh it to determine how much is missing, find and repair any leaks, and then evacuate and recharge the system using the correct amount of refrigerant as specified by the manufacturer, determined by using a refrigerant scale (weighting the 30lb cylinder containing the refrigerant).

To be clear, I don't know any DIY-er who has a recovery machine and a scale; everyone I know uses cans of R134a, and either charges the empty system, getting as close as they can to the capacity by using a combination of different-sized cans, or closes the tap on the can to keep the remainder of the can around.

The reason why I've never found recovery equipment to be necessary is that, in practice, most of the time that I'm working on the air conditioning of one of my cars, it's because I'm doing a from-scratch installation, or a rejuvenation of a long-dormant system, or because the refrigerant has already leaked out. In all three cases, there's no refrigerant in it to recover.

For more information, see the chapter on Legality.

Consumables

These aren't "tools," but you need them.

Nylog ("fitting snot")

Under no circumstances should you use Teflon tape to seal threads of a/c fittings. Instead, use Nylog Gasket and Thread Sealant (or, as it's affectionately called, fitting snot). Nylog comes as a "Red" and a "Blue" product, and it's a little confusing. The Red product says that it can be used with CFC (e.g., R12), HCFC (e.g., R134a), ammonia, or propane systems, but also says that it's mineral oil-based, which says to me that it's best used with R12 systems lubricated with mineral oil. Nylog Blue says it's made from "refrigeration-grade compressor oil" and claims to be "compatible with all systems, refrigerants, and oils." It may not matter, but just to be safe, I typically use Blue on 134a systems and Red on R12 systems with mineral oil.

Figure 27: Nylog fitting sealant.

Cork tape

Because the "suction line" (the line connecting evaporator output to the compressor input) gets cold, humidity in the air will condense on any metal fittings on the line, sweat, and drip. You don't really care about the sweating in the engine compartment, but, to make sure that the rugs inside the car don't get wet, it is necessary that any hard metal lines, or metal fittings on rubber lines, on the interior of the car are completely surrounded with cork tape, available from any refrigeration supply store. The tape must be wrapped securely around any metal, leaving no air space for condensation to form and drip.

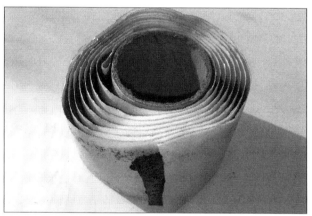

Figure 28: The roll of cork tape I bought in Austin in 1983. You don't use much of it.

Insulated tubing

As the suction line passes close to the exhaust manifold, it may be wrapped or surrounded in some sort of insulation. Remember, though, that the line isn't "carrying cold" in the way you might think. The cold is actually created in the evaporator, and what's in the suction line is refrigerant that has absorbed heat from the cabin air. Still, if you're retrofitting or rejuvenating an a/c system, there's no harm in insulating the suction line, and it may be beneficial. Make sure that whatever tubing you use, though, is heat-resistant, as it will likely be near the exhaust. There are sleeves that you can wrap around an already-installed hose, but the slide-through ones are better. 'Course then you have to remember to slide the pipe or hose through the insulated sleeve when the system is apart.

Tools summary

You're a car person. You like tools. Just buy the gauges. That way you can hang them on your garage wall and act nonchalant when someone sees them and comments "Wow! Gauges! Do you do your own a/c repair? That's so cool!" Plus, you're going to need the gauges anyway. You can't get to first base without them. Buy a vent temp thermometer, an R134a can top tap, and a bottle of Nylog as well. If you're tearing into an evaporator, buy cork tape. If you think you're going to recharge more than one car, buy the nitrogen bottle and the vacuum pump. The hose crimper is great, but if necessary, you can pay to have hoses made.

Chapter 5

Fittings and Sizes

Overview

Hoses connect the major a/c components (compressor, condenser, drier, evaporator) via fittings on the ends of the hoses that screw onto the components. Obviously, there is a relationship between the sizes of the hoses, the fittings on the hoses, and the fittings on the components they're screwed onto, but that relationship is more Byzantine than you'd think. It involves five sets of numbers.

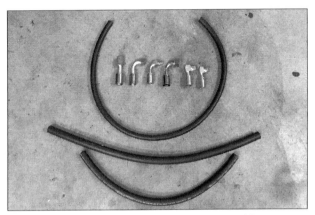

Figure 29: #6, #8, and #10 hoses with a variety of fittings.

The first parameter is a shorthand called the "hose number" which I'll explain in a moment. Next are the inner and outer hose diameter and the "fitting size," which is the physical diameter of the metal tube that goes through the fitting, which you might think would be the same as the hose's inner diameter but isn't. Next is the thread size of the threaded collar at the end of the fitting, which is not the same as the "fitting size" on the hose. This is a matter that generates endless confusion. Finally is the size of the collar nut holding the fitting. For completeness, all of these are listed in the table below.

Sizes of Common Hoses and Fittings						
Hose Size	Commonly Used For	Hose I.D.	Hose O.D.	Fitting (Tube) Size	Thread Size	Collar Nut Size
#6	Condenser to receiver; receiver to evaporator	5/16"	¾"	3/8"	5/8"-18	¾"
#8	Compressor (discharge) to condenser	13/32"	29/32"	½"	¾"-16	7/8"
#10	Evaporator to compressor (suction)	½"	1"	5/8"	7/8"-14	15/16"

In the pic below, I show that the tube size of a #10 fitting really is, as the table says, 5/8", but as you'll read below, it's an academic issue.

Figure 30: Showing that the fitting (tube) size of a #10 fitting really is 5/8".

If you want to get geeky, the shorthand of "hose numbers" originates with the number of sixteenths of the fitting (tube) size. That is, a #6 hose is used for a fitting with a 6/16", or 3/8", tube, a #8 hose is used for 8/16", or ½", fitting tubing, and a #10 hose is used for 10/16", or 5/8", fitting tubing. There. Now you know.

For the most part, no one refers much to the fitting (tube) sizes, to the hose inner and outer diameters, or to the collar nut sizes. Most of the time, we refer to just the hose numbers, even if we're talking only about the fittings on a component without a hose attached to it. Sometimes the thread sizes are referred to instead. For example, a compressor may be advertised as having "#8 and #10 fittings," or "¾" and 7/8" fittings." Both mean the same thing. Note, though, that these same hose sizes and fitting sizes are used for both flare and o-ring fitting components, so, using our example, if you want a compressor that has o-rings, look for "#8 and #10 o-ring fittings," or "¾" and 7/8" o-ring fittings," and similarly for flares.

There is also *reduced barrier hose*, whose outer diameter is slightly smaller than that of standard barrier hose. When used, it must be paired with reduced barrier-sized beadlock fittings.

Below is a table of the most commonly used inlet and outlet fitting sizes for each component. Note that the table is in order—the outlet of one row feeds the inlet of the row beneath it.

Fittings on Most Standard A/C Components		
	Inlet	Outlet
Compressor	#10	#8
Condenser	#8	#6
Drier	#6	#6
Evaporator	#6	#10

For clarity, the hose sizes are shown on the interconnect diagram on pages 16 and 18.

Fitting sizes on vintage BMWs

On the vintage BMWs I've owned, it's a little different. By the time you reach the mid-80s, popular models like the E30 3 Series, the E28 5 Series, and the E24 6 Series follow the table above and use standard o-ring fittings. However, the older models are weird.

The 2002 (dealer-installed Behr system), Bavaria (E3) and 3.0CS (E9) originally had flare fittings on everything, and York compressors with two #10 flares. The evaporator assembly on all these cars had

#6 and #10 male flares. The 2002 (dealer-installed Behr system) had a drier with a #6 inlet and a #8 outlet. The E3 and E9's drier had #8 fittings on both inlet and outlet, and an additional holding canister for refrigerant that is usually jettisoned when the system is rejuvenated. All of these driers' #8 outlet fitting had to be reduced down a size to mate with the #6 evaporator input. On the 2002, the drier had a #6 inlet and a #8 outlet, and the #8 was converted to a #6 via a hose with different-sized fittings at either end. On the E3 and E9, hard pipes were used for the section behind the glovebox and through the firewall. Where they emerge inside the engine compartment, they are no longer male threaded flares but female. In addition, the inlet hard pipe converted the #6 evaporator inlet to a #8. So, from a practical standpoint, although the evaporator fittings are #6 and #10 male flares, on an E3/E9, since you have to mate hoses to the ends of the hard lines, they're #8 and #10 female flares.

On the E12 5 Series and early 635CSi (E24), the fittings were split between flares and o-rings; they had o-rings on the compressor and condenser, and flares on the evaporator and drier. Like the E3 and E9, the hard lines in the engine compartment are #8 and #10 female flares. The drier on these cars is unusual in that it has a #6 flare input and a #8 flare output that mates directly to the evaporator inlet hard line.

Taking all that and putting it into tabular form, I believe that the fittings on vintage BMWs look like this. All fittings are male unless stated otherwise:

Stock Fittings on Vintage BMWs					
	2002 (dealer-installed Behr system)		E3/E9		E12 5 Series and Early 635CSi	
	Inlet	Outlet	Inlet	Outlet	Inlet	Outlet
Compressor	#10 flare	#10 flare	#10 flare	#10 flare	#10 o-ring	#8 o-ring
Condenser	#8 flare	#6 flare	#8 flare	#6 flare	#8 o-ring	#6 o-ring
Drier	#6 flare	#8 flare	#8 flare	#8 flare	#6 flare	#8 flare
Evaporator	#6 flare	#10 flare	#6 flare (#8 female on hard line)	#10 flare (#10 female on hard line)	#6 flare (#8 female on hard line)	#10 flare (#10 female on hard line)

If you take my advice and update all of the fittings except the evaporator to standard-sized o-ring fittings, the sizes are captured in the table below. Note that, on the E3, E9, E12 5 Series and early 635CSi, if you're using #6 hose between the drier and the evaporator, you'll then need a step-down fitting to connect a #8 fitting on the #8 evaporator inlet to the hose. For more information, see the chapter on "Making and Installing Hoses."

Likely Fittings on Vintage BMWs After Incorporation of Modern Components					
	2002		E3/E9		E12 5 Series and Early 635CSi	
	Inlet	outlet	inlet	outlet	Inlet	outlet
Compressor	#10 o-ring	#8 o-ring	#10 o-ring	#8 o-ring	#10 o-ring	#8 o-ring
Condenser	#8 o-ring	#6 o-ring	#8 o-ring	#6 o-ring	#8 o-ring	#6 o-ring
Drier	#6 o-ring	#6 o-ring	#6 o-ring	#6 o-ring	#6 o-ring	#6 o-ring
Evaporator	#6 flare	#10 flare	#6 flare (#8 female on hard line)	#10 flare (#10 female on hard line)	#6 flare (#8 female on hard line)	#10 flare (#10 female on hard line)

O-ring and flare fittings

As I repeat, well, repeatedly in this book, many vintage cars originally used flare fittings that have a bevel-cut sealing face and metal-on-metal sealing surfaces on both the component and the fitting. These were superseded by o-ring fittings that have a rubber o-ring interposed between two flat sealing faces. O-ring fittings are simply superior to flares. They're far less leak-prone, and unlike flares, don't require an enormous amount of torque to tighten or loosen. If you're retrofitting or rejuvenating a system, you should take that opportunity to replace as many of the flare fittings with o-rings as possible.

Figure 31: Old drier with flare fittings (left) versus modern drier with o-ring fittings (right).

Barbed fittings

The simplest kind of hose fitting is the barbed fitting. A hose is slid over a fitting with a barbed tube and held in place with a traditional hose clamp. In these days where discharge of refrigerant into the atmosphere is a no-no, the use of barbed a/c hose fittings is frowned upon. People used to use them when replacing a compressor and/or converting from R12 to R134a and trying to avoid the expense of new hoses. They're generally not a good idea. Taking a cracking 40 year-old hose, chopping the end off, and hose-clamping a barbed fitting onto the end is a good recipe for leakage. Even if the hose is intact, barbed fittings are leak-prone when used with R134a systems due to the smaller refrigerant molecule size. And, when used on the high-pressure side of the

system, they can easily blow off. Which is *exactly* what happened the last time I used one thirty years ago.

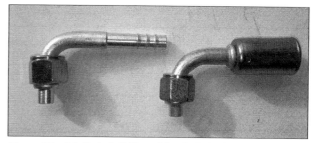

Figure 32: #6 Barbed (left) and beadlock (right) 90 degree male o-ring fittings.

Beadlock fittings

For just about any a/c rejuvenation or retrofit application, "beadlock" fittings are employed. These have a ferrule (collar) that slides over the outside of the hose. A crimping tool, usually hydraulic, is employed to squeeze the hose between the ferrule and the tube inside the hole, creating a tight, long-lasting, leak-free connection.

Figure 33: Beadlock-style #10 o-ring hose fitting and #10 hose.

Beadlock fittings are available in the three sizes widely used in automotive a/c systems (#6, #8, and #10), with choices in the connection type (flare or o-ring), gender (male or female), angle (straight, 45°, and 90°), fitting material (steel, aluminum, or mixed), and whether or not charging ports are incorporated into the fitting. "Step-up" fittings can be employed if the hose end is larger than the fitting size, and "step-down" if the hose end is smaller than the fitting size. For more information, see the chapter on Making and Installing Hoses.

Regarding the gender of the fittings, generally the

compressor, condenser, and drier have stationary threaded male fittings that are proud of the component, requiring the corresponding hose fitting to be female with a threaded collar. The hard lines connecting vintage evaporators, however, typically terminate in flare fittings with female ends and a captured threaded collar, requiring the mating hose fittings to be male with a stationary threaded nut.

Flare to o-ring adapters

There are adapters that convert flare fittings to o-rings. They exist in male-to-male and male-to-female form, and those two are very different in both size and function. If you have an old evaporator, like on a BMW 2002, with male flare fittings, you can, if you like, use adapters to convert the male flares to female o-rings. There is a certain utility in this. Flare fittings need to be tightened down with a lot of force to get them to seal, and on an already-installed evaporator assembly, it's sometimes not easy to get wrenches on the fittings and apply the force necessary to connect or disconnect the hoses from them. Instead, you can install flare-to-o-ring adapters before the evaporator is installed in the car, and tighten them down with a lot of force. Then, when the hoses are installed, since the fittings on them will now be o-ring fittings, they require much less force to be tightened or loosened.

Figure 34: #6 and #10 male flare evaporator fittings and flare sealing washers on a BMW 2002 prior to installing flare-to-o-ring adapters.

Figure 35: #6 and #10 male-to-female flare-to-o-ring adapters installed over the evaporator flare fittings.

The other kind of flare-to-o-ring adapter is a male-to-male used if you have an existing hose with a female flare end on it and wish to connect it to a female o-ring fitting on a component. These adapters are very small and elegant, simply converting the flare sealing face into an o-ring sealing face. It is very tempting to use these if you're installing, say, a new rotary-style compressor or parallel flow condenser with o-ring fittings and want to re-use your existing hoses that have female flare fittings. Unfortunately, while they may work, they're not the best idea. Here's why.

The problem is that flare fittings require a lot of force to tighten them so the metal-on-metal faces seal, whereas o-ring fittings require very little force to tighten them so the o-ring seals. In the male-to-female adapter shown above, the flare sealing face is tightened independently of the o-ring sealing face, but with the male-to-male adapter shown below, you're screwing the collar nut of the flare fitting directly onto the o-ring fitting. You need to tighten that single collar nut down enough to get the flare faces to seal, and that typically means you need to get it really tight. But, in doing so, you're squeezing the o-ring with far greater force than you'd normally use, and it's pretty easy to crush the o-ring and create a leak.

Figure 36: Male-to-male flare-to-o-ring adapters.

Hard lines and block fittings

When repairing, resurrecting, or retrofitting a/c into a vintage car, what you generally encounter are beadlock fittings crimped onto both ends of a hose, and each end is connected to a component that has a #6 (5/8") or #8 (3/4") or #10 (7/8") fitting. However, this is *not* what you will typically encounter on a newer car. Newer cars typically instead use "block fittings" where the hoses aren't all rubber and instead are model-specific hose assemblies with alternating sections of rubber and hard metal lines. The metal lines terminate in a metal block that has a flat mating surface with an o-ring beneath it. The block is typically bolted onto the component via an Allen-head fastener. Block fittings save space by having model-specific bend radiuses in the metal lines, allowing components to be packed in tightly. The obvious downside is that you can't make hoses with a crimping tool, or substitute a generic component, at least not easily.

Figure 37: Block fittings used on the drier of a 2003 BMW 530i.

Charging fittings (service ports)

Let's start with the fittings on the manifold gauge set (you *did* take my advice and buy a manifold gauge set, right?) and work downward. It'll make more sense that way.

Manifold gauge fittings for red, blue, and yellow hoses

If you look at the three fittings for the three hoses on the manifold gauge set, you'll see that they're threaded on the outside (obviously), they've got a hole in the middle (obviously), and the face is cut at a 45 degree angle. These are commonly called ¼" SAE fittings, but are also confusingly referred to as 7/16-20 fittings. Or both—you'll see it written as "¼" (7/16-20)." For clarity, in this book, I write out the whole thing—¼" 7/16-20 SAE.

Figure 38: ¼" 7/16-20 SAE fittings on manifold.

What do those numbers mean? The 7/16-20 refers to the external thread size (diameter and threads per inch), the ¼" refers to the "tube size" (the size of the hole in the middle), and the SAE refers to it being a "flare fitting," even though it really doesn't look like the flare fittings on larger components. It's much smaller.

Wait. *Tube size?* To be clear, there *is* no "tube," but if you think of it as a fitting for a ¼" diameter brake line, where there's a physical pipe through the middle of a threaded fitting, it makes sense. But since there's no "tube" in the middle, there's nothing about the fitting or the hose that attaches to it that is ¼". It's just called a ¼" fitting by convention. And it's a stupid, confusing convention. So, you need to learn to recognize that a ¼" charging fitting and a 7/16-20 charging fitting (sometimes written as simply 7/16) are the same thing. Did I mention that this is stupid?

Next, let's look at the ends of the red and blue hoses that thread onto the manifold. Obviously these have the same ¼" 7/16-20 SAE fitting, but in female form. They have a little rubber washer to help them to seal against the flare faces.

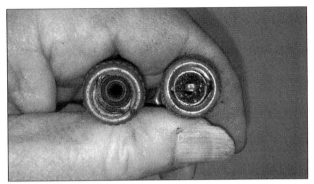

Figure 39: R12-style ¼"-7/16 SAE hose fittings with rubber sealing washer, and with (right) and without (left) post to depress valve stem. You attach the left one to the manifold gauge set, and the right one to the car's charging fitting.

What happens next depends on whether you have an R12 or an R134a gauge set (or, more accurately, R12 or R134a charging hoses on the set). Let's start with R12.

R12 charging port fittings

Continuing to work our way from the manifold gauge set down to the charging fittings… If you have a gauge set with R12 charging hoses, the fittings at the other end of the hose are the same as the ones that mate to the manifold. Well, almost the same. They're the same size (¼" 7/16-20 female SAE), and they have the same rubber sealing washer, but as per the above photo, they also have a little post that depresses the valve stem in the center of the charging fitting.

So that means that the R12 charging fittings on the car's a/c components should be the same size as the fittings on the manifold—namely, ¼" 7/16-20 SAE. And most of them are. Indeed, if you buy a Sanden 508 clone compressor that has small threaded charging fittings on the back of the head, those fittings are ¼" 7/16-20 SAE, and the R12 charging hoses thread directly onto them. ¼" 7/16-20 SAE fittings are almost universally used for the low-side service port

(charging) fitting on R12-equipped cars, and are also used for the high side on many cars.

Figure 40: Two R12-style ¼" 7/16-20 SAE fittings on the back of a Sanden 508 clone compressor head.

On many vintage cars that originally had R12, the charging fittings were located on or near the compressor. Sometimes the high-side fitting was located on the drier.

Due to the possibility of misconnecting the low and high sides and accidentally introducing refrigerant into the high side (which is dangerous—it can cause the can to blow up), unique low and high-side R12 charging fittings were introduced. It can vary by car brand, but generally the low side remains ¼" 7/16-20 SAE, with the high side using a smaller 3/16" 3/8-24 SAE fitting that looks very much like a tire valve. As with the low side, the smaller high side fitting is sometimes referred to only by the "tube size" (3/16"), and sometimes only by the thread size (3/8-24, or simply 3/8); you need to learn to recognize that they're the same thing.

Figure 41: High-side 3/16" 3/8-24 SAE (left) and low-side ¼" 7/16-20 SAE (right) fittings.

Certain R12-equipped General Motors cars from the early 1990s, shortly before the switch to R134a, use a different high-side fitting, requiring a unique "deep access" charging adapter to fit it to a standard gauge set.

R134a charging port fittings

In order to avoid the possibility of accidental refrigerant cross-contamination, R134a charging port fittings are very different from those used for R12. They're much larger, and they're not threaded on the outside. Instead, they have ridges that allow the collars on the fittings at the ends of the charging hoses to lift up and then snap over them. The low and high sides are two different sizes to prevent misconnection. The smaller one, 13mm in diameter, is on the low-pressure (blue, suction) side. The larger 16mm one is on the high-pressure (red, discharge) side.

On most new-ish cars with R134a, the charging fittings aren't buried deep in the engine compartment, but are instead up high for easy access. Sometimes they're on stalks that stand up from other components, as on my 2003 E39 5 Series 530i pictured below, but often they're integrated into the hard metal parts of hose assemblies.

Figure 42: 13mm low-side (left) and 16mm high-side (right) R134a charging fittings on a 2003 BMW 530i. Dust caps removed for clarity.

Both the low-side and high-side R134a charging

fittings have a valve stem in the middle that is depressed when a service hose is snapped on.

Figure 43: Gauge hose fitting showing post to depress valve stem in charging fitting.

Figure 44: High-side gauge hose fitting snapped in place on charging fitting. This is the "good kind" of hose fitting where you turn the knob to depress the valve stem.

On some manifold gauge sets, the red and blue hoses have ¼" 7/16-20 SAE fittings on the ends, and they come with screw-in adapters with slide-up collars that allow them to also be connected to R134a charging ports. The idea of this to let you have one manifold gauge set and hoses that can be used on both R12 and R134a systems simply by attaching or detaching the R134a adapters. However, in general, if you work on both R12 and R134a systems, it's better to have two sets of gauges and hoses. R12 reacts with the PAG oil that's often used in R134a systems and can form a sludge inside the hoses and manifold that needs to be flushed out.

R12 to R134a charging port adapters

When R12 systems are converted to R134a, the charging fittings need to be changed to prevent future owners and mechanics from cross-contaminating R12 and R134a supplies. On the one hand, the amount of energy that went into these adapters during the heyday of conversion in the early to mid-1990s was ridiculous—as if the adapters were the most important issue in conversion—but on the other hand, 25 years later, when you buy a vintage car that's passed through the hands of several owners, the charging fittings and adapters may be the only way to know which refrigerant is in the system.

From the context I've provided above, you can now understand that, if you have a large and a small R12 charging fitting, the correct R12 to R134a charging adapters have the specifications below. I've listed both the "tube size" and the thread size. Note that, as with the R12 charging fittings, sometimes only the tube size or only the thread size is specified.

Figure 45: Low side (left) and high side (right) R134a charging port adapters.

Note that if you have a Sanden 508 or a clone that has ¼" 7/16-20 SAE fittings on the back, and if you are using R134a, although there *is* sufficient room for R134a adapters, there is *not* sufficient room to get the R134a manifold gauge hose fittings on, so this is not an EPA-compliant solution. If it's your car, you can do what you want, but if you ever take the car in for service or sell the car, you should hang a tag on the compressor that clearly says which refrigerant is in it.

R12 to R134a Charging Port Adapters		
	Inner	Outer
Low side	¼" 7/16-20	13mm snap-on
High side	¼" 7/16-20 or 3/16" 3/8-24	16mm snap-on

Figure 46: R134a charging port adapters on R12 fittings on the back of a Sanden head. There's no room to fit even one of the gauge hoses on, much less two.

If your two R12 charging fittings are the same size, your high side charging adapter should have an inner thread of ¼" 7/16-20. If the R12 fittings are two different sizes, the high size adapter should have an inner thread of 3/16" 3/8-24. Adapter sets often come with both.

Figure 47: Showing that two R134a gauge hoses would never fit.

There is the issue of the valve core. Charging port adapters usually have a valve core in them. How this valve core interacts with the one in the charging port that the adapter is screwed onto varies. Some adapters require you to first remove the valve core from the R12 charging port. Since doing so would let all the refrigerant escape, this would need to be done before the system is charged. Other port adapters are designed to daisy-chain the two valve cores, having the upper one depress the lower one. Be certain of which kind you're buying.

Note that, if an R12 to R134a charging port adapter that requires the R12 charging port's valve core to be removed is on a car, and if you remove that adapter while the a/c is charged with refrigerant, the refrigerant will escape. Keep this in mind and be circumspect about unscrewing these adapters if the system is charged.

Lastly, note that these R12 to R134a charging port adapters are somewhat a focus of a bygone era. If you are rejuvenating or retrofitting a system that originally used R12, and using R134a, you're much better off simply installing R134a charging ports on the hose fittings for the compressor or splicing them in-line into the hoses.

The yellow hose

The fitting at the other end of the yellow hose depends on the gauge set. On an R12 gauge set, the yellow hose has a ¼" 7/16-20 SAE female fitting on both ends, but on an R134a gauge set, the far end typically has a female ½"-16 ACME fitting with a flat face. The ½"-16 is the actual thread size; there's none of this nonsense about "tube size" as there is with ¼" SAE fitting. It's usually referred to as a ½" fitting or a ½" ACME fitting.

Figure 48: Yellow hoses with 1/4" 7/16-20 SAE R12 fitting (left) and larger ½"-16 ACME R134a fitting (right).

On both kinds of yellow hoses (as well as on R12 blue and red hoses), one end of the hose has a post to depress the valve core, and the other doesn't. If the hose ends are swapped—if the end with the post isn't over the charging fitting with the valve core—no connection will be made because the valve won't be opened. But when connecting to something without a valve core, such as a tank of refrigerant, the presence or absence of the post is irrelevant.

Copper flare gaskets (washers)

If you have components and hoses that have flare fittings, you need to use copper flare gaskets (washers) between them to provide a malleable sealing surface. These are specified either by the hose size or by the "tube size," which, in this case, is the size of the hole in the middle. Thus, a small copper flare gasket for the drier would be specified as a #6 or 3/8", a medium-sized one between the compressor and the condenser would be specified as a #8 or ½", and a large one between the evaporator and the compressor would be specified as a #10 or 5/8".

Figure 49: #10 (5/8") copper flare gasket used to seal a #10 flare fitting.

Use two wrenches on most fittings!

When you loosen or tighten most a/c fittings, you need to use two wrenches—a *holding wrench* on the hex nut on the stationary piece the fitting with the collar nut is attached to, and a *turning wrench* on the collar nut on the fitting being installed or removed. The holding wrench must be braced with your hand to prevent the stationary side of the fitting from twisting. This is especially crucial on flare fittings on old components that have been in place for decades, where corrosion of dissimilar metals has bonded the fittings tightly to each other, and where the stationary side of the fitting is attached to a brass or aluminum component. Those are soft metals, and the torque needed to break loose an old fitting can easily rip the stationary part right out of the component it's attached to (ask me how I know). If the fitting isn't breaking free, don't risk ripping it off. Stop and apply some penetrating oil and maybe a little carefully-directed heat.

On certain components such as driers and evaporators, there may be no obvious stationary hex nut. Instead the fitting is usually attached to a square boss that you can get the jaws of a wrench around to hold it still. Compressors are sometimes the exception, as the fittings are usually steel and are often directly integrated with the compressor in such a way that the compressor and its attachment to the engine via the bracket keeps it from twisting when the fitting is loosened or tightened.

Figure 50: Holding wrench (left) and turning wrench (right) used on an expansion valve's capillary tube.

Cans of refrigerant and charging taps

R134a

If you had a 30lb cylinder of R134a (which almost no do-it-yourselfer does), it would have a male ½"-16 ACME thread with a flat face on it, a hole in the middle, and no valve core. The flow of refrigerant is turned on and off with the hand valve on the tank. The yellow hose on an R134a gauge set would connect directly to it.

An inexpensive small can of R134a has the same ½"-16 ACME fitting with a flat face, but there's no hole; it's solid in the middle. To use one of those cans, you need a can tap. A top-tap has a female ½"-16 ACME thread that screws onto the top of the can. There's a T-handle that screws in a needle and pierces the center of the solid threaded boss on the top of the can. On the side of the tap is another fitting, either ¼" 7/16-20 SAE or ½"-16 ACME, that the yellow hose on the gauge set screws into. Typically there's no valve core in the can tap. The flow of refrigerant can be controlled (somewhat) by twisting the T-handle and re-inserting the needle in the hole in the top of the can, but it's not a permanent seal.

Figure 51: R134a can and top tap. The threads on the can, the tap, and the side fitting for the yellow hose are all 1/2"-16 ACME.

R12

If you had a 30lb cylinder of R12 (which no DIY-er has), it would have a male ¼" 7/16-20 SAE flare fitting on it with a hole in the middle and no valve core. The flow of refrigerant is turned on and off with the hand valve on the tank. The yellow hose on an R12 gauge set would connect directly to it.

Figure 52: ¼" 7/16-20 SAE fitting on a tank of R12.

Unlike small cans of R134a, new old stock cans of R12 have no threaded fitting at all on them. There was a leak-prone top-tap that you used to use that latched onto the ring collar at the top of the can. Over time, use of these was largely supplanted by side can taps that clamp around the can and pierce the side. Older side can taps usually have a ¼" 7/16-20 fitting for an R12 yellow hose, but new side taps may have both this fitting and a ½"-16 ACME fitting, allowing direct connection to yellow hoses for either R12 or R134a gauge sets. Both fittings typically have a valve core, making it so refrigerant won't immediately gush out of a tapped can, but requiring connection of a hose with a post in the center to depress the valve.

Figure 53: Miserable ill-fitting R12 top tap with ¼" 7/16-20 SAE hose fitting. Don't use these.

Figure 54: Side tap with ¼" 7/16-20 SAE side fitting. Use these instead.

Bulkhead fittings

Hoses or hard lines must come through the car's firewall in order to connect to the evaporator. A bulkhead fitting replaces the hose-through-a-hole with a threaded connection on both sides to which hose fittings are connected. You still need to have a hole in the firewall through which the threaded connection must pass, but a bulkhead fitting permits the use of right-angle hose fittings, which may enable a refrigerant line to make a tighter bend than a rubber hose can. Initially popularized in the hotrod world, bulkhead fittings are finding their way into more rejuvenations and retrofits.

Figure 55: Bulkhead fittings used on the firewall of a BMW 2002. Photo courtesy Gary York.

Drier switch port

The threaded port on the receiver-drier for a low/high pressure cut-off switch is usually the metric size M10x1.25 (10mm diameter with 1.25mm thread pitch), but can be M12x1.5.

Figure 56: M10x1.25 threads on switch fitting and drier.

I think that just about covers fittings. Whew!

Chapter 6

The Compressor

Overview

As its name implies, the compressor is the part of the system responsible for compressing the refrigerant. Low-pressure gaseous refrigerant leaves the evaporator. The compressor sucks it in and compresses it into a high-pressure gas. It is condensed in the condenser into a liquid so that, when it hits the expansion valve and the evaporator, it can boil, expand, cool, and absorb heat from the cabin, which as we've explained, is what it's all about. Thus, the compressor is literally the beating heart of the a/c system.

Up through the 1970s, automotive air conditioning systems used upright piston-style compressors that were large and heavy. The York compressors employed in many domestic and imported cars look a little bit like lawnmower engines and weigh about 25 lbs. There were other units as well, very few of them small or light. Chrysler RV-2 compressors look like little Harley v-twin engines and weigh about 40 pounds.

Starting in the late 1970s, manufacturers began changing from these upright piston compressors to small cylindrical rotary-style compressors. I say "rotary-style" instead of "rotary" because they're not a rotary like a Wankel engine, and many aren't rotary in any sense at all. Technically, the distinction is between "reciprocating" compressors where a piston, driven by a crank, a swash plate, or a wobble plate, makes a reciprocal movement to compress and discharge the refrigerant, and "rotary-type" compressors where the refrigerant is compressed and pushed out by some sort of rotor (vane or scroll) making a rotational movement. It's confusing because many swash-plate or wobble-plate compressors have a cylindrical form, not an upright one, and thus are incorrectly called "rotary compressors." For clarity's sake, I use the term "rotary-style" to refer to any small, modern, compact compressor with a cylindrical form-factor.

The most popular aftermarket rotary-style compressor is the Sanden 508 and its myriad of dimensionally-identical Chinese-made copies. They can be had on eBay for as little as a hundred bucks.

Many people are surprised to learn that the 508 is actually a reciprocating (piston-based) wobble-plate compressor with five pistons.

Figure 57: The ubiquitous Sanden 508 clone compressor. #10 and #8 o-ring ports are under the dust caps on the top, and R12-style charging fittings are on the back. The single wire engages the magnetic clutch.

In addition to the smaller size and weight, the appeal of a modern rotary-style compressor is that it's quieter and more efficient; it doesn't bog the engine down as much as an old upright compressor and rob it of as many horsepower.

In this book, we're not going to talk about rebuilding compressors. We're going to treat them pretty much as black boxes. It *is*, though, sometimes necessary to unscrew the top to change an o-ring or seal under a block hose fitting, or change the "head" on the back of the compressor.

Hose ports and charging fittings on the compressor head

The Sanden catalog lists different part numbers for their R12 and R134a versions of the 508. As of this writing, Sanden says that, due to low demand, they no longer sell R12-specific compressors. However, in the rejuvenation world, it is generally regarded that the 508 clone compressors work with both R12 and R134a. It's just a question of which hose fittings and charging port fittings the compressor comes with, and which oil they're filled with. The hose and charging fittings on a Sanden clone are on a plate on the back of the compressor called the "head." Be certain you're buying a compressor with the correct head – that is, if your car has R12 and your hoses have the original flare fittings and you want to try to re-use the hoses, be certain the compressor head has flare connections and R12 charging ports (see the caution on this in the chapter on flare versus o-ring fittings). Even when I'm using R12, I typically source the compressor with a head with o-ring hose fittings. And, if you're wrong, the head can easily be easily changed; it's just a plate held on by five bolts.

Regarding the charging port fittings, the Sanden head is typically available either with R12-style ¼" 7/16-20 SAE threaded fittings, or with no charging fittings. As shown in the previous chapter, although there is enough space on the head to put R134a charging adapters onto the ¼" fittings, there's not enough space to get R134a snap-on charging hoses onto them.

Figure 58: Sanden compressor head with flare fittings and threaded ports to receive 1/4" 7/16-20 charging fittings. The five other holes are to receive the bolts holding it to the back of the compressor.

Clutch

Just about every automotive a/c compressor has a pulley on the front, spinning on a hub, and driven by a belt from the crankshaft on the engine and coupled to the compressor with a magnetic clutch. When the compressor is off (when it isn't fed voltage), the belt spins the pulley freely on the hub, but when it is fed 12 volts, the magnetic clutch engages, locks the pulley to the hub, and causes the compressor to do its thing. In addition to hearing the metallic "th*wank*" the clutch makes when it receives 12V, you can tell if the clutch is engaged by simply looking at the hub in the center of the pulley. The pulley is always spinning, turned by the belt from the engine, but if the clutch is engaged, the hub in the center will also be spinning. If the clutch is disengaged, the hub will remain still.

Electrical connection

The only electrical connection on most compressors is a single 12V connector feeding the magnetic clutch. This is usually a quick-connect bullet or spade connector. Touch that connector to a wire running to the battery, and you should hear the clutch engage. There is no ground wire because the body of the compressor is grounded to the engine through the compressor's bracket.

Failure modes

Compressors certainly can and do go bad. They can run out of oil and flat-out seize, which is pretty obvious because as soon as you turn on the a/c, the belt squeals spectacularly. Or, in the opposite of seizing, the magnetic clutch can die and prevent the compressor from engaging at all. One or more of the internal valves can go bad, preventing the unit from successfully compressing the gaseous refrigerant.

Note that, in retrofit and rejuvenation applications on cars where the a/c never functioned terribly well even when new, one frequently deals with a compressor that has been abandoned in place, or jettisoned entirely when the engine was replaced or rebuilt. As such, much of the a/c work on vintage cars involves replacing an upright piston compressor with a small rotary-style unit without ever evaluating whether or not the upright compressor is working.

The bracket issue

Unless you are looking for concours-winning

originality, no one in their right mind would choose the original big upright heavy York compressor and its bracket for a rejuvenation or a from-scratch installation (though, I have to admit, the v-twin RV-2 compressors have such a distinctive look and feel that I can understand why people consider them part of the under-hood landscape on vintage Chrysler products). Because Chinese-made Sanden clones are so inexpensive, there's a temptation to use them when performing a from-scratch installation or rejuvenating a dead system. You'd think that attaching the rotary-style compressor to the engine wouldn't be a big deal—and conceptually, it's not—but in practice, it can be a total and complete pain in the ass.

Here's the issue. Owing to the size and weight of old upright piston compressors, they're attached to the engine with a bracket which is also fairly large and heavy. The Sanden rotary-style compressor is much smaller and lighter, but it has a completely different form-factor, and thus needs a different bracket to mount it to the engine. Or let's say, for a moment, you're not replacing a big old upright compressor. Let's say you have a newer car that came from the factory with a rotary-style compressor, but not a Sanden 508. If that compressor goes bad, the cost of a new one from the dealer can be prohibitive, and the lure of procuring a Chinese-made Sanden copy for a hundred bucks and slapping something together to mount it to the engine it is pretty strong. I mean, how hard can it be, right?

Harder than you think.

First, understand that the purpose of a compressor mounting bracket is not only to hold the compressor to the block in a location where one of the grooves in its pulleys aligns parallel with the groove in the crankshaft pulley, but also to provide a mechanism to adjust and tighten the belt. That function can be achieved in three ways. The first is to employ an idler pulley on a little adjustable swing arm. The second is for the bracket to have four slotted holes so that the entire compressor can slide linearly. The third is for the compressor to pivot in an arc about a fixed point and then tightened in place.

Second, understand that when I say that a rotary-style compressor is smaller and lighter than an upright compressor, it is still by no means light. A Sanden 508 weights about 18 pounds. It is absolutely essential that it be mounted rigidly to the engine block. The high-vibration environment will cause it to work itself free if it's not. The pulley also must be kept in very close alignment to the crankshaft pulley or the belt will prematurely wear, loosen, and work itself off.

For both of these reasons, the bracket really needs to be an engineered assembly. It's difficult to jury-rig these functions with pieces of angle iron from Home Depot and get them right.

With that in mind, you can search eBay for "Sanden compressor bracket" and find two kinds of adapter brackets that mount to the flat side of the original York bracket. One kind has four slotted holes, but they're typically to help align the compressor to the crankshaft. They may not provide enough adjustability for belt tightening, and an idler pulley on a short swing-arm may still need to be employed.

Figure 59: Flat Sanden adapter bracket without belt adjustment. Photo courtesy Vintage Air.

The other type of Sanden adapter bracket is the "claw" type with two curved tracks. It provides the fixed-point-and-pivot approach to belt-tightening mentioned above.

Figure 60: "Claw"-style Sanden adapter bracket with built-in belt adjustment. Photo courtesy Red Dot.

Figure 61: A deteriorated rubber bracket bushing like this can make the bracket move around and mis-align the compressor pulley with the crankshaft pulley.

BMW-specific bracket information

2002 / M10 motor

In the vintage BMW world, aftermarket brackets used to be readily available to allow you to bolt a Sanden compressor to a BMW engine block. However, as cars like the BMW 2002 passed from daily driver into pampered classic, the demand for these brackets dried up, and thus so did the supply. They haven't been commercially available for several years.

On a 2002, the York bracket is especially offensive, as it wraps around the front of the engine and is supported by the bolts holding on the water pump. This means that, in order to change the water pump, you have to remove, or at least loosen, the compressor bracket, which is a total pain. Thus the bracket-on-a-bracket solution is particularly egregious. You want the compressor and that big old heavy bracket *outa* there. This, coupled with the fact that the a/c wasn't great even when the car was new, helps explain why so many of these compressors and brackets were pitched and hoses were simply left hanging.

However, neither of these "Bracket on a Bracket" (BOAB?) approaches are a great solution, as using two brackets makes things big, heavy, and rife with opportunity for misalignment. For example, the original big brackets usually had four big rubber bushings in them, and after decades of exposure to heat and oil, these bushings have usually badly deteriorated, creating a lot of play that often results in the compressor pulley being misaligned with the crankshaft pulley. If you're going to the trouble to update the compressor, you really should mount it via a single secure bracket. By far the better approach is to use a small mounting bracket specifically designed to mount the Sanden to the engine block of your car.

The problem is that the availability of these engine-specific Sanden adapter brackets appears to have plummeted. Below, I'll talk about the problem, and how it is addressed, in the vintage BMW world.

Figure 62: A Sanden 508 clone installed on an original York bracket that wraps around the front of the water pump. Arrows show bolts that must be removed to access the water pump.

Fortunately, for a BMW 2002, there is a solution, though it's not exactly click-and-buy. Understand that no BMW 2002 had factory air conditioning. Those that had a/c were was dealer-installed. There were three options. The first was a Behr system whose console looks factory-correct because the Behr system was, in fact, in the BMW parts catalog. The second was a Frigiking system. Both of these used an upright York compressor. But the third option was a Clardy system, mainly installed on late 2002s sold in California and Texas. The Clardy system was unique in that it did not use the York upright compressor; instead, it used—taDA!—the Sanden 508. So it *had* a bracket that directly mounted the 508 to the M10 block.

Four decades later, a guy on bmw2002faq.com who goes by the handle of "02hobiedave" makes reproductions of this Sanden bracket in small batches. The "hobiedave bracket," as it's typically called, is what you need in order to install a Sanden 508 clone compressor in a BMW 2002. Other than the "bracket on a bracket," there's really no other viable option I'm aware of. Typically Dave will solicit orders on

bmw2002faq, then have a batch of brackets made. It may be a few years between batches. But, hey, at least they're out there. Search bmw2002faq.com and you'll find his contact information.

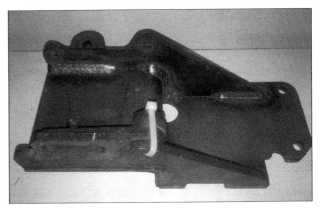

Figure 63: The "hobiedave" bracket. The zip tie is just holding the belt tensioning tabs so they don't get misplaced.

Figure 64: The "hobiedave" bracket bolted up to the 2002 M10 block.

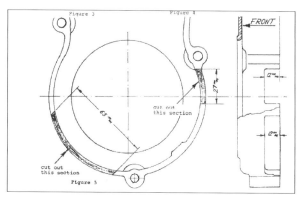

Figure 65: "Hobiedave" bracket and Sanden 508 clone compressor installed on my BMW 2002tii.

Note that, on a 2002tii, a special tii-only pulley, with the groove for the a/c belt located behind the cogged pulley for the toothed injection belt, is required. When a/c was installed in tiis at the dealer, the lower timing cover and the plastic lower injection belt cover were both slotted to receive the a/c belt, so if you're doing a from-scratch installation, this is a necessary part of the process.

Figure 66: Page from the Behr 2002 installation manual showing the necessary cut-outs in the tii's lower injection belt cover. Illustration courtesy Behr of America.

Note also that, because the Sanden 508 and the Hobiedave bracket put the compressor in a different place than the original York, the angle of the belt as it comes on and off the crankshaft is different. On a regular 2002, it doesn't matter, but on a 2002tii, the cut-outs where the belt enters and exits the plastic lower injection belt cover typically need be widened. Below I show how I had to rout out the top notch to get the belt to clear. Issues with the bottom notch are similar.

Figure 67: Top notch (presumably cut at the dealership when new) before additional routing.

Figure 68: Top notch after routing.

Figure 69: Top notch with belt installed.

Bavaria / 3.0CS / 635CSi / E28 5 Series / M30 motor

The M30 "big six" motors that were in E3 Bavarias, E9 3.0CS coupes, E12, E28 and E34 5 Series sedans, E24 6 Series coupes, and E23 7 Series cars from 1968 through 1994 used several different a/c compressors. If you had a Bavaria or an E9, the compressor was same big fat York that most 2002s was saddled with, albeit with a different big bracket for the M30 motor. Unless you are looking for concours-winning originality, no one in their right mind would choose the York compressor and its bracket for a rejuvenation or a from-scratch installation. But at least it didn't wrap around the water pump like it did on a 2002 engine.

When the a/c maintenance needs of M30-equipped cars were in the automotive mainstream, M30/Sanden-specific brackets were sold by Air Products Group (APG), part number 0151A, and widely available through WorldPac, eBay, Amazon, and other outlets. Unfortunately, these brackets are simply no longer available. I called APG directly and chased the issue to ground. APG said they purchased the brackets from another company who has long since gone out of business.

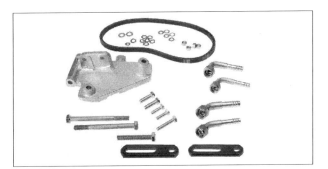

Figure 70: The no-longer-available Air Products Group 0151A bracket to mate a Sanden 508 to a BMW M30 block. Funny, and somewhat wishful thinking, that it also came with barbed-style hose fittings with O-ring ends.

Figure 71: The Sanden 508 clone and 0151A bracket installed in my Bavaria.

So the question then becomes how to mount a Sanden 508 compressor to the M30 block when there is no longer any click-and-buy solution to do so. I wrote about this at great length a few years back on the E9Coupe.com forum, and concluded there was no turn-key solution. (Google "The great Sanden M30 compressor bracket mystery." This was, for years, where Google immediately went if you typed in "BMW Sanden bracket.")

To be absolutely clear about this, one solution is not to use a Sanden 508 compressor at all, and instead use one of the later compressors that BMW used on the M30 that is less objectionable than the boat-anchor York. A number of different compressors were used during the lifetime of the M30 cars. By the late 1980s, the 535i, 635CSi, and 735i all used a fairly compact Bosch Behr rotary vane compressor commonly called a "wing cell" compressor. It has four rounded mounting ears and attaches to the block via a fairly compact mounting bracket with a tensioning tray on the bottom that acts as the belt adjustment mechanism, using the same nifty little toothed track and gear nut used to tighten the fan belt. The BMW E30 3 Series used this same compressor, though with a different mounting bracket. I believe that the Behr Bosch wing-cell compressor is no longer available new unless you find a NOS one in some dusty corner of a dealership, but there's absolutely nothing wrong with buying a rebuilt one and its mounting bracket. The 4 Seasons part number for the wing-cell with the four rounded ears is 57400. Be absolutely certain it has four rounded mounting ears and not two rounded ones and two flat ones; that's a different compressor that uses a different bracket.

For many years, the price of rebuilt 57400s seemed to start at about $350, which, as long as the Sanden adapter brackets were readily available, made the economics clearly in favor of using a new Sanden clone instead of a rebuilt wing-cell. However, some wing-cell rebuilds have been recently appearing on eBay for as low as $160. And, *new* Chinese-made knock-offs of the wing-cell compressor are beginning to show up on eBay for about the same price.

If you read my lengthy post on the E9 forum, you'll see that, after my original "I don't see a turnkey solution" sum-up, some others commented that folks in the E28 world had been working the same Sanden/M30 bracket problem, and a few enterprising individuals had figured out that there was a way to hang a Sanden 508 from a wing-cell bracket and adjust it via the tensioning tray, albeit with a nightmarish kluge of spacers and angle iron. Then, about three years ago, a gentleman named Will Nolan posted on MyE28.com that he'd developed a pair of adapter brackets that allow the Sanden 508 to be adjusted fairly cleanly and easily via the tensioning tray. Mr. Nolan charges about $50 for the pair of adapter brackets. He can be reached at bimmerbrackets@gmail.com.

To use this approach, you need three main pieces:

• A Sanden 508 compressor, or one of its clones. I buy mine for about $110 from one of the eBay suppliers in Irving Texas I've had good luck with. I buy the configuration with a head with o-ring hose fittings and small threaded R12-style charging fittings on the back of the compressor so I don't need to splice charging fittings into the hoses.

• The two main pieces of the wing-cell bracket (the cast aluminum piece, part number 64 52 1 284 953, that mounts to the block, and the tensioning tray, part number 64 52 1 289 076, that attaches to the bottom of the bracket) from a late M30 car like an '89 E24 635CSi. A link on Realoem to the parts diagram can be found here (http://www.realoem.

com/bmw/enUS/showparts?id=5374-USA-04-1989-E24-BMW-635CSi&diagId=64_0430). The bracket and tray are fairly readily available used on eBay; just don't confuse the M30 bracket with the shorter more squared-off M20 bracket. If you can buy a used bracket and tray with all of the bolts that mount the bracket to the block, and the long bolt that holds the tensioning tray to the bracket, and the bolt with the adjuster gear for the toothed track, so much the better.

• The pair of adapter brackets from Will Nolan.

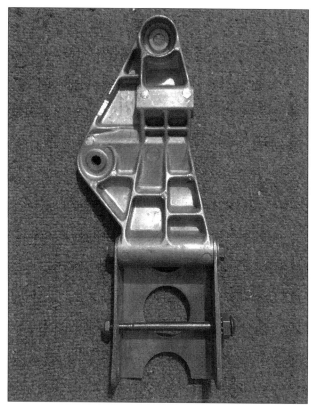

Figure 72: The wing-cell bracket, tensioning tray, and necessary bolts.

Figure 73: Will Nolan's adjusting brackets.

Be aware that, even with Will's adapter brackets, there are some issues with this approach. It is *not* turn-key. If you want a turn-key solution, a fellow named Layne Wylie sells what appears to be a very nicely-engineered solution for about $150. It attaches to the wing-cell bracket but replaces the adjustment tray. You can find more information about it at www. facebook.com/LCWylieAutomotive/.

Figure 74: Layne Wylie's turnkey compressor bracket. Photo courtesy Layne Wylie.

If you're going down the wing-cell bracket route, you have to understand that the purpose of the Will Nolan adapter brackets is *not* to hang the Sanden from the wing-cell bracket. For that, you need to make two modifications listed below to the wing-cell bracket, and hunt down a bolt and a spacer. The purpose of Will's adapter brackets is to allow the bottom of the compressor to be attached to the tensioning tray so it can pivot out and tighten the belt. And it, too,

requires bolts and spacers.

The first required modification to the wing-cell bracket is enlarging the pivot bolt hole. The upper through-hole in the wing-cell bracket that forms the main mounting and pivot point for the compressor is sized for a skinny M8 bolt, whereas the mounting holes in the ears of the Sanden are larger, for a 3/8" bolt. Thus, you either need to use a skinny M8 bolt and risk the compressor moving around (if you take this approach, a 5/16" ID 3/8" OD sleeve available through McMaster-Carr, part number 2868T54, will take up some of the play), or drill out the upper through-hole in the bracket to receive a larger bolt. I found that an M10 bolt is an even better fit to the holes in the Sanden's ears than a 3/8" bolt, so, wanting to minimize slop and misalignment in the mounting of the compressor, I drilled out the bracket's upper hole with a 10mm (0.406") drill bit. I was initially concerned that, since I'm not a machinist and don't have a milling machine, if I didn't keep the drill bit absolutely square with the bracket, the hole could wander off at some angle, but looking at the back of the bracket, I could see that much of the drill path was punctuated by open space. This has the effect of centering the bit whenever it enters a new section of a path through metal.

Figure 75: Note how the holes in the wingcell bracket go through sections, making it easier to drill them out larger without the drill bit wandering.

Figure 76: Drilling out the hole for the pivot bolt in the bracket.

Second, the rear of the bracket needs to be routed out so that the hex head of the M10 (or 3/8") bolt will clear the ridge. It would be nice if you could slide the bolt through the front instead of the rear, but the bolt's hex head won't clear the compressor pulley (at least it wouldn't with my M10 bolt). A Dremel tool with a carbide cutting bit makes routing the needed clearance in the aluminum bracket pretty easy. Make sure that the hex head not only clears the ridge, but that you can get a socket on it.

Figure 77: Wing-cell bracket before and…

Figure 78: …after routing out clearance for the pivot bolt head.

Third, once the bigger bolt can be put through the upper hole in the bracket and the compressor hung from it, you see that the bracket's upper mounting boss is much smaller than the space between the compressor's ears, leaving nearly an inch and a quarter of space where the compressor can slide back and forth on the bolt, so some sort of spacer must be used. And, with all that axial play, where should the compressor even go? The enterprising souls in the E28 world found that, if the compressor is slid all the way forward so the back of the bracket's boss is flush with the compressor's rear mounting ear, the front pulley of the compressor aligns very well with the crankshaft pulley, so any spacers should go *in front of the bracket's boss, between it and the front mounting ear of the compressor.*

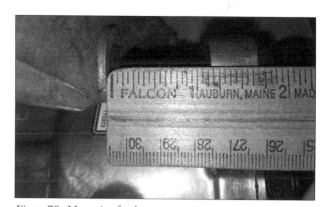

Figure 79: Measuring for the spacer.

Some of the posts on the myE28 forum show the space on the pivot bolt filled up with washers. Perhaps it's a sign that, as I'm getting older, I'm getting less Hack-y, but the thought of using that many washers drives me crazy, so I sought out a solution for a spacer. Using calipers, I measured the size of the gap as 1.236", so you either can use a slightly smaller spacer and make up the difference with washers, or a slightly larger spacer and file it down to fit. 1.25" aluminum spacers with a 3/8" hole are readily available on McMaster-Carr (part number 92511A107), but because I'd elected to use an M10 bolt, I needed a spacer with a slightly larger hole (some 3/8" spacers will let a 10mm bolt through, and others won't). The actual M10 bolt diameter is 0.386". I wound up ordering a 32mm (1.26") long spacer with a 10mm hole from aluminumspacers.com (part number MAS-19-10-32, $3.04 plus $6 shipping), and filed it down to fit. I have to say that that spacer is a simple thing of beauty sitting in that gap.

Figure 80: My spacer is a thing of beauty.

Regarding the length of the pivot bolt, because I was using metric M10 bolts, I was stuck with metric lengths. The 120mm bolt (about 4.72", McMaster part number 91287A381) didn't quite have enough thread length to fit on both a nut and a lock washer, and the 130mm bolt (91287A383) protruded far enough that I thought it would interfere with the inner groove on the pulley. As it happens, it comes close to the pulley but doesn't actually hit it, and you put the belt on the outer groove, not the inner one, so 130mm (5.12") was the right length. If you're using 3/8" bolts, 5" would be correct.

Figure 81: A 130mm bolt just clears the pulley.

The adapter brackets also require some "spacing engineering" to get them to sit flush with the rear-facing sides of the tensioning tray. I used one 10mm washer as a thin spacer between the adapter brackets and the ears of the compressor on the rear-facing side. On the front-facing side, I found some ½" long spacers at my local hardware store that are sized for a 3/8" hole but fit my 10mm bolts (the McMaster part number for a spacer that'll fit both 3/8" and M10 is 93320A315). For the bolts securing the adapter brackets to the compressor, I used 40mm ones (McMaster part number 94036A641) on the rear ears, and 50mm ones (94036A651) on the front ears, the extra length needed to accommodate the spacers.

Figure 82: The wing-cell adjusting tray with Will Nolan's brackets and the appropriate washers and spacers.

Now that the 8mm through-bolt with the adjusting gear nut has to go through not only the adjusting tray but the adapter bracket, it's a little short. The nut still threads on it, but there's barely enough room for a lock washer. The original length is 110mm, so 120mm would be a better length. Unfortunately I don't see any metric carriage bolts on McMaster-Carr longer than 90mm. The other option is to use spacers to put the adapter bracket on the inside of the adjusting tray rather than on the outside. For now, I'll just live with the short bolt.

It's best to test-fit everything (compressor, brackets, adapters, spacers, bolts) on the benchtop and make sure it's right, then take it partially apart and bolt things onto the block. With this Sanden / wing-cell arrangement, you can simply withdraw the main pivot bolt and spacer, and leave the adapter brackets bolted to the compressor. Bolt the main bracket to the block. Compressor brackets experience a fair amount of vibration. I've had bolts back out several times, so even when using lock washers, I also now use a dab of Loctite.

Lastly, test-fit the compressor to the bracket. When you use a non-stock compressor or bracket, you can sometimes have nasty surprises trying to fit the pivot bolt. I've had them not fit from the rear due to obstruction by something else on the engine block, and not fit from the front unless the radiator is first removed. It's best to be aware of these situations so you can plan the rest of the installation accordingly. Note that the radiator usually has to come out anyway in order to install the condenser and fan.

Compressor summary

Although I use the Sanden 508 as the archetypal replacement compressor throughout this book, the approach of using a Sanden 508 clone has been made more difficult by the lack of availability of proper adapter brackets. If the engine in your car had a long service life, there may be a factory compressor and bracket from a later car that used that same engine. As long as you have a new or rebuilt small modern efficient rotary-style compressor, you should be good.

Chapter 7

The Evaporator Assembly

Overview

Of all of the big pieces of the air conditioning system, the evaporator assembly requires the most attention, both in terms of deciding what path to take for retrofit or rejuvenation, as well as the actual time it takes to remove, repair, and re-install. It's really a bit of a pain in the ass.

The **evaporator core**—the part of the a/c system that actually gets cold—almost always lives under the dash, along with **the expansion valve** that the gas expands through, and the **blower fan** that blows the cold air at you. In a modern car, the evaporator core and expansion valve may be somewhat easily accessible, sliding into a compartment behind a side panel on the console (see photo below), but on a vintage car, the evaporator core, expansion valve, and blower fan are usually part of an **evaporator assembly**, often constructed as a plastic case whose top and bottom are clamped, screwed, or riveted shut, requiring the entire assembly to be removed and disassembled in order to service any individual component. Rather a pain, actually.

Figure 83: Evaporator assembly of the type commonly used on a vintage car. It contains the evaporator core, expansion valve, and blower motor. This one was retrofitted into my '79 BMW 635CSi.

Figure 84: A somewhat easy-to-access evaporator core and expansion valve on a 1987 BMW E30 325is, being slid out from the right side of the console.

On an original a/c system or a well-engineered aftermarket one, the evaporator assembly usually sits on the transmission tunnel and is usually surrounded by a well-integrated console, but on some vintage and aftermarket systems, the evap assembly may be a "knee-knocker" that hangs down from the underside of the dashboard. There are also units that sit on top of the dash, and some that mount inside the trunk.

Note that some cars have an **orifice tube** at the inlet to the evaporator instead of an expansion valve. For more information, see the next chapter.

Vintage air conditioning means no "climate control"

First, understand that vintage cars (say, pre-late-70s) generally do not have climate control systems. This means there is no mixing (well, no *intentional* mixing) between the a/c and the heat. The heater box and the evaporator assembly both have their own fan and temperature control switches. The evaporator assembly produces cold air that emerges from a hole in the enclosure. Depending on the car, it may only blow that cold air out the center vent, or it may let you direct the cold dehumidified air at the windshield to defog it, but it doesn't mix the cold air with heated air to allow you to set a less-than-cold temperature. The temperature knob on the evaporator assembly governs only how frequently the compressor cycles (turns on and off), which makes the air alternately warm and cold, but this is *not* the same as a modern car where adjusting a single temperature knob will move a blend door to mix cold air with heated air and produce a single stream of air at a relatively constant temperature. If you're freezing in an old car because the a/c is too cold, count yourself lucky, then you don't complain about it too loudly for fear your friends with non-air-conditioned cars will beat the crap out of you, and finally, lower the fan speed and aim the blowers away from you.

Now that you understand this, you can appreciate the different options for the evaporator console and how they affect the look and feel of the interior.

Things you need to know for rejuvenation or retrofit

The evaporator work has the potential to be the most time-consuming and most nerve-wracking of all of the tasks. Or it can be nearly no work at all. Here's why.

The gamble of leaving it in place versus removing it and opening it up

As I said, on later cars, the evaporator core and expansion valve are usually accessed by removing the right side of the console and simply sliding them out (in the BMW world, this starts with the E30 3 Series and the E28 5 Series), but in a vintage car (in the BMW world, in a 2002, Bavaria, E21 3 Series, E9, E12, or early E24), the evaporator core, expansion valve, and blower motor are contained inside an evaporator assembly, a plastic tub with lower and upper halves. The assembly is mounted under the dash. On a front-engine rear-wheel-drive car (which most vintage cars are), the evap assembly sits on the transmission hump.

If a car has a long-dormant a/c system that you want to rejuvenate, and you're staying with the original R12 refrigerant, and the system has remained closed, and when you remove the hoses to the compressor you find no evidence of contamination (no metal shavings or powdery residue or black goo fall out of the compressor line), and the evaporator blower fan works fine, then you can roll the dice and leave the evaporator assembly alone, update the other

components, pressure-test, evacuate, and recharge, and, with a little luck, it'll be okay.

But if the system was left open (if, for example, the compressor was removed to save weight and the hoses were left hanging, or if a hose hit the exhaust manifold and melted), you're foolish to go to all the work of a/c rejuvenation without flushing the system to remove contamination, and that requires removing the evaporator assembly, disassembling it, removing the expansion valve, and flushing the evaporator core. And, if you're doing that, you should probably replace the expansion valve while you're in there. If you can rig something up to pressure-test the core and the attached expansion valve, do it. Feed the fan motor 12v and test it. It has to move enough air over that evaporator core to make this whole exercise worthwhile. If the motor seems anemic, or is loud and squeaky, you might want to have it and the squirrel cages rebuilt. At a minimum you can oil the bearings and wash the fan motor brushes down with contact cleaner.

Remember also that the evaporator assembly has to allow water formed through condensation to drain. Typically there's a small rubber hose that exits from the bottom. You need to verify that this hose is present, that it isn't blocked, and that it protrudes through the hole in the transmission tunnel.

Figure 85: Drain tube from evaporator assembly in a BMW 2002 passing through hole in transmission hump.

Flushing when changing refrigerants

There are several other fulcrum points for the decision on whether to remove the evaporator assembly. First, if you are changing refrigerants (e.g., converting from R12 to R134a), you need to make sure that all of the old mineral oil is out of the system, and the best way to that is to disassemble the evaporator and flush it. You can't really properly flush the evaporator with the assembly in the car, as the expansion valve blocks the flow of the flushing chemical. You can try to "pop-flush" it (see below), but it's not as effective.

Replacing the expansion valve

Second, if you're converting to R134a, some folks say that you should change to an R134a-specific expansion valve. On a car with a slide-out evaporator core, the expansion valve is fairly easily accessible, but on a car with an evaporator assembly, it's inside the box, requiring removal and disassembly of the evaporator assembly. If I'm rejuvenating a system, and if I have to open up the evaporator assembly, I make sure to install the expansion valve that's correct for the refrigerant I plan to use, but I can't say whether I'm certain it really matters or not.

Synergy with heater box repair

Third, the evaporator assembly sits behind the heater box, and in vintage cars, it's very common for the foam to wear off heater box's flaps, making it so you can't ever fully block off the flow of hot ambient air into the passenger cabin, which, obviously, impedes the performance of the a/c system. In addition, it's common for the blower motors in heater boxes to die. The heater box has to come out to re-line the flaps with foam, and, depending on the model, may have to come out to change the fan. The point is that it's kind of silly to pull the evaporator assembly and re-install it without doing the "while you're in there" thing and addressing any needed issues with the heater box. This makes sense, but it magnifies the scope of the job.

Risk of damage

Last, and perhaps most important, taking the evaporator assembly out is simply a colossal pain in the ass, and on a vintage car, risks damage to the assembly and to the parts you need to remove in order to get it out. The console has to come out, and on a vintage car, there's risk of tearing the vinyl on the side pieces and having the ancient particle board side pieces crack or dissolve. With a system that originally used R12, the hoses or hard pipes that connect to the evaporator usually have flare fittings, and they're very tight. If they weren't leaking, you run the risk of making them leak when you disassemble them and put them back together, or, worse, twisting them off.

Plus, in a car like a BMW 3.0CS or a Bavaria, there's a plastic duct piece (the "intermediate piece") that connects the evaporator assembly to the dashboard vents. This kind mid-1970s plastic is *very* brittle and often cracks if you disturb it and shatters if you twist it.

My approach

For these reasons, I've adopted the following approach: If the system was closed, and if I'm not converting from R12 to R134a, and if the heater box doesn't require attention, and if, when I pull the hoses off the compressor, I don't find any contamination, then I roll the dice and leave the evaporator assembly alone. I did this with my Bavaria, and the gamble paid off; it has knee-freezing air conditioning without my ever having touched the evaporator assembly. But if any of those assumptions is false, then I pull the evaporator assembly out, disassemble it, flush it, and replace the expansion valve.

Flushing

To fully flush the evaporator core, remove and disassemble the evaporator assembly, remove the expansion valve, and flush the core using a canister of a/c flush chemical in a container pressurized by a compressor and fed through an air gun with a rubber tip. By putting a rubber hose on the other end of the evaporator and feeding it into a jar, you can collect the waste chemical. As I said, if there's no evidence of contamination, you can instead leave the assembly installed and try "pop-flushing" it in place, squirting in the pressurized flushing chemical until the pressure builds up and it sprays back out, but it's really messy (if you do it, **wear eye protection**) and not nearly as effective as removing the expansion valve and fully flushing the evaporator core.

Figure 86: Only when the expansion valve is removed can the evaporator core be thoroughly flushed.

Replacing the expansion valve

When replacing the expansion valve on a vintage system that uses flare fittings, use new copper flare crush washers coated with Nylog gasket and thread sealant. Note that, when you tighten flare fittings, it's very different from tightening o-ring fittings. The latter need only be tight enough to lightly squeeze the o-ring, which is what is actually doing the sealing. With flare fittings, though, it's the copper-on-copper part that's the actual sealing surface. You want them tight, though you need to take care not to overtighten them and crack the copper flares (been there, cracked that). Be sure to put the "holding wrench" on the square part of the expansion valve to hold it still while you tighten the collar nut with the other wrench.

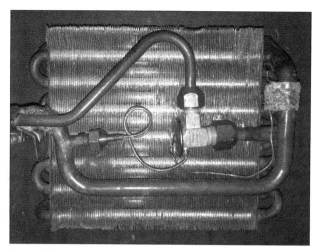

Figure 87: A new expansion valve installed. Note the square bosses where a holding wrench can be put while tightening the collar nuts.

Pressure-testing

There are few things in the auto repair world more frustrating to me than going to all the work to install or repair an a/c system, carefully removing the evaporator assembly, rebuilding it, and reinstalling it, only to find that the evaporator core is leaking at one of the joints to the expansion valve and the whole assembly has to come back out. So these days, I pressure-test a newly-assembled evaporator core and expansion valve before I install it.

To do this, you need to plug up one end of the evaporator/expansion valve, and make a hose with a charging fitting on it that connects to the other end. On the '79 BMW 635CSi evap assembly that's in the photos below, this meant using a ½" (#8) flare plug and a 5/8" (#10) flare union, both of which can be purchased at any hardware store. This is a perfect example where you need the table I have in the Fittings chapter showing the correspondence between the hose numbers and the so-called tube sizes. Hardware stores will have the flare unions and block-off plugs, but you need to know that the #10 fitting is 5/8", and the #8 fitting is ½".

Figure 88: 5/8" (#10) flare union (left) and ½" (#8) flare plug (right) for evaporator pressure testing.

Next, you make a hose that, at one end has a 5/8" flare fitting and a charging port, and at the other end is blocked off.

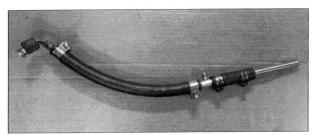

Figure 89: My home-made block-off hose with a 5/8" (#10) flare fitting and a charging port.

Then you connect the charging port to the blue (low pressure) side of a manifold gauge set, and connect the yellow hose of the gauge set to a nitrogen bottle. This lets you pressurize the evaporator with nitrogen. Then you shut off the nitrogen, close off the blue valve on the manifold gauge set, and wait 24 hours to see if the pressure drops. For more information, see the chapter on Pressure-Testing with Nitrogen.

Figure 90: The evaporator core and expansion valve connected to the nitrogen tank for pressure testing. Photo for reference only. Any pressurized cylinder should either be chained or in a self-supporting cart.

The added complexity of evaporator issues in a late '70s car

It is useful to step through the increasing level of complexity of installing an evaporator assembly in an early '70s BMW 2002 and a 3.0CSi, and a late '70s 635CSi. By modern a/c standards, they're all primitive, but it provides a window into why, the older the car is, the easier a/c retrofit or rejuvenation is.

2002 evaporator

A 2002s evaporator assembly has the electrical controls (temperature and fan speed, where zero fan speed shuts the a/c off) dangling right off it, and the output vent is right there on the front of the box. There's no ventilation interface to the car, and the electrical interface is just a few wires. There is a bracket that you're supposed to screw into the tunnel to hold the assembly there, but it's often missing or the attachment points on the box are often cracked. As long as the evaporator drain is over the hole in the transmission hump, you almost *can* just sit the assembly on the tunnel and hook up the refrigerant lines. Any other clearance and alignment issues are virtually nonexistent.

E3 / E9 evaporator

On an E3 or an E9 (3.0CS or Bavaria), it's a little more complicated. Electrically, the switches still dangle from the evaporator assembly and mount to a faceplate, but the assembly doesn't have its own front-mounted air output vent like a 2002. Instead, the evap assembly is open at the top, and uses what's listed in RealOEM as the "intermediate piece," sort of like a box of Kleenex turned on its side and open at the top and bottom, that connects it to the dashboard vents. Therefore, servicing the evaporator assembly on these cars involves removing and installing the intermediate piece. It's plastic from the mid-1970s, and it cracks into splinters if you even look at it too hard. For this reason, I try not to pull the evaporator assembly out of E3s or E9s unless there is incontrovertible evidence of contamination or a failed component inside.

BMW E24 (635CSi) evaporator

On my 1979 Euro 635CSi, like the E3 and E9, the evaporator assembly is open at the top (see photo at the start of the chapter), so clearly some sort of intermediate piece was required.

Block-off plate for intermediate piece

When I bought the pieces to retrofit air into the car, I was incredibly fortunate that the gentleman from whom I purchased the evaporator assembly sold me not only the assembly, but *everything* it touched on the inside of the Euro '79 635CSi he was parting out. This included the "intermediate piece." Though it wasn't immediately clear to me, it turned out that, on the underside of the dashboard ventilation ductwork in my car, there was a block-off cover with guitar case–like latches that snapped it in place. I needed to unsnap it and substitute the intermediate piece.

Figure 91: The snap-on under-dash cover in an early BMW 635CSi that is replaced by intermediate piece.

I replaced the deteriorated foam around the openings of the intermediate piece to reduce the chance that the precious chilled air from the evaporator assembly would leak out before blowing in my face, then installed the piece.

Figure 92: The intermediate piece, with the sealing surface to the evaporator assembly lined with foam to prevent cold air from escaping.

Figure 93: The intermediate piece snapped into place.

Securing the bracket to the hump

Before installing the evaporator assembly, I needed to mount the bracket that holds it on the transmission hump and drill the drain hole. Fortunately, when I pulled back the carpet, I found that there were cutouts in the sound deadening material where the feet of the bracket needed to go.

Figure 94: Cut-outs in the sound deadening material in my 635CSi for the evaporator bracket and drain locations.

Unfortunately, once I pulled the cut-outs away, there was nearly an inch of uncertainty in the bracket position. I shrugged, put the bracket about in the middle of the cutouts, eyeballed it so it wasn't cocked side to side, and marked and drilled the holes for the screws holding it in place. I then marked the hole for the drain and drilled it.

Figure 95: Routing out the drain hole.

Figure 96: The placed bracket with the drain hole guide over the drain hole.

I attached the bracket, but left the screws loose so it had some play on the transmission hump. I then test-fit the evaporator assembly onto the bracket, sliding it in place at an angle, then up and into the intermediate piece. I looked up top to make sure that the assembly was seating correctly on the intermediate piece and not twisting it, and looked beneath the assembly to verify that the drain tube went into the hole I'd drilled. I appeared to have gotten the bracket location about right, so I took the assembly back out, tightened the bracket in place, then reinstalled the assembly.

Dual-use fan and temperature controls

Unlike the other cars in which I'd done retrofits, the evaporator assembly on the 635CSi had no temperature or fan speed controls hanging off it. Instead, the heater control panel in the center of the dash needed to be replaced with a climate control panel whose temperature and fan speed knobs controlled both the heater box and the evaporator assembly, switching between them via a relay. Fortunately this was part of the parts package I'd bought, and swapping it was pretty straightforward.

For more information, consult the Electrical and Retrofit chapters.

Issues in adapting a modern climate control box

If you're performing a from-scratch a/c retrofit, one tempting option is to try to adapt one of the modern aftermarket units that offer genuine climate control—an evaporator and heater core in the same box with their streams blended together—that gives you a single-knob single-fan single-air-stream solution. Part of the appeal is that a modern box has a modern fan motor that likely moves a lot more air than the ancient squirrel cages in an original evaporator assembly. These boxes are quite popular in the hot rod world, where much of the gestalt is a roll-your-own one anyway, and there's little eyeball-rolling at components that aren't original.

However, there are four substantial issues with trying to make one of these boxes work in your car. I wish I could say that I've solved them. I haven't. I'm just warning you at the think-it-through level.

The first is that the unit has to physically fit under the dashboard. On a front-engine rear-wheel-drive vintage car, this means the unit has to fit on top of the transmission hump and under the dash. On a small car like BMW 2002, there's very little space there. I was interested enough in trying this in my

2002tii that I paid $75 to buy a "mock-up box" (the empty plastic housing) of a Hurricane 2000 climate control unit, and it did not fit, at least not at the level of the box simply sliding into place without trimming anything off it or the underside of the dash.

Figure 97: My attempt to test-fit a Hurricane 2000 climate control box in my BMW 2002tii. I couldn't get it to fit under the dash and on the transmission hump.

Next is that, because these boxes contain a heater core, the car's existing heater box needs to be removed. Since the stock heater core and fan usually reside in a heater box that sits against the firewall in a very specifically-sized cut-out, it's likely that the firewall cut-out needs to be completely blocked off. As part of this blocking off, you have to understand that, on most vintage cars, the path that the fresh air takes is through this opening and then through the heater box. Thus, if you block off the opening, and if the climate control box doesn't offer another path for fresh air (and most don't), you've eliminated the ability to get fresh air into the car unless you open a window. To me, this alone is a non-starter. Maybe it's not to you, but you should be aware of it.

Figure 98: The large rectangular cut-out in the firewall of a BMW 2002 for a heater box. If you replace it with a climate control box, this entire opening must be blocked off.

Next, you need to interface the knobs and the flap controls on one of these units with the existing dash sliders and ductwork on your car. If you have a common well-supported vintage American car like a Mustang, you may be able to find a kit that does this for you from a company like Old Air Products, Vintage Air, or Nostalgic AC Parts, but if you're looking to, say, interface one of these to a BMW 2002, you're probably on your own.

Lastly, there's the issue of the console. Since none of these units is even remotely stock, good luck wrapping it all in an original console, or at least one that looks remotely period-correct. Of course, you might not care how it looks. Maybe you *want* it custom. Maybe you want to build your own console out of burled walnut, an old saddle, and pieces of Barbie's playhouse, and if that's the case, more power to you. But the console is literally in the center of the dashboard. It's something the eye is immediately drawn to, particularly if it's non-original. The more non-stock a console looks, the more it is a reflection of your personal taste, and thus the more chancy it is that, when you sell the car, the prospective buyer will share your taste. The more valuable the car is, the larger an issue this is. For this reason, folks are well-advised to, whatever they do for an evaporator assembly, stick with a console that looks as close to stock as humanly possible.

Adapting a modern evaporator assembly

The second option is to abandon the pipe dream of climate control but opt for a modern aftermarket evaporator assembly. This gives the benefit of an evaporator core and expansion valve optimized for R134a, and a modern fan that moves more air than the original antiquated unit. You won't have to remove the heater box like with the climate control option, but you still have the other problems. You're on your own regarding getting the new evaporator assembly to fit under the dashboard and on the transmission hump. And there's no guarantee you can sandwich one of these units inside an original console. You may start off thinking that a universal evaporator assembly will fit the bill perfectly fine, but then decide that it's out of sync with the look and feel of your car (trust me, there's no value judgment here). This was precisely what happened to me with my BMW 3.0CSi.

Using a stock evaporator assembly

The last option is the one many people, including me, select, and the one that I document throughout this book—finding an original, used evaporator assembly, flushing it out, replacing the expansion valve, testing the motor, and surrounding it with a stock console. Particularly when combined with a new rotary compressor and a larger parallel-flow condenser, most folks find this provides the right compromise of look, feel, and performance.

BMW 2002-specific evaporator information

As I said in the compressor chapter, no BMW 2002 had factory-installed air conditioning. There were, however, three dealer-installed systems: Behr, Frigiking, and Clardy. Of the three, the one that is generally regarded as having the most factory-looking console is the Behr system. This is not accidental, as the Behr system was the one that was in the BMW parts catalog. In look and construction, it is very similar to the factory-installed Behr systems in the BMW E9 (3.0CS) coupe and E3 (Bavaria) four-door sedan. The family resemblance of the 2002 console to that of its two big brothers includes side panels with two long ears that extend past the shift lever. This adds quite a bit to the factory look.

Figure 99: The Behr a/c console in a 1972 BMW 2002tii.

However, the Behr system does have drawbacks. The evaporator core, expansion valve, and motor with two "squirrel cage" fans are all inside an evaporator assembly with a plastic housing, the upper and lower halves of which are held together with snap-on clips. Service of any of the three major components requires removal and disassembly. With age, the plastic gets brittle, and sometimes pulling the clips to disassemble the housing causes the plastic that the clips snap around to crack off.

There is a single louvered vent at the top of the assembly, though the left and right sides can be aimed independently. The faceplate is trapezoidal in shape, with a single cutout at the top for the louvered vent from the evaporator. Like the assembly itself, the faceplate is plastic and tends to become fragile with age.

But even with these drawbacks, a Behr console and a period-correct radio provide a great stock look, and when coupled with a rotary-style compressor and large parallel flow condenser and aux fan, gets cold and moves enough air.

Figure 100: The Behr evaporator assembly showing its integrated louvers and snap-on clips holding it together.

The next dealer-installed system is the Frigiking system. Like the Behr, the Frigiking system has a plastic evaporator assembly that houses the core and fan. However, unlike the Behr evaporator assembly, on the Frigiking, the expansion valve protrudes from the back and can thus be replaced without disassembling the assembly. The front of the assembly has a large rectangular hole that lets the air blow through two vertically-oriented louvered vents in the console faceplate. The Frigiking doesn't have a full length console that extends past the shift lever. There are side-pieces that hide the evaporator assembly, but it lacks the overall factory look of the Behr evap assembly and its console.

Figure 101: The Frigiking console. Photo courtesy Chris Roberts.

Figure 102: The back of the Frigiking console, showing the accessible expansion valve. Photo courtesy Chris Roberts.

Figure 103: Front view of Clardy console. Wood ashtray surround is non-stock. Photo courtesy Earl Meyers.

Figure 104: Right side of Clardy console showing fan bulge into passenger side footwell. Photo courtesy Earl Meyers.

The third option, the Clardy system, installed primarily on late (1974–1976) 2002s sold in California and Texas, is very different, and, well, a little weird looking. Unlike the Behr and Frigiking, it does not use a closed plastic evaporator assembly with two squirrel cage fans. Instead, the blower motor—a single squirrel cage in a wrap-around horn housing—is located on the right side, hanging into the passenger side footwell, making the whole thing look a bit asymmetric. The fan blows sideways into the right side of the evaporator core, which is surrounded by an enclosure that smaller than the Behr or Frigiking. The faceplate has two vents side-by-side at the top allowing independent air placement for the driver and passenger.

Below is the Clardy evaporator assembly and its side-mounted fan. You can clearly see how, with the fan outside the enclosure, the enclosure itself is smaller and thinner than both the Behr and Frigiking evap assemblies.

Figure 105: The Clardy evaporator assembly from the front, showing the thin enclosure surrounding the evaporator core, and the side-mounted blower fan. Photo courtesy Clyde Gates.

Like the Frigiking console, the Clardy console has the expansion valve outside the assembly, making it so that disassembly is not required to change the expansion valve. Further, the expansion valve is not the older-style externally-regulated valve used by both the Behr and Frigiking systems, but is instead the newer-style internally-regulated expansion valve found on BMW E30 3 Series and E28 5 Series cars.

Figure 106: The rear of the Clardy evaporator assembly, showing the accessible internally-regulated expansion valve. Photo courtesy Clyde Gates.

After working on a 2002 that had the Clardy system, I was very impressed. As I said, because there's not a hard evaporator tub like the Behr and Frigiking, the fan (which I was replacing) can be accessed without removing and dismantling an evaporator assembly like the other two systems. The fan moved a lot of air. And, most important, I shot one can of R134a into it, and it blew nice and cold.

Although the Clardy system is the least common of

the three, I mention it for an additional reason. There is a vendor (ICE AC) who sells an a/c system for the BMW 2002 whose console appears to be patterned after the Clardy console, with a fan that protrudes into the passenger footwell. ICE AC also claims to have a bracket, different from the "hobiedave" bracket, that allows a Sanden 508 clone compressor to be mounted to the BMW 2002's M10 engine block. Another vendor (Dtechparts) claims to offer an a/c climate control box for a 2002, and their website shows it fit into a console whose side-by-side vents somewhat resemble those of a Clardy console. I include this reference only, as I have no direct experience with the products from either vendor. Whether you regard either of these options as satisfying the goal of "looks stock but performs new," as the vendors doubtless would like, is your call

Evaporator summary

If an OEM evaporator assembly and console exists for your car, I recommend that you err on the side of using it. The more valuable the car, the more of an issue the look of originality of the interior is. If you are considering using a climate control box instead, I recommend you look at photos of a successful installation (or, better yet, see one in person), and decide whether you can live with its non-stock appearance.

Figure 107: For preserving the value of a car, nothhing beats an original console, faceplate, and vent.

Chapter 8

The Expansion Valve / Orifice Tube

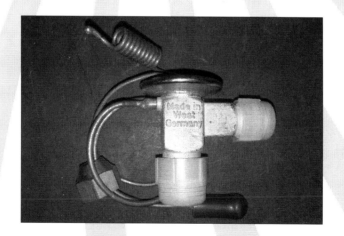

Overview

I briefly discussed the expansion valve in the previous chapter on the evaporator assembly, but it deserves its own moment in the sun. (Whereas it's usually deeply buried. A little air conditioning humor there.)

If the compressor is the beating heart of the system, the expansion valve is the, well, I'm actually hard-pressed to come up with a good bodily organ analogy, but it's the component that enables the whole "a gas cools when it expands" principle. Maybe the pyloric sphincter. Yeah, we'll go with pyloric sphincter.

Since another heat transfer analogy is that our bodies cool themselves by perspiring—by pumping sweat out our pores and letting it evaporate on our skin—you could say that the expansion valve is like a skin pore. Nah, I'm sticking with pyloric sphincter. Way funnier.

At the heuristic level, the expansion valve (or, its sister, the orifice tube) imposes a restriction in the path of the liquid refrigerant. More formally, the expansion valve and orifice tube are *metering devices* controlling the amount of refrigerant released into the evaporator. The restriction creates a Venturi effect—there's a reduction in pressure as the liquid refrigerant spits through the valve. This allows the refrigerant to boil, evaporate into a gas, expand, and absorb heat inside the evaporator assembly to cool the passenger compartment. The compressor gets all the glory, but the expansion valve is where all the action is.

Orifice tube

Let's actually start with the orifice tube. It lives inside the connection (inside the metal pipe) heading into the evaporator assembly from the condenser. It's a small cylindrical brass tube that's coupled with a cylindrical mesh screen that acts as a filter. Both the tube and the filter are part of a small package that looks a little like, I don't know, say, a slightly nasty-looking rectal thermometer in that it has a tab on the end that allows you to grip it and stick it in or pull it out. (Hey, I'm not the one who named it an orifice tube. But I do need to justify that pyloric sphincter

analogy.)

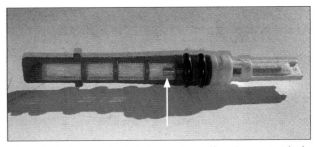

Figure 108: Orifice tube. The brass tube itself can be seen inside the mesh filter.

If a system has an orifice tube instead of an expansion valve, it also has an accumulator instead of a receiver-drier. The accumulator is located on the low-pressure side of the system, between the evaporator outlet and the compressor inlet, and holds excess liquid refrigerant that may come out of the evaporator.

The main thing about an orifice tube is that it is simply a fixed restriction with no moving parts. There's a constant pressure drop across it. The pressure drop doesn't change in response to evaporator temperature or pressure like the expansion valve does. A compressor clutch cycling switch on the accumulator is employed to turn the compressor on and off in response to evaporator outlet pressure.

Expansion valve

Unlike the orifice tube, the expansion valve (sometimes called a *thermal expansion valve* or TXV) *does* have moving parts. It is a metering device that adjusts the amount of refrigerant entering the evaporator in much the same way that a mechanical thermostat adjusts how much antifreeze passes through the radiator. If the output from the evaporator is warm, the valve opens to let more refrigerant in so it can boil, evaporate, expand, and cool. If the output from the evaporator is very cold, the valve may close for a short amount of time and not allow refrigerant in in order to prevent the system from freezing up.

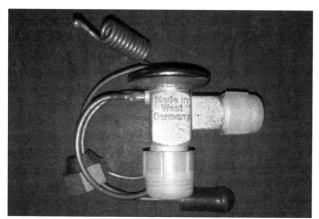

Figure 109: A "New Old Stock" (NOS) externally-equalized expansion valve for a vintage BMW. Nothing says NOS like "Made in West Germany."

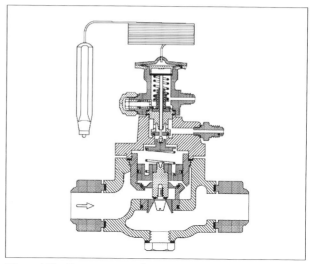

Figure 110: Cutaway view of an expansion valve. Photo courtesy wikicommons.

The opening and closing of the valve is handled as follows. A spring-loaded diaphragm (the disc-shaped piece about the size of a quarter that's on the outside of the expansion valve) moves a rod which, in turn, opens and closes the passageway that the refrigerant flows through. A sensing bulb is attached to the output pipe of the evaporator. The sensing bulb is ideally filled with the same kind of refrigerant that the system is using. The refrigerant travels up a capillary tube from the sensing bulb and pushes against the spring-loaded diaphragm. The refrigerant inside the evaporator core is pushing at the diaphragm from the other side. Together, the temperature / pressure from the sensing bulb, the pressure inside the evaporator core, and the spring tension determine whether and how far to open the valve. When driving a vintage car with an expansion valve, you can often hear the evaporator "sigh" as the valve opens a bit, lets more refrigerant in, and it boils.

There are a few things to note. First, the room-temperature state (or, for that matter, the steady-state state) of the valve is open. So if the system is empty of refrigerant and you have access to the inlet and outlet pipes, either because the hose connections are off or because the evaporator assembly has been removed from the car, you should be able to blow into the input pipe and have *some* air come out the outlet pipe, though not a gushing flow because, even when the valve is open, it *is* a restriction.

Second, the fact that the sensing bulb is filled with the same kind of refrigerant as used in the evaporator is the reason why there are R12-specific and R134a-specific expansion valves. As I've said, if I have the evaporator removed and apart, I install a new version of the correct expansion valve, but I can't swear that it makes a big difference one way or another.

Third, when replacing the expansion valve, the sensing bulb should be wrapped in cork tape to ensure that it only senses the temperature of the outlet pipe at the evaporator.

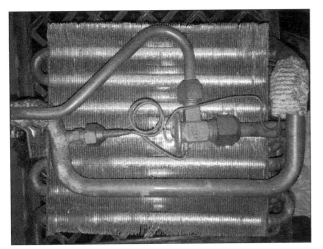

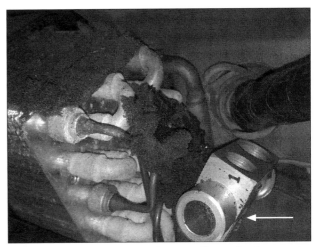

Figure 111: Sensing bulb should be wrapped in cork tape, as shown upper right.

Figure 112: Modern block-style internally-equalized expansion valve.

Last, there are two types of expansion valves—externally-equalized and internally-equalized. Technically, as the names imply, the externally-equalized valves monitor the pressure externally at the evaporator outlet, and the internally-equalized valves monitor at the evaporator inlet. But, from a practical standpoint, at least in the BMW world, the internally-equalized expansion valves are the more modern-looking block-shaped devices pictured below, with holes in them to receive pipes with o-ring fittings, and are easily removable from the outside of the evaporator core without having to remove and disassemble an evaporator assembly. In contrast, the externally-equalized valves are the older ones as pictured above that are hidden inside an evaporator assembly that must be removed and disassembled, and have flare fittings and a long capillary tube to the sensing bulb.

Expansion valves can fail in a number of ways. They can simply become clogged with debris, or they can mechanically fail in the open or closed position, or a fixed position in between. For more information, see the Troubleshooting chapter.

Chapter 9

The Condenser

Overview

The condenser is the part of the a/c system that dumps the heat produced by the compression of the refrigerant from a gaseous to a liquid phase. In virtually every front-engine car, the condenser is in front of the radiator in the nose of the car, and is almost always coupled with an electric cooling fan. In mid- or rear-engine air-cooled cars without a grille opening in the nose (e.g., vintage Porsches and Volkswagens), the condenser may be in the deck or trunk lid, or multiple condensers may be employed and stuck wherever they'll fit and wherever there's air flow (under the car, behind fender scoops, etc).

Owing to their front-mounted location, condensers are susceptible to punctures from road debris. It's also not uncommon for them to develop leaks from corrosion where sand and salt have been kicked up and it sits between the fins and tubes and causes corrosion.

Figure 113: Road debris?! I'll give you road debris! The condenser in my BMW 3.0CSi had a clevis pin from a truck smash into it. Miraculously, the pin embedded right between two passes of the serpentine tubes without puncturing the condenser.

However, in the vintage car context, the condenser is the part of the a/c, along with the compressor, that is most frequently replaced and updated as part of a systematic rejuvenation whose goal is to not only resurrect a long-dormant a/c system but also to improve system performance (below).

Serpentine versus parallel flow

Remember from the Theory chapter that heat always flows from a warmer body to a colder one. The condenser must run at a hotter temperature

than that of the ambient air in order to shed its heat. The way any condenser (or radiator, for that matter) maximizes its ability to dump heat is to maximize the surface area between the liquid carrying the heat and the outside world. Original condensers in vintage cars have a tube-and-fin-style "serpentine flow" design, meaning that one continuous tube snakes back-and-forth through the finned condenser. The smaller the tube, the more of the refrigerant is actually touching the inside of the tube, facilitating heat transfer. Similarly, the higher the fin density, the more efficiently that heat can be shed to the outside. Early condensers had 3/8" copper tubes and a fin density of 10-12 per inch. Over time, the industry gravitated to ¼" aluminum tubes with a fin density of 14-16 per inch. Both of these worked well for R12 systems, but they are often found to be inadequate when systems are converted to R134a, particularly when the systems are small and the climate is very hot.

Parallel flow condensers use tubes that are each about one or two square millimeters in diameter, ganged together in parallel so they appear to be one wide tube. Because the tubes are small, much more of the refrigerant is in direct contact with the inside of the tube. This greatly improves heat transfer. These groups of tubes are replicated and stretch horizontally across the condenser looking like rungs on a ladder. So the "parallel" thing is going on at two different levels—a very small one, and a very obvious one.

The fin density of parallel flow condensers is also higher than old serpentine flow units, typically 18-24 fins per inch. This also aids in cooling.

In the photo below, an original serpentine condenser from a BMW 2002 and a replacement parallel flow condenser are both shown. The old serpentine unit is in the foreground, with its serpentine tubes clearly showing. The new parallel flow condenser is in the background.

Figure 114: Serpentine flow (foreground) and parallel flow (background) condensers.

Parallel flow condensers were first introduced in the late 1980s, shortly before the changeover from R12 to R134a. They were eventually adopted by all manufacturers to help compensate for R134a's decreased cooling performance in comparison to R12, but that didn't happen instantly. This is one of the reasons why many folks feel that cars sold just after the federally-mandated change in 1994, or cars that were retrofitted from R12 to R134a, don't cool as well as the R12-charged brethren and sistern. Depending on the manufacturer and model, a car may have been supplied with a less-efficient serpentine flow condenser up through about the year 2000.

Figure 115: New parallel-flow condenser retrofitted into my 1973 BMW 3.0CSi.

To improve a/c performance in a vintage car,

particularly when converting from R12 to R134a, you want to install as large a modern parallel-flow condenser as will fit in the nose. In extreme cases, folks have been known to daisy-chain two of them together, running the output of the first into the input of the second.

The only real downside of parallel flow condensers is that, owing to the tiny diameter of the cooling tubes, they are much more prone to blockage and resist cleaning if the system is contaminated by "the Black Death" (see the Compressor chapter). For this reason, in the event of system contamination, it is strongly recommended that a parallel flow condenser be replaced instead of flushed.

Drop-in versus universal fit

Whether they're serpentine or parallel flow, condensers are classified as "universal fit" or "drop-in replacements." Universal fit models have brackets with dozens of equally-spaced holes on all four edges, and hose fittings that usually stick straight out one side.

Figure 116: Universal-fit parallel flow condenser.

In contrast, the drop-in replacements are designed to replace the original condenser, and as such have brackets and hose fittings in the same places as the original. The hose fittings are sometimes "block fittings," where rather than individual threaded input and output hose fittings, there's a flat mounting flange for one or both fittings to which the hoses—which also have block fittings—attach with a single bolt.

Unfortunately, unless there was a manufacturer-ordered change as part of the car's life cycle, it's pretty rare to find a drop-in replacement parallel flow condenser for a car that originally only ever had a serpentine flow unit.

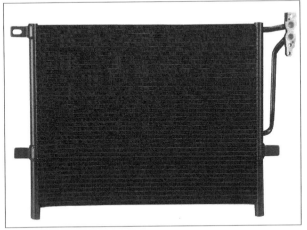

Figure 117: Drop-in parallel flow condenser with proper brackets attached. Photo courtesy TYC.

Installing a universal fit parallel-flow condenser

In order to select and install a "universal fit" parallel flow condenser, what you need to do is measure carefully and determine the largest unit that'll fit into the nose of the car, mount it by hook or by crook, mount a big electric fan either on it or in front of it, and either adapt your existing hoses to fit the new condenser or fabricate new ones. If you're doing a from-scratch installation, you're fabricating new hoses anyway, but if all that you want to do is replace the original obsolete serpentine flow condenser with a modern parallel flow unit to get the system to cool better, the bracket and hose adaptation are a fair amount of work.

Because of this, in the BMW 635CSi world, for a brief period, an enterprising company sold a drop-in parallel flow condenser specifically designed to replace the 635CSi's original serpentine condenser, with the mounting brackets and hose fittings in the same place. Unfortunately these appear to have been like Brigadoon, emerging from the mists only to disappear from the marketplace a short time later. Folks still ask about them on web forums. Perhaps

in a hundred years they'll become available again. Until then, you just have to roll up your sleeves and adapt a universal unit. (Note that, for a BMW E30 3-series, there *does* appear to be a drop-in parallel-flow condenser; see the section at the end of this chapter.)

I mention the 635CSi because I recently did a from-scratch a/c retrofit into mine. I'm going to use it in this chapter as a very specific example of exactly what you need to do to spec, procure, and install a universal parallel-flow condenser.

Measuring to determine the biggest condenser that'll fit

The process I use for determining condenser size is this: Measure, sanity-check against web forums, decide whether to err on the conservative or aggressive side, purchase, test-fit, return if necessary, install the cooling fan (see next chapter), then permanently mount. Fortunately, the universal fit units are inexpensive enough (often $60 or less) that even if you need to eat one before you come up with the optimal size, it's not big money.

When measuring and ordering, the condenser's width measurement is much more critical than the height measurements. This is because the quoted width dimension of the condenser doesn't include the brackets or the hose fittings that have to attach to the side, so it's easy to get the width wrong. In contrast, the height measurement is less squishy. You do need to understand the difference between the height of the cut-out in front of the radiator through which you need to pass the condenser to get it into the nose, and the height of the space inside the nose. Typically, if you tilt the condenser, you can get a bigger one in there than the size of the cut-out. But the height is less critical than the width; I've never bought a condenser and had it not fit because I'd blown the height measurement. The cut-out height in my 635CSi is about 17 inches.

Here's how the width measurement works. Accurately measure the side-to-side width inside the nose (NOT THE WIDTH OF THE CUTOUT), making sure to take into account any bulges in the sheet metal or other things that protrude into the space. In the 635CSi, as you can see in the picture below, this side-to-side measurement is a little less than 24 inches.

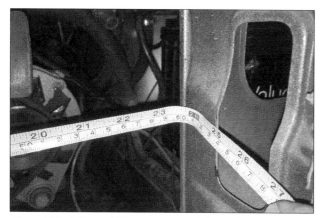

Figure 118: A direct width measurement of the condenser space in the nose of my '79 BMW 635CSi shows about 23 5/8 inches.

Now, subtract three inches from that, and that will give you the "zero-clearance width" for the condenser.

What do I mean by "zero-clearance width?" And why subtract three inches? The specified width of these universal-fit condensers is very misleading because it is the measurement between the outer edges of the vertical tubes that run down the sides. That measurement doesn't take into account the side brackets with the mounting holes, which typically add 3/4" per side (1.5" total), or the hose fittings on one side, which typically add on another ½". So you need to add two inches to the condenser's stated width to get the total physical width of the condenser. Even if there is a drawing for the condenser, this is rarely shown.

But then you need to figure in the added width of the fittings on the ends of the hoses you'll be attaching. The tightest narrowest fittings I've found are what are known as short-drop 90 degree fittings, and once they're screwed onto the condenser, they add an extra inch in width.

In the photos below, I show that when you take a condenser specified as 19 inches wide, temporarily screw 90-degree short-drop fittings into the side, the

resulting measured with is 22 inches. If you're using standard 90-degree fittings instead of short-drop 90-degree fittings, it adds even more, about another inch. So *the absolute best case is that the condenser takes up three inches more than its specified width*.

Figure 119: With one end of the ruler on the left edge of this 19" condenser...

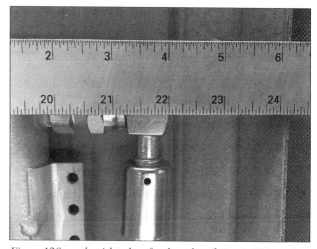

Figure 120: ...the right edge of a short-drop fitting is 22", or three inches larger than the specified width of the condenser.

Theoretically, if you could screw the hose fittings onto the side of the condenser and then slide the condenser with the hoses already attached into the nose, you could get by with zero clearance. This is why I say "subtract three inches from the width in the nose, and that'll give you the zero-clearance width of the condenser."

The problem is, you can't ever do this. It's not realistic. The zero clearance width isn't a number you can actually use. It's only a reference point for an ideal case that never exists. If you buy a condenser whose width is three inches smaller than the width of the nose, it won't fit. There won't be enough clearance for you to get the hose fittings on. **You need to subtract one or two inches more from the zero-clearance width to get a condenser that will actually fit.**

So, which is it? Do you need to subtract an extra inch, or an extra two inches? To answer that, you need to know how the condenser will actually mount. And, to know *that*, you need to look carefully inside the nose.

If, looking through the holes where the grilles were, you see that there are flat surfaces behind and parallel to the plane of the condenser, then you can mount the condenser on stand-offs. If that's the case, the mounting itself shouldn't eat up much if any space, and subtracting one inch from the zero-clearance width should be sufficient. But remember that you can't center the condenser—you need to slide it all the way to the side that doesn't have the hose fittings on it so that the hose fittings have the benefit of all of that one inch of clearance.

If, on the other hand, there aren't mounting surfaces parallel to the plane of the condenser, and instead you need to mount it with right-angle brackets, the brackets themselves typically take up some amount of space, and it's safer to subtract two inches from the zero-clearance width.

Just to make sure I haven't confused you with too much detail about zero-clearance widths as opposed to actual widths that will work, let's go over it again:

- Measure the side-to-side width inside the nose.

- Subtract three inches to get the zero-clearance width. This is a reference number only. As its name implies, it leaves zero clearance to put the hoses on the fittings once the condenser is installed. You need to subtract one or two inches from it to get a condenser that you'll actually be able to get the hoses on once it's mounted.

- If both condenser mounting surfaces are parallel with the condenser, and if you can mount the condenser slid all the way over to the side without the hose fittings to maximize the clearance on the side *with* the hose fittings, subtract one additional inch for hoses and brackets. This gives you the biggest condenser that'll fit, with one inch to spare, which ain't much.

- If, instead, one or both mounting surfaces are at right angles to the condenser, the brackets will take up more space, and you'll need to be more conservative and subtract two inches for hoses and brackets. This gives you the biggest condenser that'll fit, with two inches to spare.

- Obviously, you need to take into account the fact that the nose width is probably not an exact number of inches, so you need to round up or down accordingly.

Note that mounting the condenser is one thing, but getting the hoses on it is another, and *tightening* those hoses is a third. These problems are typically magnified when one tries to maximize condenser size, as the wider it is, the closer the fittings will be to sheet metal, and the more difficult it will be to get wrenches on them and tighten them without hitting something.

Note also that original condensers typically have the hose fittings somewhere convenient for both accessing (removing and installing) them and for passing the hoses into the engine compartment. In contrast, universal fit condensers almost always have the fittings at the top and bottom of one side. In particular, once the condenser is installed, the one at the bottom may be quite difficult to reach. Keep this in mind when deciding on whether you want that extra one inch or two inches.

So, with the 635CSi's 24" nose width measurement, if I wanted to be aggressive, I could order a 20" wide condenser, but if I felt like I wanted to err on the safe side, I'd go for a 19" wide unit. In fact, my nose wasn't 24" wide, but 23 5/8" wide, so rounding down to 23" and subtracting four inches yielded a condenser width of 19 inches.

On the height, there was additional room in the nose, so I figured I could go up to 17 or possibly even 18 inches.

Once you've honed in on your target size, you need to see if that size is even available. I try to buy my condensers off Amazon since, if they're the wrong size, returns are easy, but eBay has also proven to be a good source. You can go to boutique vintage a/c parts sellers such as Old Air Products, Vintage Air, or Nostalgic AC Parts, but depending on the condenser, they may simply be reselling it.

In my case, a web search revealed that both 16"x19" and 16"x20" were readily available, but I struck out on trying to increase the height to 17" or 18"; I simply could not find anything of that height.

I then pored over a 635CSi-specific web site (bigcoupe. com) to see what size condensers folks were using, and the consensus seemed to settle on 16"x19", with a few comments saying that you might be able to get a 16"x20" unit to fit, but it would be tight.

On other projects, I've ordered both a conservative and an aggressive-sized condenser and returned the one I didn't use, and I might have done here that if there was one that was not only wider but taller. But because the 635CSi's nose width wasn't exactly 24 inches but a little under it, I erred on the safer side and ordered the 16"x19" unit.

The condenser arrived, and I did a quick test-fit with the short-drop fittings screwed in, which is by far the best way to judge side-to-side clearance. Even having to negotiate the right side around the bracket supporting the oil cooler, there appeared to be gobs of room; with the condenser slid all the way to the right, a direct measurement appears to show that, with the short-drop fittings screwed on, there's about 1 5/8" of space to the left of the fitting. Which meant that, if I went with a condenser an inch wider, I'd still have 5/8" of space to get the hoses on.

Figure 121: There was a minor clearance issue on the lower right side due to an oil cooler bracket.

Figure 122: There seemed to be oodles of room on the left when using the short-drop fitting.

Figure 123: A direct measurement seemed to show 1 5/8" clearance to the edge of the short-drop hose fitting.

I nearly ponied up for a 16"x20" condenser, but I decided to wait until the brackets I'd ordered arrived and I could begin the mounting process. Sometimes what appears to be available space vanishes as you actually begin to mount the unit.

Fabricating mounting brackets

Dealing with the condenser mounting brackets for a universal condenser is the part of the a/c installation process that takes up way more time than you think it should. If you're using a drop-in replacement instead, you'd have it installed in 90 seconds, but unless you own a common car for which companies like Old Air Products, Vintage Air, or Nostalgic AC Parts sell a condenser and pre-made brackets, this is what you need to do to fit a modern parallel-flow condenser in a vintage car. I've done six of these (three 2002s, my Bavaria, my 3.0CSi, and now the 635CSi), and in each one, mounting the condenser has had its own set of challenges and required its own unique solutions. You'd think it's trivial, but in all likelihood you'll

be test-fitting everything a dozen times before you finally snug it down for good.

All of these universal condensers have rows of regularly-spaced holes down the sides, and usually across the tops and bottoms as well. The first problem is that the hole spacing is not standardized. On many of them, the side hole spacing is ½", but it can also be 5/8". Vintage Air and other companies sell Erector Set-like universal mounting brackets (boy, does *that* description date me, huh?) with ½" hole spacing, but I have yet to find a set of these brackets with 5/8" hole spacing. Even the redoubtable McMaster-Carr, whose website is widely regarded to be the best organized in the world (go ahead; go to www.mcmaster.com and type in "brackets") doesn't sort their brackets by hole spacing. To make matters worse, the hole spacing along the tops and bottoms of the condenser is usually different from the sides. Go figure.

But even if you had brackets whose hole spacing matched the condenser perfectly, they might not be enough, because the next problem is that you need to look carefully in the nose of your car and determine exactly which surfaces you're going to mount the condenser to. If there are vertical surfaces behind and parallel to the condenser on both sides, then it's pretty easy. You slide the condenser all the way to the right to create clearance for the hose fittings on the left, mount the right side on stand-offs directly attached to the brackets on the side of the condenser, and mount the left side on stand-offs, either with or without the Erector Set-like brackets, depending on whether the available mounting surface is directly behind the condenser or offset to the left. (To be clear, "left" and "right" are as you're looking at the condenser through nose, so yes I'm violating the "left is driver's side and right is passenger side" convention.)

Below, I show the recent condenser retrofit in my 3.0CSi, and the use of hard standoffs on the right and a bracket combined with hard standoffs on the left. The first two pics are of the stand-offs on the right side. They're taken from inside the engine compartment, so in the photo they're on the left (sorry). The first picture shows the additional complication that, on the

3.0CSi, there was an obstruction at the bottom of the inside of the nose that the condenser needed to clear, requiring longer stand-offs than would otherwise be needed. The third photo, also taken from inside the nose, shows the Erector Set-like bracket being employed to take up the gap between the left side of the condenser and the stand-off mounted on the nose's sheet metal. But overall, this is a relatively simple condenser mounting configuration.

Figure 125: Adapter brackets were required, along with standoffs, on the right side.

Figure 124: Hard standoffs used to mount a parallel flow condenser in my 3.0CSi on the left side at the top.

Wait. Did you say "mounted on the nose's sheet metal?" Exactly *how* are those stand-offs mounted?

Ah. You need to... just a minute, let me get my pit helmet and running shoes on... *drill holes.* (The Hack Mechanic now cowers beneath the nearest car, waiting for the jeering crowds to disperse).

Now, there are two schools of thought on this. One is that, on a car like the subject Euro '79 635CSi with 220,000 miles and a non-original engine and transmission, who cares, really, about a few holes drilled in the nose? But, on cars like 3.0CSis and mint 2002tiis, you really need to present a lawyer's case to drill any holes anywhere in the body.

When I updated the condenser in my E9 to a modern parallel-flow condenser, I took advantage of the fact that, 19 years ago, I drilled holes in the nose of the car and used stand-offs to mount the condenser, so I felt entitled to re-use the holes for mounting the new condenser but honor-bound not to drill *any more* of them (re-using an old sin makes it okay :^). Thus, even though the 3.0CSi's new condenser was a different size, with a different hole spacing on its side brackets, the mounting holes in the nose of the car were fixed points. The result satisfied my "no new holes" requirement, but it wasn't pretty.

Back to the 635CSi. Normally, what you'd do is procure or make mounting brackets whose hole spacing is the same as that of the side brackets, test-fit the condenser, put it as far right as it'll go, split the difference between any space at the top and bottom, mark the holes you need to drill on the right, drill them, test-mount the right side, test-fit the brackets on the left, mark the holes you need to drill on the left, drill them, then mount everything for real. It sounds pretty straightforward, right?

The question of whether you *should* drill holes notwithstanding for a moment, there's also the question of whether you *can* drill them. Sometimes the places you'd like to drill the holes are occluded by other sheet metal, and you can't get a drill in there. Sometimes you need to buy or borrow one of those right-angle drills to get it done. Sometimes you need to drill the holes from the back (the radiator side). This is a less-precise method, as when you slide in the condenser and brackets, test-fit it, and mark the holes, you have to mark them from the front, not the back. I'll admit that I've eyeballed where the holes should go, drilled them from the back, and futzed with the brackets to get things to line up. It's not something I'd do again.

If there isn't a vertical mounting surface that's parallel to the plane of the condenser, and the only available mounting surface on one or both sides is at a right angle to the condenser, it's more complicated. You need to procure, or make, right-angle brackets, and do a fair amount of measuring and cutting.

I sussed all this out on the 635CSi. On the right side of the nose, there is no vertical surface directly behind the condenser's side brackets, only one at 90 degrees to it, so I needed to buy or make some sort of right-angle bracket. At the bottom of the right side, there is already a small bracket that supports one side of the oil cooler. Initially I thought, great, I can drill holes in a bracket and slide it right over those existing bolts, but the nuts on the oil cooler bracket are captured, meaning I'd need to get a new bracket behind the existing one, not on top of it. I decided it was more trouble than it's worth. I did make a mental note that the bottom of the condenser needed to be in either front of or behind the protruding bolts for the oil cooler bracket. Eventually I got tired of that

corner of the condenser snagging on those two bolts during test-fitting, and used the Dremel tool to cut a few inches off the bottom off the bracket on that side of the condenser so it wouldn't keep interfering.

Figure 126: Cutting and routing the condenser bracket to address a clearance issue.

On the left side of the 635CSi's nose, there is a narrow vertical mounting surface behind the condenser, but because the condenser must be slid all the way to the right to gain clearance for the hose fittings on the left, the surface isn't directly behind it; it's offset. So I'd need some combination of standoffs and universal brackets.

However, since I couldn't find *any* brackets, flat or angle, that had a 5/8" hole spacing like the side brackets of the condenser, I figured that I'd just order 1.5"-wide flat and angle aluminum from McMaster-Carr and make my own brackets, cutting it all to length and drilling mounting holes exactly where I needed them. Makes sense, right?

I looked in the nose again and noticed that, on both of the right-angled surfaces flanking the condenser, there were already two holes, halfway down, one inch apart. They were for the brackets that held the car's original non-functional auxiliary cooling fan. I'm replacing that fan with a lighter fan for both the condenser and auxiliary cooling of the radiator. I thought that I might be able to use those existing holes and their mounting surfaces to hold the condenser, freeing me from having to drill *any* holes.

Figure 127: The mounting face on the right side of the nose was perpendicular to the condenser bracket. Existing holes are pictured.

Normally I'd attach the condenser with brackets at all four corners, but I thought that, if I used very beefy brackets in the middle of each side, and also supported the condenser at the top as well, it would be plenty secure. I noted that there was already a row of holes in the top of the nose over where the condenser would go. Plus, as I said, it would be challenging to attach a bracket at the lower right because that's where the oil cooler was attached. Even though this wasn't one where a no-drill approach was strictly necessary, I became attracted to the idea of test-driving a no-drill

approach so I could use it elsewhere.

I could still make brackets from the aluminum stock I'd bought at McMaster, but since I was now using the existing holes that were at a right angle to both sides, and since the condenser needed to be slid all the way to the right to get hose clearance on the left, that created a big gap on the left that would require a home-made right angle bracket bolted to a home-made straight piece of aluminum. A combination of both the klugey mechanical and questionable aesthetic nature of this approach gave me pause.

So, back to McMaster. I found some very sturdy-looking right-angle corner brackets where the long side was 3.5 inches (part number 15275A66). A measurement showed that this was long enough to use on the left side and would offset the condenser nearly flush with the right side. I'd need to trim the bracket on the right side to length. I ordered some smaller lighter brackets with elongated oval holes (15275A51 and 15275A53) to use to hang the condenser from the top.

When the brackets arrived, I first test-fit one needed for the left side of the condenser. I knew that all the holes in the bracket wouldn't line up perfectly with the 5/8" holes on the side of the condenser, but in addition, I found that I needed to grind about an eighth of an inch off the end of the bracket to get even one hole to line up.

Figure 128: Test-fitting and modifying a right-angle bracket to get the holes to line up.

I then installed the left side bracket, test-fitted the condenser, marked where I needed to drill holes in the bracket to align with the 5/8" holes on the sides of the condenser, took it all back out, drilled what I needed to in the brackets (not in the car), put it all back in, test-fitted it again, and carefully measured how much I'd need to cut the right bracket to accommodate the fixed 3.5" length (minus a little grinding) of the left bracket. I cut it and drilled some elongated holes 5/8" apart, test-fit the brackets on both sides, and verified that I could indeed get the hose fittings on and off the left side of the condenser.

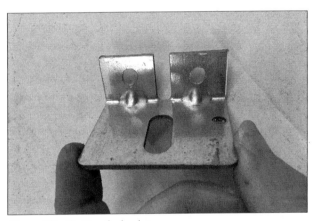

Figure 129: Cutting the bracket.

All that was left was to secure the condenser at the top. This was less to bear any real weight than to just make sure the condenser couldn't somehow rotate about the two attachment points on the side. (By the way, you don't really want the top of these universal condensers to bear a lot of weight anyway, as the bracket material is typically thinner along the top and bottom edges than it is on the sides). Unfortunately, the small brackets I'd bought for the top were just a skosh too short. And in addition, when I looked carefully, I found that the section of the nose above the condenser was angled slightly, so right-angle brackets wouldn't work. I came very close to drilling holes and mounting extra right angle brackets in the upper corners instead.

Then I looked at some right-angle brackets I'd bought at Home Depot. I'd already mangled one during some test fitting, so I only had one left. I gave it a few gentle taps with a sledge to increase its angle, then test-fit at the top of the condenser. Iterating this process a few times got the angle so the bracket was flush with both the condenser and the underside of the nose. By chance, the bracket was the right length, and I could even use its existing holes and simply mark new holes to drill in the bracket at the top of the condenser. But I only had one bracket.

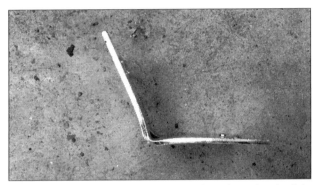

Figure 130: Bending a bracket to hang it from the underside of the top of the nose.

Sometimes you remember things that people have said to you that made a lot of sense. My friend Lindsey Brown, shop foreman at The Little Foreign Car Garage in Waltham, once said to me: "At the shop, we have a saying: *Put the god damned part in the god damned car!*"

I cut the bracket in half length-wise with the Dremel tool. Voila! Two brackets!

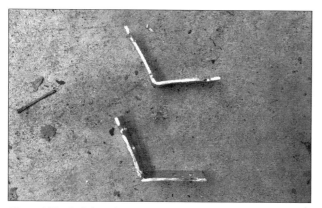

Figure 131: And then there were two.

I test-fit both brackets at the top of the condenser, and used them to mark new hole locations to drill in the condenser's top bracket, then test-fit all brackets with bolts in them.

Figure 132: Bracket installation on the left...

Figure 133: ...right...

Figure 134: ... and top.

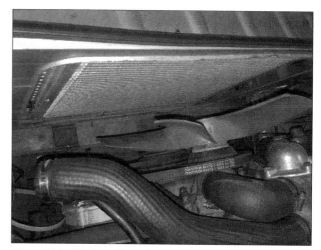

Figure 135: Checking the condenser installation from the back.

Lastly, I inspected the condenser from the back and made sure nothing was protruding into the radiator's space. Test-fitting the radiator itself is five minutes well spent.

The next step is to install the fan, and then put nyloc nuts or lock washers on everything and install the brackets and condenser permanently. In truth, you need to deal with the fan in parallel with the condenser installation because, most of the time, you mount the fan on the condenser and thus need to verify that, when you mark any holes to drill for any brackets, the fan doesn't hit anything. We'll cover the fan in the following chapter.

But the main thing in these condenser installations is that you're comfortable that the condenser is secure, and that you're not going to look at it in a month and go "geez, what a bloody kluge." For me, this installation passed those tests.

Largest condenser sizes for vintage BMWs

My experience is this:

- On a BMW 2002, many folks on bmw2002faq.com report that a 10"x18" condenser is the biggest you can get to fit without cutting anything on the car. I was able to fit a 10"x19" by cutting into the condenser bracket. However, the horns on a 2002 hang down from the top of the inside of the nose on small brackets, and by cutting the passenger-side horn bracket, I was able to fit an 11"x21" condenser (see the "Rejuvenation Case Studies" section of the Rejuvenation chapter for more detail).

- On an E9 (3.0CS), others have used a 16"x20" condenser, but I had no trouble installing a 16"x22" when using short-drop fittings on the hoses on the sides.

- On an E3 (Bavaria), I couldn't find any information online, so I measured, then ordered several. The 16"x22" I tried was too big, so I used a 16"x20".

- On an early (1979) 635CSi, folks on bigcoupe.com reported that 16"x19" was the biggest that could fit. I took their advice and used a 16"x19" coupled with short-drop fittings. It may be possible to get

another inch, but it would be tight.

On other vintage BMWs I don't have direct experience retrofitting condensers into:

- On an E28 (533i / 535i), several posts on MyE28.com report that the biggest parallel flow condenser that'll fit is 16"x19".

- On an E30 (325e / 325es / 325i / 325is / 318i / 318is), in contrast with the other cars above where folks used a universal-fit parallel-flow condenser, folks on r3vlimited.com report using a drop-in parallel flow condenser that's a direct replacement for the original unit. The Nissens part number appears to be 64538391509, the Spectra part number appears to be 7-3464, and the APDI part number appears to be 7013464. However, care must be taken to make sure that when you order using the part number, you actually get the parallel flow version of the condenser, not the serpentine flow version.

Condenser summary

If no drop-in parallel flow condenser exists for your vintage car (and it usually doesn't), buy a universal-fit model. Measure the inside width of the nose, and subtract four inches (aggressive) or five inches (conservative) to calculate the width of the condenser that'll fit and still allow you to get the hoses on the side. Mounting it isn't much different from putting up shelving, but does take a bit of time. At least it lets you familiarize yourself with the McMaster-Carr website.

Chapter 10

The Condenser Fan

Overview

Just as a radiator needs a fan on it to help to dissipate the heat that it is trying to dump, the condenser needs to have a front-mounted electric cooling fan pushing air through it to help carry the heat away. And, just like a radiator, the condenser fan is least important while driving on the highway, and most important when stuck in traffic in hot weather.

My advice for any retrofit or rejuvenation is to pair the biggest condenser that'll fit with the biggest most powerful fan that'll fit ("a fan that can suck a schnauzer off the sidewalk" is how I've previously phrased it). You usually select a fan whose diameter is the same as, or slightly smaller than, the smaller dimension of the condenser, which is usually the height. Using my 635CSi as an example as I did in the previous chapter, I planned to use a 16" fan on its 16" condenser unless a test-fit showed that the space directly in front of the top or bottom of the condenser was occluded. Nothing looked like it was in the way, so 16 inches it was.

Selection

However, the selection of a fan requires considering parameters other than diameter. These include weight, depth, cost, and, probably most important, the number of cubic feet per minute (CFM) of air flow. This last one is the parameter most affecting whether an actual schnauzer can actually be sucked off the sidewalk, and it is here that I can be accused of not following my own advice. Here's why.

Since I began doing air conditioning retrofits and rejuvenations almost 20 years ago, I've used Spal Italian-made sealed bearing pusher fans. They have an excellent reputation. I've yet to have one go bad. The Spal fans come two main styles—low-profile and high-power. The low-profile fans, as their name implies, are very thin (like two inches) front-to-back. Their main application is to be inserted into the small space between the engine and the radiator to replace or augment a mechanical fan. In that configuration, you want a "puller" fan that pulls the air through, whereas if you're mounting one in front of a condenser, you want to be certain to order one

in a "pusher" configuration. Some vendors claim that their fans are reversible. Spal says that their fans will certainly spin backwards if wired backwards, but that the fan blades are designed for one-way operation, so be sure you're ordering a pusher fan.

To be clear, for a condenser fan, you usually don't care about the actual profile (thickness) dimension, as the fan is thickest in the center where the electric motor is, and when it's mounted, that's in the center of the nose where there's usually oodles of room. It's neither the low profile nor even the moderate price that has me often using low-profile fans. **It's the weight**. A 16" Spal low-profile pusher fan weighs just 3.2 pounds. And the weight is a crucial issue affecting how you mount a condenser fan.

Figure 136: Newly-installed big fan on newly-installed parallel flow condenser

The original condenser fans on vintage BMWs were heavy, about eight pounds, and, if memory serves me correctly, were mounted to the nose of the car using brackets with rubber washers or bushings to cut down on the transmitted vibration. These brackets are usually very specific to the original fan. So if you wish to mount another heavy fan, you're faced with the prospect of having to do what you just had to do with the condenser— fabricate brackets and either drill holes or try to re-use old ones.

Mounting

There is, however, an easy alternative. If you use a lightweight fan like a Spal low-profile model, you can instead mount it directly to the condenser using what are essentially zip ties (search for "Derale 13001 Plastic Rod Mounting Kit"). The first time I used one of these, nearly twenty years ago on the 3.0CSi, I was very suspicious, as you're hanging the fan off the condenser's cooling tubes, but it held up fine. Note that it's advised that you don't use this mounting technique for a vehicle that spends a lot of time driving off-road, as the jostling of the fan can loosen the mounting ties, and the subsequent motion can bend the cooling tubes.

Figure 137: The zip-tie-like plastic fan mounting kit from the front...

Figure 138: ...and back

Over the years, the deal I've made with myself is this: "You can use the zip mounting kit for an a/c condenser fan *as long as it's employed on a lightly-used vintage car, not a daily driver,* and *as long as it's used to mount a lightweight fan.*" So, lightweight low profile Spal fan + zip mounting kit = fan mounted on condenser in two minutes. With all the ins and outs of a/c retrofit, it's a pretty appealing shortcut. And the fact that the low-profile fans aren't as expensive as some of the other models is an added benefit.

There is some middle ground between the two options of quickly using plastic ties to attach the fan to the condenser's cooling tubes and spending half a day elegantly mounting it independently to the nose. You can instead mount the fan to the brackets on the sides or tops of the condenser, which are considerably stronger than the cooling tubes. Spal sells mounting brackets with Erector Set-like multiple holes and plastic ends that snap into the circumference of the fan shroud. They're about $20 for a set of four. In some cases, the brackets are included when you buy a new Spal fan; it depends on the vendor you're buying it from.

These brackets work fairly well, though the result often isn't quite as clean as you'd expect. The process of mounting the condenser in the nose always takes up some of the mounting holes along the sides, so they're all not readily available for the Spal brackets. And the condenser's side brackets aren't flush with its face, so spacers (or at least washers) need to be employed between them and the Spal brackets. The top and bottom brackets *are* flush with the face, but they're not as strong as the side brackets. And once the long Spal brackets are installed, they need to be trimmed to length with a jigsaw or a Dremel tool. Below is a photo from another project (the Bavaria) of a Spal fan and its stock brackets mounted to the top and bottom of a condenser. Here, the fan is smaller than the condenser because there was a clearance issue at the top.

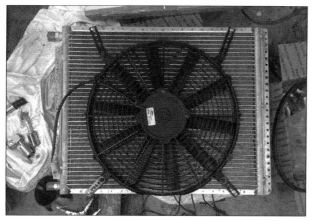

Figure 139: A Spal fan hard-bracketed to the condenser.

Weight, air flow, and power

In contrast to the lightweight low-profile fans, Spal's high-performance (full-profile) fans move about 50% more air, but they also are twice as heavy, draw more than twice as much current, and cost more. The salient parameters for the 16" pusher fans I was considering for the 635CSi are summarized in the table below. Prices, obviously, will change over time, and are just shown for comparison, but the specs shouldn't. Fans in sizes other than 16 inches have a similar spread of specifications.

Parameters of Spal 16" Pusher Fans						
Spal Model	**Blades**	**Weight (lbs)**	**Depth (in)**	**Air Flow (CFM)**	**Current (amps)**	**Price (Amazon)**
30100401 (low profile)	Straight pusher	3.2	2	1298	8.5	$78
30102048 (high performance)	Curved pusher	6	3.9	1959	19	$136
30102047 (high performance)	Straight pusher	5.8	3.5	2036	22.5	$146

Regarding the blade shape, according to Spal, all other factors being equal, straight-bladed fans move more air, but curved-bladed fans are quieter. Indeed, nearly all of the Amazon reviews for the Spal straight-bladed 20102047 say "great fan, moves a ton

of air, but man this sucker is *loud*." Spal's low-profile 16" fans are only available straight-bladed, but their high-performance pusher fans are available with either blade shape.

Note that in buying a name-brand fan like a Spal, there's a decent chance that when they say the fan puts out 1298 CFM, that spec is accurate. There are certainly other reputable manufacturers of high-quality fans (Mishimoto, for example). In my humble opinion, you should treat the CFM specifications of unbranded Chinese-made fans with a healthy degree of suspicion. Just because an ad says a $40 fan puts out 3000 CFM doesn't mean it's actually so.

Another thing to consider is whether the fan will be employed only as a condenser fan or whether it also will perform double duty as an auxiliary fan for the radiator. Early 1970s era BMWs like 2002s, Bavarias, and 3.0CSis had no aux cooling fan; if the car originally didn't have air conditioning, there was no electric fan. 1980s-era U.S.-spec BMWs like 635CSi, E28s 5-Series cars, and E30 3-Series cars all had air conditioning, and on those cars, the electric fan in front of the condenser was both a condenser fan and an aux cooling fan. A gray market car like my Euro '79 635CSi falls into an odd niche, as it did not have air conditioning (the reason for my from-scratch retrofit), but it did have an aux cooling fan.

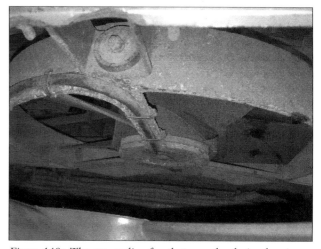

Figure 140: The aux cooling fan that was already in place in my 635CSi. Dead, but in place.

The newer the car is, the greater the chance that

the aux cooling fan is a multi-speed fan that, in addition to being turned on by a relay triggered by a temperature sensor, is being fed a speed signal by a fan speed controller, in which case it's more involved to replace it with an aftermarket fan.

Lastly, when selecting a fan, keep in mind that the higher the CFM rating, the more current the fan will draw. The three that I've presented above draw 8.5, 19, and 22.5 amps respectively. We'll get to the wiring issues later, but for now, the point is that you need to be mindful of the electrical limitations of vintage cars. The 635CSi's 65-amp alternator should be sufficient for any of these alternatives, but the original alternator on a round tail light 2002 may only output 40 amps. You can see that your selected fan may use up half of the headroom. So, sure, put a schnauzer-sucking fan on the condenser, but be aware of what the ramifications are on the alternator.

Which raises the question: How many CFM do you *need* for a condenser cooling fan? Instead of sucking a schnauzer, how about a Chihuahua? Perhaps a star-nosed mole? Maybe just a really big spider? More is always better, but there is some guidance offered on the Spal website for the amount of CFM needed when a fan is employed as a primary radiator cooling fan. They recommend minimum ratings of about 1250 CFM for a 200 to 250 hp motor, about 2000 CFM for 400 to 425 hp motors, and 2500 CFM for more powerful motors. Granted, these are radiator cooling numbers, not condenser cooling numbers, but they provide some scale for the CFM numbers needed to dissipate certain volumes of heat.

For my '79 635CSi, taking all of that into account, and trading off air flow, weight, cost, ease of installation, and the anticipated use of the car, I ordered the Spal 30100401 16" low-profile fan that weighs 3.2 pounds, moves 1298 CFM of air, wasn't reviewed as sounding like a passing helicopter, and cost about $78. I test-fit it in the nose of the car, with the condenser behind it, made sure there were no clearance issues at the top or bottom, took everything out, then mounted the fan to the condenser with the plastic zip tie kit. I then had a small surprise as the assembled condenser and fan nearly wouldn't fit pass

between the mechanical fan on the water pump and the sheet metal on the nose of the car. I eventually got them in with some careful positioning. Not a big deal; worst case would've been that I simply needed to temporarily remove the mechanical fan.

Figure 141: Maneuvering the condenser with attached cooling fan into position through the opening in the nose.

Once the condenser and fan were in the nose and all brackets were threaded with bolts and nylock nuts, I snugged it all down, taking care to tighten the fasteners in stages so the brackets could seek their best alignment and not twist the condenser.

Figure 142: Condenser and fan installed.

Condenser fan summary

Absolutely, buy the biggest fan that'll fit on the nose

of the car, but be aware that the hardest-blowing fan may draw twice as much power and weigh twice as much as another option. If you don't live in a stinking hot and humid climate, a lightweight low-profile fan that can be easily plastic-tied to the condenser may be adequate. If you have any doubt, though, go with a high-powered fan, mount it rigidly, and make sure that the alternator puts out enough juice to power it.

Chapter 11

The Receiver-Drier / Accumulator

Driers

Most air conditioning systems have a drier, also called a receiver, which is a beer-can-sized bottle of desiccant located on the line between the condenser outlet and the evaporator inlet that removes moisture from the refrigerant. It's the simplest and least expensive component of the air conditioning system. If the a/c system is opened to replace any component, unless the drier is very recent and is kept capped while the system is open, it should be replaced. They're cheap, usually less than twenty bucks.

Most driers have two #6 fittings, either o-rings or flares, that enter and exit in line with each other at the top of the drier, as shown above.

Certain vintage BMWs and Mercedes use an unusual drier that has a #6 flare input and a #8 flare output, with the two fittings at 90 degrees to one another.

Figure 144: The oddball drier used on certain vintage Mercedes and BMWs where the inlet #6 fitting is at 90 degrees to the #8 outlet fitting. Note that the third hose doesn't actually go into the bottom of the drier; it passes beneath it.

Figure 143: A generic aftermarket drier with #6 inlet and outlet fittings in-line with each other.

Basically, any drier will work. It's mostly a question of selecting one with the appropriate fittings for your hoses, making sure it has a switch port on it if your car's a/c is wired for a cut-off switch, and mounting it somewhere convenient. They're not refrigerant-specific. And although a larger drier has more desiccant in it and is appropriate for a system that holds more refrigerant, a/c systems aren't terribly sensitive to drier volume. Replace it with one that's about the same size and you'll be fine. A little larger or smaller won't kill the a/c.

Accumulators

Receiver-driers are sometimes also called *accumulators,* but there's a major distinction. If an a/c system has an expansion valve, it has a receiver-drier located between the condenser output and the evaporator input. However, if instead of an expansion valve, the system has an orifice tube, then instead of the drier connected before the evaporator inlet, it has an accumulator located between the evaporator outlet and the compressor inlet. The function of the accumulator, in addition to removing moisture, is to act as a liquid / vapor separator and store excess liquid refrigerant coming out of the evaporator so it can vaporize before reaching the compressor. The accumulator has a compressor cycling switch on it to monitor the low-side pressure and turn the compressor on and off. If your car has an orifice tube and an accumulator, disregard what I said about how "any drier will work." Replace the accumulator with one that's the same size.

Figure 145: Large accumulator and cycling switch on a late-model truck. Photo courtesy Layne Wylie.

If you are making your own new hoses, the required input and output fittings for whatever drier you select can simply be incorporated into the new hoses. And, if you're doing that, if the original drier had flare fittings, you'd be well-advised to select a new drier with o-ring fittings, as they're far less leak-prone than flares, and just make new hoses with o-ring fittings on them.

Regarding mounting, certain OEM driers have mounting brackets integrated right into the drier. If they do, it may be best to buy the original part even if that means continuing to use flare fittings. However, many driers simply use what are effectively large hose clamps to hold the drier against a bracket or post, in which case, they can be replaced with an inexpensive generic drier.

Figure 146: Drier on a 1987 BMW E30 325is, with site glass on the top and pressure switch, and integrated bracket tabs, located in a small well in the right front of the engine compartment.

Many driers have an M10x1.25 threaded fitting to receive a safety switch that cuts off the compressor if the system pressure is too high (usually above about 400 psi) or too low (usually below about 28 psi). If a safety switch isn't used (and it isn't on many vintage cars, at least not the stock way they're wired), the plug that comes screwed into the switch port can be left in place.

Some driers have a small clear sight glass on the top. This can be a diagnostic aid for a number of conditions. When R12 was used, one metric for proper charging was the absence of bubbles in the sight glass. With R134a, this is no longer as reliable a metric. Sight glasses seem to be in fewer and fewer new OEM driers, but are readily available in universal fit driers such as the one pictured below.

Figure 147: Some driers have a sight glass, but with R134a, it's not a reliable charging indicator.

That's about it. Nice to have an easy chapter :^)

Chapter 12

Electrical

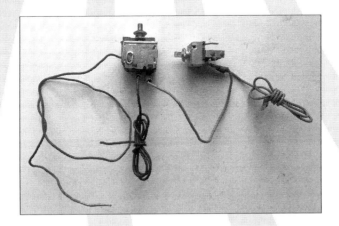

Figure 148: **Basic A/C Electrical Diagram**

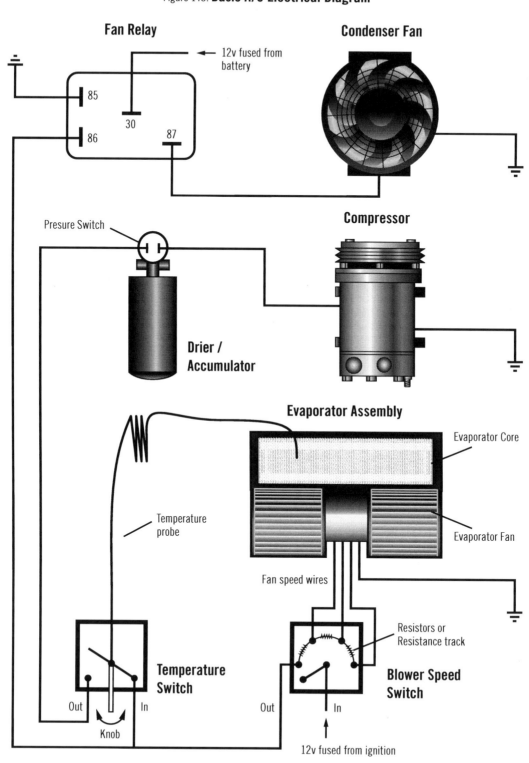

Overview

The electrical needs of a vintage car's air conditioning system are very basic.

- The compressor is powered by a single wire and grounded through the engine.

- The condenser fan in front of the radiator needs power and ground.

- The blower motor in the evaporator housing needs power and ground.

That's it. It's simple, but on a vintage car, I've seen all three of the above without power, and for three different reasons. If you need to, you can troubleshoot the three individual major electrical components by bypassing the wiring and powering them directly off the battery.

Basic a/c wiring diagram

Of course, to be useful, the system has to be able to be switched on from inside the car, not just hard-wired for testing. Below, I'm going to describe the basics of how the electrical systems on vintage a/c units that I've worked on are wired. It follows the diagram shown at left. Your car may vary, and you may need a wiring diagram for it to figure it out, but this should give you an overview.

In a vintage a/c system, typically there are two knobs in the middle of the console—the blower speed switch and the temperature switch. Even though they're rotary knobs, they're often referred to as switches because they contain switches that turn components of the a/c on and off.

Blower speed switch

On a modern car, the blower speed may be continuously adjustable, so the blower speed switch may be an actual variable rheostat (like a volume control), but in a vintage car, it's more likely that there are three selectable blower speeds, in which case the switch has a resistor pack associated with it. The resistor pack may be integral with the switch, or it may be near the blower motor. In either case, you should think of the blower speed switch, the resistor pack, and the blower motor as a tightly-coupled subsystem. The blower motor itself, like any motor, has just two wires (12V and ground), and can be tested by wiring it directly to the battery, but when looked at as a subsystem, there are typically several wires running from the blower speed switch to the evaporator assembly. In the drawing below I've labeled these wires somewhat generically as "fan speed wires."

The other thing to understand is that the blower speed switch serves two functions. The obvious one is to turn on the blower fan. But the other function is that it turns on the rest of the a/c system. Turning the blower speed switch from "off" to any fan position switches on the a/c by, in addition to powering the blower fan, sending 12 volts to two places.

Temperature control switch

The first place voltage is sent by the blower switch is to the temperature control switch (the other knob). It is this switch that actually turns the compressor on and off. If the evaporator temperature is warmer than the setting on the knob, the switch sends 12V to the compressor to engage the electromagnetic clutch which starts the compressor doing its thing. Typically the rotary temperature knob is a relative setting. It's not calibrated in degrees. There's no in-cabin temperature sensor to compare the reading to. It doesn't really matter; you usually peg the knob hard right to set it to maximum cold and leave it there. Note that the temperature control switch should automatically shut the compressor off if the probe tells it the evaporator is freezing.

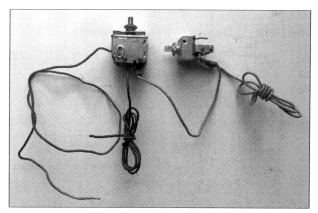

Figure 149: Temperature switch with probe (left) and fan control switch (right).

Pressure control switch

Before the voltage hits the compressor, though, it may or may not be passed through a pressure control switch. There are two types. On the first type, for a Clutch Cycling Orifice Tube (CCOT) system, there is a pressure switch on the accumulator that is used to cycle the compressor on and off in response to evaporator output pressure. On the second type, for an expansion valve system, there may or may not be a binary pressure control switch on the drier. These both serve an analogous function of gating the compressor, but only the pressure switch on a CCOT system cycles the compressor on and off during normal operation; the binary pressure switch on an expansion valve system instead is a fail-safe switch that cuts the compressor out if the pressure is too high (above about 400 psi) due to a restriction in the high side, or too low (below about 29 psi) due to a blown line. Some aftermarket a/c systems use a trinary switch, where the third function is to turn on the condenser fan above about 225 psi.

Note that the generic electrical diagram above is for both an expansion valve system and a CCOT system, where the "pressure switch" can be a CCOT cycling switch or a drier binary switch. The wiring of the trinary switch is not pictured in the diagram.

See the following chapter on Compressor Cycling for additional information.

Condenser fan and relay

The second place voltage is sent when the blower switch is turned on is the condenser fan in front of the radiator. This is a big honking electric motor that can easily draw 10 to 20 amps of current, so in order to avoid having high current running from the fan to the dashboard switch and back, the condenser fan is controlled by a relay. As with any relay, there's a low-current control side ("the switcher") and a high-current load side ("the switchee"). On the low-current control side, terminal 86 is connected to the on switch, and terminal 85 is grounded. On the high-current load side, terminal 30 is connected to the battery, and terminal 87 is connected to the thing you want to switch on, which in our case is the hot lead to the condenser fan. The other leg of the fan wire is grounded. Thus, switching on the a/c sends voltage to 86, energizing the little electromagnet inside the coil, which closes the internal switch, connecting 87 and 30 together, sending high current to the fan without having to rout thick wires inside the passenger compartment. (I love relays.)

As I've said, one of my definitions of "vintage air conditioning" is an a/c system that doesn't have climate control—one that doesn't have a blend door to combine cold air from the a/c evaporator with heated air from the heater core. There are, however, electrical configurations that complicate things while falling short of climate control.

For example, my 1979 BMW 635CSi is one generation newer than a BMW 2002 or E9 or Bavaria, and as such, its electrical connections are more complex. It doesn't have the two knobs on the console's center panel. Instead, the a/c has its hooks into the heater control panel. It cleverly uses one temperature knob and one fan speed knob to control both the heater box and the evaporator assembly. Note that this isn't true climate control—you don't dial in a degree setting and have the system use a variety of sensors and blend the heat and a/c to maintain it. The a/c in this car is switched on by setting the temperature control—the same one that's used for the heat—to the right of zero. This action also makes the heater blower fan control change its function to instead control the evaporator blower fan. Fortunately, the fan-switching is handled flawlessly by two relays that are built into the air conditioned version of the climate control panel, and when I swapped panels and installed the air-conditioned version, that part of the wiring worked flawlessly (for more information, see the "Rejuvenation Case Studies" section of the Rejuvenation chapter).

Wiring diagrams for BMW 2002 Behr a/c installation

For reference purposes, pages 128 and 129 include wiring diagrams straight out of the Behr a/c installation manual for the 2002. As I've said, I'm not a big fan of wiring diagrams—they often contain detail you don't want but miss things you do want—but some may find them helpful. As they are in the installation manual, two versions are included, one without a heater blower relay, and one with. The heater blower relay is a nifty little way of using a single pole double throw "changeover" relay so that when the a/c blower is switched on, the heater blower fan is automatically switched off.

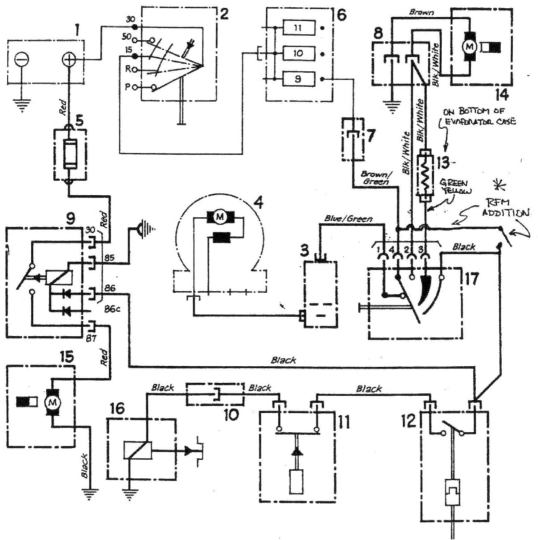

Figure 150: BMW 2002 Behr wiring diagram without heater blower relay. Illustration courtesy Behr of America.

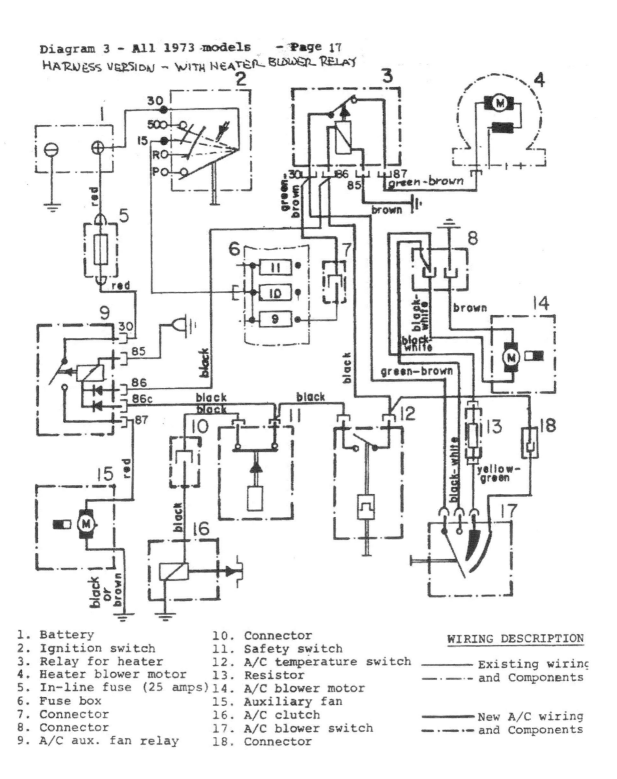

Diagram 3 - All 1973 models - Page 17
HARNESS VERSION - WITH HEATER BLOWER RELAY

1. Battery
2. Ignition switch
3. Relay for heater
4. Heater blower motor
5. In-line fuse (25 amps)
6. Fuse box
7. Connector
8. Connector
9. A/C aux. fan relay

10. Connector
11. Safety switch
12. A/C temperature switch
13. Resistor
14. A/C blower motor
15. Auxiliary fan
16. A/C clutch
17. A/C blower switch
18. Connector

WIRING DESCRIPTION

——— Existing wiring
—·—·— and Components

——— New A/C wiring
—·—·— and Components

Figure 151: BMW 2002 Behr wiring diagram with heater blower relay. Illustration courtesy Behr of America.

Chapter 13

Compressor Cycling

Overview

Compressor cycling is an issue that spans the compressor, the evaporator, the expansion valve or orifice tube, the receiver or accumulator, and the electrical system. Since there's a lot of confusion over it, I thought it deserved its own short chapter.

The a/c system is designed to have the compressor cycle on and off. You can think of this as analogous to the thermostat in your house turning the furnace on and off, and you'd be partially right. Depending on the age of the car and the style of a/c system (expansion valve versus orifice tube), there can be one, two, or three different mechanisms that cycle the compressor on and off, but only one of the three performs the thermostat-like function, and another one of the three is the one likely to result in the rapid on-off referred to as "short-cycling." As I said, it's the source of some confusion. I will describe all three.

Temperature control switch (controlling temperature and preventing freezing)

The first compressor cycling mechanism is the temperature control switch. It has a capillary tube with a small sensing bulb on the end. The capillary tube snakes inside the evaporator housing, and the bulb snuggles between the fins on the evaporator core and monitors it for signs of freezing. I believe that all automotive a/c systems have this. Even if you have the temperature control cranked all the way cold, the switch is supposed to shut off the compressor if the evaporator temperature reaches 32°F, and turn it back on when it warms up slightly. As you adjust the temperature knob to the right, you make the compressor switch off and turn back on at a lower temperature, though the accuracy with which it does so is pretty crude.

So the temperature control switch really serves two functions—it prevents the evaporator from freezing, and provides rudimentary temperature control. On a pre-1980 car with an expansion valve, this may be the *only* thing that cycles the compressor.

Figure 152: Temperature control switch with capillary tube.

And now I must digress and tell you my Rambler story. I used to have a '63 Ramber Classic, which had the coolest a/c system in the world. I don't mean that from the cold-generation standpoint, although it worked fine. No, what was cool was the control switch. It had three labels. They said "Cold," "Colder," and—and I swear I am not making this up—"Desert Only." It actually wasn't just marketing hokum. The "Desert Only" setting bypassed the compressor cycling from the evaporator temperature sensor. The idea was that, if you drove the car in a low-humidity (e.g., desert) environment, you could run the compressor below the point of freezing and, with no water to condense on it, it wouldn't ice up.

Figure 153: The "Desert Only" setting on the a/c switch of early 1960s Rambler Classics and Ambassadors.

Clutch cycling switch (evaporator control on orifice tube systems)

A second mechanism is employed on systems with an orifice tube instead of an expansion valve and an accumulator instead of drier. These are sometimes called Clutch Cycling Orifice Tube (CCOT) systems. In these systems, an accumulator is employed on the low side, between the evaporator output and the compressor inlet to hold excess liquid refrigerant that may exit the evaporator. A pressure switch is screwed into the top of the accumulator (see photo at start of chapter) that monitors the low-side pressure and cuts power to the compressor if the pressure gets too low (below about 20 psi). When people talk about "short-cycling" (the rapid turning on and off of the compressor, typically when the system is undercharged), they are generally talking about CCOT systems.

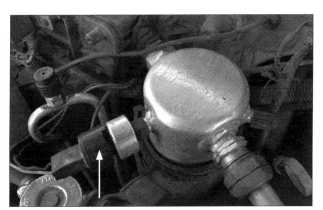

Figure 154: Clutch cycling switch on an accumulator. Photo courtesy Layne Wylie.

If you read the chapter on the Expansion Valve / Orifice Tube, you'll see that the clutch cycling switch exists on orifice tube systems because the orifice tube has a fixed opening, and thus the system needs some other mechanism (e.g., switching the compressor on and off) to control the pressure in the evaporator. In contrast, an expansion valve has a variable opening that automatically responds to evaporator pressure, and thus doesn't need the compressor to be cycled. Note that, when driving a car with an expansion valve, you can often hear the evaporator "sigh" as the valve opens a bit, lets more refrigerant in, and it boils. This is the analogous function to the compressor

cycling back on in a CCOT system.

High-side pressure cutoff switch (safety and preservation of compressor)

There is a third mechanism for pressure control—the switch on the drier. As described in the previous chapter, a binary switch is often employed that cuts off voltage to the compressor if the pressure is higher than about 400 psi due to a restriction in the system, or if the pressure is lower than about 20 psi because the system has blown a line and lost all its refrigerant, and with it, its oil. Note that the high-pressure case is a safety issue, and the low-pressure case is a compressor preservation issue. In both cases, this switch has nothing to do with cycling the compressor to keep the system running at a certain pressure like the cycling switch on a CCOT system does If the system has a high-side restriction, though, it is possible that the compressor may cycle as the compressor is turned on, the pressure builds and hits the limit on the switch, and the compressor is shut back off.

There. When broken out like that, it's not so confusing after all.

Chapter 14

Connecting and Using Manifold Gauges

Overview

Because the use of manifold gauges is central to a/c work, I discuss what the gauges are and how to connect them to perform specific tasks in several chapters (Tools, Fittings, Leak Detection, Rejuvenation, Retrofit, Evacuation, Charging), but let me put also put it all in one place.

Figure 155: Manifold gauge set

The manifold gauge set, along with its three hoses, acts as a kind of adapter between the car and the outside world. When connected to the charging ports—also called service fittings—on the car, the gauge set provides the pathway to pressure-test, then get air and moisture out of the system, and refrigerant into the system. Note that if you need to get *refrigerant* out of the system, you need to take the car to a shop and pay them to recover it, or buy your own recovery equipment, which is outside the scope of this book.

Different types of charging ports

R12 and R134a charging fittings are different, but they both have valve cores in the center that are depressed when the gauge set hoses are put on. As described in great detail in the Fittings chapter, R12 systems use ¼" 7/16-20 SAE threaded fittings that look like large tire valve stems. The low and high side may be the same size, in which case the two R12 hoses on the manifold gauge set thread directly on them, or the high side may be a smaller 3/16" 3/8-24 SAE fitting, in which case you need an adapter. Some

refrigerant loss typically occurs when the hoses are threaded on and off, so wear gloves to avoid the risk of frostbite, and eye protection as well.

Figure 156: ¼" 7/16-20 SAE R12 charging ports on the back of a Sanden 508 clone compressor.

The charging ports on R134a systems look very different from R12 charging ports. They use 13mm and 16mm snap-on fittings with ridges on the side, and the fittings on the red and blue hoses on the manifold gauge set have a collar that you slide back as you press the fittings on. A small amount of refrigerant loss may occur when snapping or unsnapping the fitting. The better gauge sets have hoses whose fittings have knobs on the ends that you turn clockwise to depress the valve cores in the charging fittings. These eliminate refrigerant loss during connection and disconnection.

Figure 157: 13mm and 16mm R134a charging fittings.

Locating the charging ports

Every car has charging ports on both the high side (between the compressor discharge outlet and the evaporator inlet) and on the low side (between the evaporator discharge outlet and the compressor suction inlet). On cars with original factory air, the ports are usually part of components or integrated with hard lines. If the car has a drier and an expansion valve, it's common to find the high-side port on the receiver-drier, which is always between the compressor outlet and the evaporator inlet. Conversely, on cars with an orifice tube and an accumulator, it's common to find the low-side charging port on the accumulator, which is always between the evaporator outlet and the compressor inlet. It is also possible that both of the original charging ports are on the fittings that connect to the compressor. On late-model cars, the charging ports tend to be easily accessible. They're often integrated either with hard metal lines that are up high in the engine compartment, or they rise up stalk-like from a line or component as shown in the previous pic.

Figure 158: R12 charging ports spliced into custom-made a/c hoses.

On a car with rejuvenated a/c and upgraded components, there are some additional possibilities. The charging ports may be spliced into the rubber hoses, either near the compressor, near the evaporator, or, in the case of the high-pressure fitting, near the condenser. Or the charging ports can be on the compressor itself. As pictured above, some Sanden 508 compressors and their clones have small R12-style charging ports on the back of the compressor. Considering the presence of a hot exhaust manifold,

it is sometimes necessary to reach these from beneath the car.

The manifold gauge set itself

A manifold gauge set has a blue low-pressure gauge and a red high-pressure gauge, both connected to a metal tube (the "manifold"). There are three threaded fittings on the manifold—one to connect the blue hose to the low-side charging fitting, one to connect the red hose to the high-side charging fitting, and a center one to connect the yellow hose to a can of refrigerant, a nitrogen bottle, or a vacuum pump.

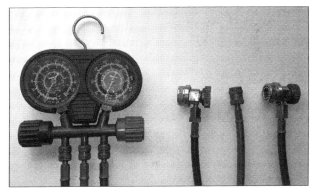

Figure 159: A manifold gauge set with R134a fittings.

CLOSE THE GAUGE KNOBS before connecting the hoses to the charging fittings!

People are often confused regarding the function of the knobs on the gauge set. Let's start off without them. Make sure the knobs are closed (turned all the way to the right), and connect the red and blue hoses to the charging fittings. If the ends of your R134a charging hoses have small knobs on them, turn them clockwise to depress the valve stems in the middle of the charging fittings. Ta-DA! The gauges now read the low and high side pressure in the a/c system.

If all you ever needed to do was monitor system pressure, you would never need the knobs or the center yellow hoses. The gauges are always directly connected to their charging hose fittings, no matter whether the knobs are open or closed.

What the knobs do

So, then, what do the knobs do? *The knobs on the ends of the manifold control which of the charging fittings have access to the yellow hose – the blue one, the red one, or both.* When they're open, they connect the blue and / or the red hoses (and the charging fittings on the car that they're connected to) to the center port on the manifold, to which the yellow hose is usually connected. The other end of the yellow hose can be connected to a can of refrigerant, or a nitrogen bottle, or a vacuum pump. This is useful because, in addition to providing pressure readings of the low and high sides of the system while running, the other functions of the manifold gauge set are to allow evacuation (pump-down) of the system, pressure-testing with nitrogen, and charging.

The numbers on the gauges

The blue (low side) gauge is a "compound gauge," meaning that it will read pressure in pounds per square inch (psi), but there's a small section near the bottom of the dial that's calibrated to read out vacuum in inches of mercury (inHg).

Figure 160: Dissimilar scales on low-side and high-side manifold gauges.

If you look at the gauges, you'll notice several other things. The first is that there are concentric circular scales of numbers on both gauges. The outer set of numbers are the pressure readings in psi. These are the numbers that, most of the time, you want to pay attention to.

The second thing is that the blue and red gauges don't have the same scale. The blue gauge tops out at about 120 psi, the red gauge at about 500 psi. That's because the normal low-pressure readings for a healthy system are, well, low—about 30psi, whereas the high-pressure reading are, um, high—just to pull out a number, about 250psi on a hot day (consult the tables in the Charging chapter). But the fact that they have different scales is important. For example, when we check if there's refrigerant in the system, we use the rule of thumb that the static pressure is about equal to the ambient temperature in °F, so 80° = about 80 psi. On the blue gauge, 80 psi is about ¾ around the gauge, whereas on the red gauge, it's in the lower 1/6. It's something you have to get used to.

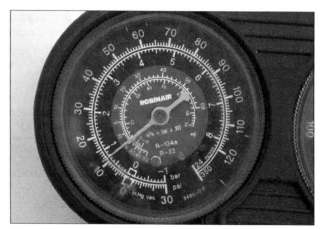

Figure 161: Blowup of low-side gauge showing concentric temperature scales.

The third thing to notice is the inner sets of numbers on the concentric circular scales. These represent the temperature readings for different refrigerants at different pressures. In the picture above, the innermost scale is for R134a. You can see that, for example, 35 degrees corresponds to a low-side pressure reading of about 30 psi. You can also read this off the little folded laminated pressure chart that comes with the gauge. So, on an operating R134a system, if the low-side pressure is 30 psi, the temperature of the refrigerant at that point should be 35 degrees, or just a bit above freezing. A certified a/c technician may make frequent use of the temperature/pressure charts. Do-it-yourselfers, however, typically don't, and instead use a combination of factors to judge if a system is properly charged. I'll talk about using the temperature/pressure relationship to calculate superheat and subcooling in the Troubleshooting chapter.

Pressure-testing for leaks with nitrogen

If you are pressure-testing, connect the manifold gauge set to a nitrogen bottle using a ¼" NPT to ¼" 7/16-20 SAE adapter. This is easiest if you have an R12-style yellow hose with ¼" 7/16-20 SAE fittings at both ends.

Figure 162: 1/4" NPT to 1/4" 7/16-20 SAE adapter in pressure regulator on nitrogen bottle.

Figure 163: Yellow hose on manifold gauge set hooked to nitrogen bottle using an R12-style yellow hose with ¼" 7/16-20 SAE fittings at both ends and ready for pressure-testing. Photo is for reference only. Any pressurized bottle should be chained to the wall or in a tip-resistant cart.

As per the Pressure Testing chapter, connect both the low and high pressure fittings to the car, set the

regulator on the nitrogen bottle to about 120 psi, open the valve on the tank, then slowly turn both the blue and red knobs counter-clockwise to open them. This allows nitrogen to flow into both the low and high sides of the system.

Evacuation

Similarly, if you're evacuating prior to recharge, connect the yellow hose to a vacuum pump (this may require a ¼" 7/16-20 SAE to ½"-16 ACME adapter), and open up the red and blue knobs. This allows a vacuum to be pulled on both the low and high sides of the system. Then connect the high and low fittings to the car, turn on the pump, and open up both of the knobs on the gauge set.

Figure 164: Yellow hose on manifold gauge set hooked to vacuum pump using an R12-style yellow hose with ¼" 7/16-20 SAE fittings at both ends and ready for evacuation.

Recharge

If you're recharging the system after evacuation, connect the yellow hose to a can tap, then *turn only the blue knob*, which connects the yellow hose to the low pressure side of the system. You always charge on the low side only, *never* on the high side (more about this in the Charging chapter).

Figure 165: R134a can hooked to manifold gauge set via yellow hose with ½"-16 ACME fitting on one end, manifold gauge set connected to car, ready for charging. Picture is for reference only. Don't put a can of refrigerant on a hot engine.

Again, there's much more detail on the fittings, leak detection, evacuation, and charging in their appropriate chapters.

Chapter 15

The Basic Steps for A/C Rejuvenation

Overview

As those of you who read my *Hack Mechanic* column or have read my other books know, I'm not a "do it once, do it right" guy. I reserve the right to be, shall we say, thrifty, and to cut corners when I think I can do without shooting myself in the foot.

However, I am, above most things, a practical guy, and I've learned that, when you're resurrecting an a/c system, it pays big time to err on the side of "do it once, do it right." If you don't like that motto, use "clean and tight" instead. By flushing a system, making new hoses, installing new components, keeping things assiduously clean during assembly, and prophylactically testing for leaks, a/c systems usually come up running cold, and that's what you want, because then you simply enjoy a cold car instead of spending more time trying to diagnose what went wrong.

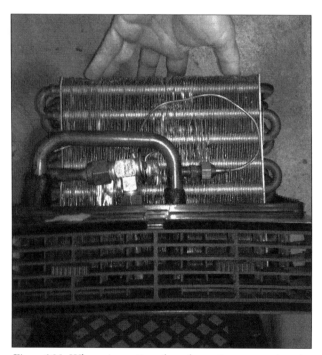

Figure 166: When rejuvenating a long-dormant system, you're going to need to take it apart further than you'd probably prefer.

When you read through this, you'll see that, as part of the rejuvenation sequence, I recommend replacing all, or nearly all, of the under-hood a/c components. You might think that this takes you close to a from-scratch a/c retrofit. There are, however, substantial differences. On a rejuvenation, the framework is already in place (the a/c wiring harness, for example), even if you update substantial portions of it.

The basic steps that I go through for rejuvenating a present but long-dead a/c system on a vintage car are listed below. Most of these subjects have their own chapters, or sections in chapters, but it is useful to see them as part of an overall rejuvenation sequence.

The steps are:

- Perform an inspection of the existing system.
- Test if refrigerant is present in the system.
- Decide if you're changing refrigerant from R12 to R134a.
- Decide if you're replacing the compressor.
- Decide if you're replacing the condenser.
- Decide how much work to do on the evaporator assembly.
- Decide if you're replacing all the hoses.
- Verify that the compressor clutch works and compressor isn't seized.
- Perform a gross leak test.
- Test compressor functionality.
- Flush the system.
- Refill the system with oil.
- Replace the receiver / drier.
- Replace needed components.
- Test for small leaks.
- Evacuate the system and test for vacuum integrity.
- Recharge.
- If necessary, perform further small leak detection.

Perform an inspection of the existing system

You have to start somewhere. Start here. Are all of the necessary a/c components even still *there*? If it's an old car with a replaced or rebuilt engine, the large bulky upright piston compressor may have died at some point and been pitched into the scrap heap when the engine was out. Does the crankshaft have the pulley needed to run the belt for the compressor? Is the condenser present in front of the radiator? If the car has had a front-end accident and the a/c wasn't working, sometimes the condenser doesn't make it back in. Are all of the hoses present and attached? Have any of them burned up against a hot exhaust manifold or simply been cut? You can't begin to assess leaks if the system isn't closed, and it can't be closed if it isn't even complete.

Figure 167: When you see cut hoses, you know that clearly the system hasn't sat closed up. Photo courtesy Steve Jones.

As part of your inspection, turn on the a/c switch. Do both fans (the one in front of the condenser and the one inside the evaporator assembly) blow air without squealing and howling? It's pretty common to need to replace, or want to upgrade, the fan in front of the condenser, but if the fan inside the evaporator assembly isn't working, you're going to need to pull the assembly out, and that's a fair chunk of work over and above simply re-charging the system.

In addition to visually accounting for the major components and evaluating the state they're in, this is a chance to truly look at the project with eyes wide open. You may wind up having to replace every single component you see. Understand it. Grok it. Be at peace with it.

Test if refrigerant is present in the system

It's possible to do this test, and other a/c work, without a set of gauges, but you shouldn't. Do *not* test for the presence of refrigerant by using a pen to depress a valve in the middle of one of the charging fitting and seeing if anything comes out. That's intentionally

venting refrigerant, and it's illegal, and in the case of systems with R12 left in them, it's highly unethical as well. Don't do it. Buy the gauges. You're a car person. You *like* tools.

However, *do* realize that, on long-dormant systems, anything can happen. Charging fittings can be gummed up. It is possible to screw the charging hoses onto the charging fittings, have a valve stick open, and accidentally discharge all the refrigerant. (My friend and pro Terry Sayther adds "And be fined $10,000, go to jail, lose your wife and family, have your house repossessed, become a drug addict, live under a bridge…")

The use of gauges to fine-diagnose a/c issues and troubleshoot down to the component level is discussed in the Using Manifold Gauges and Troubleshooting chapters, but for the refrigerant-present test, we're basically just using the gauge set to see if there's *any* gas in the system. Make sure both knobs on the gauges are closed (rotated clockwise). Using the blue and red hoses, connect the gauges to the car's service fittings. These may be on the compressor, or the low side fitting may be on the line from the receiver to the compressor and the high side fitting may be on the line from the compressor to the condenser. Once the gauges are connected, they will register the pressure of the refrigerant in the system.

If the gauges read zero, then there's no refrigerant, and you can proceed with the leak test. But if the gauges read a fair amount of pressure (a good rule of thumb is that, with the car off, "resting pressure" of the refrigerant should be about equal to the ambient temperature in degrees Fahrenheit – that is, if it's 80° out, you should see about 80 psi on the gauges), your system has a fair amount of liquid refrigerant in it, so if it's not cooling at all, the cause is likely due to something else, in which case, you can proceed directly to the compressor test.

If the pressure is less than ambient temperature but non-zero, then there is refrigerant in the system, so if any of the steps below require opening up the system, you are going to have to have the refrigerant recovered. DIYs rarely own recovery equipment, and venting refrigerant is illegal, so stay legal and take the car to a local shop to have the refrigerant recovered. In particular, if it has R12 in it, under no circumstances should you vent it, since R12 is a pernicious ozone-destroying agent.

Figure 168: For a full system, the resting pressure should about equal the ambient temperature, but any non-zero reading on the gauges indicates that the system has refrigerant in it.

Decide if you're changing refrigerant from R12 (Freon) to R134a

As I said in the Refrigerants and Legality chapters, because of the evidence of Freon's role in harming the ozone layer, it was phased out in the early 1990s in favor of R134a. The little 12 and 14-ounce cans of R12 stopped being manufactured and sold commercially in this country in 1993, but are still widely available on Craigslist, and can be legally sold on eBay and bought by anyone with an EPA Section 609 certification, which you can easily obtain via an on-line exam. Venting R12 (or R134a) into the atmosphere is illegal and unethical, though, at the price that R12 costs, I don't know why anyone would intentionally vent it. Note that, as per the Refrigerants chapter, there are choices other than R12 and R134a, but you have to be knowledgeable and committed – they're the refrigeration equivalent of voting Libertarian.

I discussed the steps necessary to retrofit R134a into a system designed for R12 in the Refrigerants chapter.

In a perfect world, an accepted retrofit technique, provided the system is leak-free and is functioning correctly, is to flush the system, drain but not replace the compressor, refill it with Ester oil, replace the drier (as should be done any time the system is opened), replace any black o-rings with green ones, and leave the hoses alone. However, we rarely live in a perfect world. If the system really *was* leak-free and functioning correctly, you wouldn't touch it, so odds are that, at a minimum, the refrigerant has leaked out of it, and it's likely it has a bad component that requires replacing as well. There's a good chance that, as part of resurrecting the system, you're going to wind up replacing the compressor, the condenser, and the hoses.

Note that we've gone from simply retrofitting R134a to raising the possibility of replacing all of the a/c components that are under the hood. This naturally leads into a discussion of…

The whole flares-versus-o-rings thing

Although there was a crossover period in the 1980s where some R12-based a/c systems such as those on BMW E30 3 Series cars had components with o-ring fittings, many a/c systems that originally used R12 had flare fittings on all of the components, and those manufactured after the changeover to R134a in the early 1990s had o-ring fittings. Make no mistake, o-ring fittings are far superior to flare fittings. In a flare fitting, it's the metal-to-metal interface of both sides of the flare that provides the seal. The seal is improved by the presence of a copper flare washer. The copper is softer than the metal on the fitting or the component and thus provides a malleable sealing face, but it's still metal-to-metal. In contrast, on an o-ring fitting, the rubber o-ring provides the seal. Not surprisingly, the rubber seal works better than the metal-on-metal seal of a flare fitting, and thus o-ring fittings are much less leak-prone than flares. This benefit is magnified when switching from R12 to R134a or other alternative refrigerants, as the molecule size is smaller than that of R12.

Figure 169: Old-school flare fitting (left) and new-school o-ring fitting (right).

But in addition to the issue of whether the car originally had flares or o-ring fittings, there's the fact that most new components you'd install to upgrade the system are going to have o-ring fittings. That is, when you're in the process of rejuvenating or upgrading a system and you change from an old large inefficient upright piston-based compressor to a new compact rotary-style unit, and also upgrade from a serpentine-flow condenser to a more efficient parallel-flow one, you're also likely changing from old components that have leak-prone flare fittings to modern ones that have better-sealing o-ring fittings. Although you can buy a new rotary-style compressors with flare fittings, and you can *try* to find a new flare-equipped parallel-flow condenser, it's not a great idea because the flare fittings don't seal as well as the o-ring versions. The *only* reason you'd buy new components with flare fittings is to try and continue to use your existing hoses, and we'll address that in a moment.

So, replacing the compressor and condenser naturally causes you to gravitate toward components having o-ring fittings. In addition, any time you open up an a/c system, you should replace the receiver/drier. If the original drier had flares, this work gives you an opportunity to replace it with a new drier that has o-rings instead.

Thus, as a natural consequence of repairing and upgrading, the compressor, condenser, and drier get replaced with new components equipped with o-ring fittings. That's three of the four major components.

That leaves just the evaporator. Unfortunately, if you have a 1970s-era car, its old evaporator likely has male flare fittings—at least it does on BMW 2002s, E3s, E9s, and E12-based 635CSis like mine—and the flare fittings are often an integral part of the evaporator's hard metal lines and can't be replaced. As I explained in the Fittings chapter, on a 2002 where the evaporator is connected to hoses, there's some value in using male-to-female flare-to-o-ring adapters on the evaporator fittings. But on the six-cylinder cars, the evaporator is connected by hard metal lines that run through the firewall, and the ends of these are female flare fittings. If you want, you can install male-to-female flare-to-o-ring adapters, but you also can just fabricate the two hoses that mate to the evaporator with flare fittings on them and keep it simple. The pros and cons are discussed in the Fittings chapter.

Figure 170: There's no getting around the flare fittings that are integrated into the hard pipes of an early evaporator.

So, the likely path is o-rings on everything except the evaporator fittings, and maybe using adapters on those. Got it? Good.

There's also the issue of the different charging fittings used for R12 and R134a. On older cars running R12, the charging ports use small screw-on ¼" 7/16-20 SAE charging fittings that look roughly like a fat tire valve. When cars switched over to R134a in the early 1990s, larger (13mm and 16mm) snap-on charging fittings were employed to avoid any chance of accidentally cross-connecting R12 and R134a recovery tanks. For more information, see the chapter on Fittings.

For all these reasons, if you're resurrecting a dead a/c system, it's best to decide on which refrigerant and which set of fittings you're using at or near the start of the project.

Decide if you're replacing the compressor

If you're rejuvenating the a/c on an older car with an original big bulky upright piston compressor, you may well want to skip over the section below on testing the compressor and simply replace it with a smaller, quieter, more efficient rotary-style unit. As discussed in the Compressor chapter, a rotary-style compressor generally requires a different bracket to bolt it to the engine block, or an adapter to bolt it to the original bracket. If you are buying a rotary-style compressor like a Sanden, the hose and charging fittings are on a plate called the "head" on the back of the compressor. Be certain you're buying a compressor whose head has the hose fittings you want (o-ring or flare), and, if you don't have them elsewhere, charging fittings.

Even if you know that the old compressor is going to the scrap heap, don't yank it out just yet; it's useful to leave it in for the gross leak detection step below.

Verify that compressor clutch works and compressor isn't seized

If you know you're replacing the compressor, obviously you can skip this and the compressor functionality test. The first test in evaluating the compressor's health is to check whether its electric clutch engages and, if so, whether the compressor turns freely. On anything but the most primitive a/c system, a low-pressure cutoff switch will prevent the compressor from engaging if the system is out of refrigerant, and if the a/c isn't working, the odds are overwhelming that it *is* out of refrigerant, so to test the compressor you may need to hot-wire it directly to the battery.

Find the wire powering the compressor. Generally there's just a single positive wire because the body of the compressor is grounded to the engine, eliminating the need for a ground wire. Trace the power wire

back from the compressor until you find a connector, then disconnect it. Attach a length of wire to the compressor side of this connector that's long enough to reach the battery. Touch the wire to the positive terminal of the car's battery, then release. Do this two or three times. You should hear a clicking sound from the compressor's magnetic clutch as electrical contact is made and broken. If you don't hear the click, the clutch is probably bad. The clutch may be separately available, and depending on the make and model of the compressor, it may be possible to change the clutch with the compressor in the car, perhaps even without losing refrigerant, but in the vintage BMWs I mostly work on, this has never been the case.

If the clutch is working, make sure the compressor belt is installed, then start the car and again touch the compressor wire to the positive battery terminal. If, when you touch the wire to the battery, you hear a spectacular squealing sound and smell burning rubber, then you are the proud owner of a seized compressor—the squealing you're hearing is that, when the clutch is engaged, the belt can't spin the seized compressor. It sucks when you find this, but at least it's a clear unambiguous diagnosis. If it's an old car with a large upright piston-style compressor, you'd be advised to replace it with a newer, smaller, more efficient rotary-style compressor and whatever bracket is needed to mount it to the block. If it's a newer car, there may be good cost-effective options for a used or rebuilt OEM compressor. As with buying any used part, this is a judgment call that's a function of cost, risk, and how long you plan to keep the car.

Note that, if the compressor is seized, there is the possibility that it threw debris into the system, in which case the hoses and all of the other a/c components need to be flushed out.

Decide if you're replacing all the hoses

Obviously, if you already know that a hose is junk because it's been cut or melted against the exhaust manifold, you should plan on replacing it. But, similar to the "just pitch the compressor" approach, if you're resurrecting a long-dead system, and if the hoses look old, the smart thing to do is to simply replace all of them. If a car has been sitting with the a/c system intact (i.e., closed up with all hoses attached), and if it's recent enough that it doesn't need a compressor and condenser upgrade, I will sometimes pressure-test the system, and if it passes, flush it, replace the drier, charge it, and see what happens, but if it fails the leak test and any leaks are traceable to a hose, I'll usually just replace every hose. I cannot state strongly enough that if there is no refrigerant in the system, it's because it leaked out from somewhere, and in addition to finding *the* leak(s), hose replacement is a great prophylactic measure so you don't have to go through the leak detection process again in a few months.

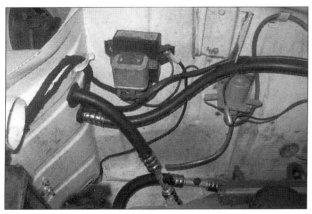

Figure 171: In a rejuvenation, the smart thing to do is go for all new hoses.

In addition, as I said above, the process of rejuvenating a system using an upgraded compressor and condenser naturally leads to replacing components that have flare fittings with ones with o-rings, and that, in turn, usually means having to replace the hoses. Really, the *only* reason you'd buy new components with flare fittings is to try and continue to use your existing hoses.

Can you reuse your existing hoses?

Let's address this question explicitly. Let's say that all of your hoses have flare fittings on them, and you're installing a rotary-style compressor and/or a parallel-flow condenser with flares. *Can* you still use your existing hoses? Is it even possible?

The answer is: It depends, but probably not, and if you're smart, you'll let go of the idea.

Here's a good example. My BMW 2002tii originally had a York compressor with flare fittings, charged with R12. During the car's a/c rejuvenation (one of my first in over a decade), I thought I'd be smart and try to save myself the work and expense of new hoses, so I decided to stick with R12, sourced a rotary-style compressor with flare fittings, and thought I'd simply see if the flare fittings on the ends of the original hoses would reach the new compressor. I mounted the compressor, stretched the old hoses over to it, and was surprised to find that the car's compressor hoses had two #10 flare fittings on them (standard then, unusual now), whereas the head on the new compressor had the standard #10 and a #8 flares.

You might get lucky and be able to chop the old fitting off a hose and crimp a new beadlock fitting on the end (or—gasp—use a barbed fitting and a hose clamp instead of crimping). Whether you can or not depends on a number of factors, including the type of hose, what condition it's in, and whether it's long enough to reach the new component.

But really, it's false economy. You're already going to all this work to repair, upgrade, pressure-test, evacuate, and recharge the system. You should ensure a leak-free system by installing all-new a/c hoses. There are usually, at most, only four hoses anyway. If you make them yourself, it's usually about twenty bucks per hose. To have them made mail-order, it's maybe $50 per hose, shipped; see the chapter on Making and Installing Hoses.

If your hoses still have flare fittings and you're switching over to o-ring components and the fittings are both the same size, there's one thing you can try. Assuming the new component has its fittings in almost exactly the same place as the old component, the hose will reach, and the fitting is at the correct angle (and the odds of these three things are not good), it's possible that you can employ little cone-shaped male-to-male flare-to-o-ring adapters. However, as I explain in the Fittings chapter, those aren't as good an idea as they sound. When you use an adapter and torque down the fitting to get the flare part to seal, it's possible to crush the o-ring and introduce a leak. Now you have *two* possible places for the fitting to leak instead of just one.

For all these reasons, usually you should plan on just replacing all the hoses. On the 1970s BMWs I usually work on, the original hoses are no longer available, so "replace" means "make new hoses." If you still have the original hoses, don't throw them out even if they're junk. They may be of value in case you need to take them or send them to a custom hose shop and have them duplicated. I say "*may* be of value" because the degree to which a duplicate of an old hose will help you depends on what else you're replacing. If every a/c component is original, sure, duplicate the hoses, but if any have been updated, it gets complicated. For example, the drier in a Behr a/c system in an old BMW 635CSi has a #6 flare input facing down and a #8 flare output facing sideways – very specific and highly unusual. The hoses connecting to the drier are equally specific. If need be, you can replace the drier with the original part and have the hoses duplicated. But, as I discussed above, if you're doing a whole-hog a/c upgrade and replacing the compressor and condenser as well, you'd be wise to select components with modern o-ring fittings, so why not just use o-rings on everything and use a conventional drier with two side-facing #6 fittings? Once you cross this Rubicon, your old hoses no longer matter – the components may be mounted in different locations than original, the fittings are different, the angles at which the hoses connect to the fittings probably change, etc. It's custom hoses for you, Jack.

However, make no mistake – the modest expense notwithstanding, there is some amount of risk in replacing every hose. The ones that are especially challenging are the two running inside the passenger compartment, attaching to the evaporator assembly up under the dash. On a newer car, o-ring connections are employed, but on older cars like a BMW 2002, they're flare fittings that were tightened with a dying strain in 1972 and may not have been touched since. The accessibility of the "holding fitting" (the one you need to hold in place with a wrench while you

loosen or tighten the collar nut on the hose fitting) at the side of the console isn't great, and the tubing connecting them to the evaporator core is fragile and easy to damage when trying to unscrew fittings wedded with 40 years of corrosion.

Another exception to the make-all-new-hoses-they're-cheap rule is if you have a car whose originality you prize so highly that you insist on keeping its original a/c hoses. Original BMW 3.0CS coupes and Bavaria sedans have red cloth-braided hoses and fittings that look completely different than inexpensive crimp-on beadlock fittings. I don't question that they're part of the look and feel of the under-hood. I can understand how, particularly as the value of mint CS coupe now exceeds $100k, an owner might want to keep the original red cloth-braided hoses. In that case, that desire for originality may continue to the compressor and condenser, in which case it's squarely at odds with the desire with cold functioning air conditioning. That's not a world I inhabit. Me, I just want the a/c to work.

I think that, for the moment, we have beaten the hose issue to death. With a hose.

Decide if you're replacing the condenser

As discussed in the Condenser chapter, the condensers used in vintage air conditioning systems are of an old serpentine-style tube-and-fin design. In comparison, a modern condenser is of a parallel flow design, greatly increasing its heat transfer capability and thus the cooling capability of the system. If you are rejuvenating an old a/c system, particularly if you are planning on converting from R12 to R134a, it is strongly advised that you also upgrade to the biggest parallel flow condenser that'll fit. Old condensers may have flare fittings, but just about any new parallel-flow condenser has o-ring fittings. As stated above, this has a ripple effect in terms of hoses.

Decide how much work to do on the evaporator assembly

As detailed in the Evaporator chapter, there's a choice of how much work to do on the evaporator assembly. If the system has not been left open, and there's no evidence of contamination in the lines, and if you're not changing the kind of refrigerant and oil used, and the blower fan turns on, then you can tempt fate and leave the evaporator assembly alone, perhaps pop-flush it as described below. But if any of those conditions aren't true, you really ought to take it out and flush it.

Another way to look at it is, if you have other reasons to disassemble the console, such as a dead evaporator blower motor, a leaky heater core, or heater flaps whose foam has deteriorated so they're letting in ambient air, then you need to take the evaporator assembly out anyway, and when you do, you can disassemble and flush it. When you do that, you might as well just change the expansion valve. When you reinstall the evaporator assembly, be sure to completely surround the fittings on the suction line to the compressor with cork tape so they don't sweat and drip on the rug.

Perform gross leak test

If the system still has refrigerant in it, skip this test.

Before going further, you need to have some idea if the system has obvious leaks. Many years ago I learned the trick of using a tank of nitrogen to pressure-test an air conditioning system. It's a three-stage process. In the first, you literally listen for hissing from massive leaks. In the second, you pressurize it and then watch the gauge. In the third, you let it sit, first for a few minutes, then for an hour, and finally overnight and see if it maintains pressure. For the gross leak test, we're using the gauge set primarily as an adapter for the nitrogen bottle, secondarily to check if the pressure drops overnight.

Buy or rent a small nitrogen bottle at a welding supply shop. Use a ¼" NPT to ¼" 7/16-20 SAE flare adapter to connect the regulator on the nitrogen tank to the center hose of the gauge set. Close the knobs on the gauge set (screw them in clockwise). Close the regulator on the nitrogen bottle by unscrewing it all the way. Open the valve on the top of the nitrogen bottle. Then screw in the regulator until the gauge on the regulator reads about 120 psi. Now slowly open both knobs on the gauge set to allow the nitrogen

to flow into the low and high pressure sides of the system.

With the valve on the nitrogen bottle and the knobs on the gauges open, the bottle is going to try to maintain 120 psi into the system. The system is either going to hold it, or it's going to leak out. You're going to need to *listen*. Turn off the radio and any other devices making noise. If there's a massive leak, you'll see the pressure on the gauges drop, but you'll also hear it. Follow your ears. Put your hands around hoses and connections.

Figure 172: An obviously leaky fitting on the drier discovered using pressurized nitrogen and soap solution.

Eventually you'll need to use a bottle of soap solution such as Big Blu, spray it on all components (particularly around connections – don't forget the pressure cut-off switches) and look for air bubbles. If you find a leaky component, shut off the nitrogen bottle and repair or replace the part. If it's leaking at a threaded connection, try tightening the nut. On newer cars with o-rings, the rubber ring is responsible for the seal so the nuts don't need to be tightened down with a dying strain, but on older cars that originally used R12 and still have flare fittings, these connections need to be very tight.

Pressure-testing is an iterative process. Let's say you pressure-test the system and discover a leak in the condenser—fairly common due to its front-mounted location and exposure to weather and stones. You'll need to procure another condenser, install it, and pressure-test again.

If there's no obvious audible leak, close the valve on the nitrogen tank and the knobs on the gauges, and watch the gauges for a minute. If they don't move, the system may still have small leaks but at least it is tight enough to see if the compressor functions.

Test compressor functionality

If there are no massive leaks, and the compressor clutch is engaging, and the engaged compressor is not seized, the next step is to see if the compressor is actually compressing anything. If the gauges showed no gas in the system, shut off the nitrogen bottle and unscrew the hose to the gauges. Open the knobs at the top of the gauges to vent nitrogen until the pressure reads about 70psi (about what the resting pressure of refrigerant would be), then close them. Start the car. Either turn on the a/c or hold the compressor wire on the positive battery terminal. Look at the gauges. If the high side (red) gauge increases and the low side (blue) gauge decreases, then the compressor is at least doing something, and it's worth a try flushing, pressure-testing, evacuating, and recharging the system. If the gauges remain static, then the compressor is not compressing anything and probably needs to be replaced.

Figure 173: Any motion in the gauges (high side going high, low side going low) indicates that the compressor is functioning.

Flush the system

If the system still has refrigerant in it, you have a choice to make. You need to decide if you're going to the minimally invasive route and simply try and top it up with refrigerant, or are indeed going to rejuvenate it with upgraded components. If it's the former, just jump out of this whole chapter and go to the Charging chapter near the end of the book. But if it's the latter, you'll need to take the car to a service station to have the refrigerant recovered, as it is illegal to vent refrigerant. If it's got R12 in it, under no circumstances should it be released, as it is an ozone-depleting agent. R134a is *not* an ozone-depleting agent, but it *is* a greenhouse gas, and it is illegal to vent as well.

As described in the Flushing chapter, if the system has remained closed, didn't suffer catastrophic failure (e.g., seized compressor), and if the refrigerant isn't being changed, then it may not need to be flushed. But if the system was left open (for example, if the compressor was removed and the hoses were left hanging), or if the compressor seized and threw metal shavings into the system, or if the refrigerant is being changed and, along with that change, there's a required change in the kind of oil used, then the system needs to be flushed. If none of these things are the case but, when you remove a hose, you see powdery residue or oily goo, the system must be flushed too.

Flushing is performed either by using pressurized cans of a/c flush, or by filling a container with a/c flush or a volatile compound such as mineral spirits, putting it in line with an air compressor, and blasting it through sections of the system. For example, you can undo the hoses coming from the condenser to the drier and from the condenser to the compressor, put the flush nozzle in the end of one hose, and flush through the condenser and out the other hose.

You have to trade off the risk of taking things apart so you can flush against the risk that the system is full of crap and it will fail if you don't flush. Err on the side of flushing.

Refill the system with oil

There's another reason to flush the system: Verifying that it has the correct amount of oil in it. Air conditioning systems use several ounces of oil to lubricate the compressor. As a system is run, the oil gets distributed through the components of the system, and because there is no way to directly measure how much oil is in there (it's a sealed system, and there's no oil dipstick), in order to be absolutely certain of the amount of oil, you need to flush it all out, drain the compressor, and start from scratch. Because this is a pain, people sometimes use a rule of thumb to add two ounces of oil whenever a major component is replaced.

Thus, for all of these reasons, the "do it once, do it right" approach to a/c repair is to completely flush the system of any old oil and contaminants, then refill it with the correct amount of the correct type of oil. If the system is completely apart, if you like, you can add 1/3 of the oil to the compressor, condenser, and evaporator respectively. If the vendor from whom you purchased the compressor is adamant that the compressor comes filled with the correct amount of oil for the entire system, and you've verified it's the correct oil for your configuration, you can take them at their word, but you must make sure other oil has been flushed out of the system. If your system had been working and recently died, and if you identified the failed component as, for example, the condenser, you can probably get away with replacing just that

one component, not flushing, adding two ounces of whatever kind of oil is in it to it, and evacuating and recharging. This usually works fine, but over time, with multiple repairs, it can result in a car with too little or too much oil in the a/c system.

When adding oil, it's a good opportunity to add dye. You can either use oil that's pre-mixed with fluorescent dye in it, or add dye to oil without it. In any case, dye can be greatly helpful in locating a leak if one develops down the road.

Figure 174: The only way to verify the system has the correct amount of oil in it is to flush it, drain the compressor, and refill it with the correct amount of oil. Here I'm adding oil with dye pre-mixed into it.

Replace receiver / drier

As described in the Drier chapter, air conditioning systems that have an expansion valve have a drier (also called a receiver), basically a beer-can-sized bottle of desiccant that removes moisture. If the system is opened to replace any component, unless the drier is very recent, it should be replaced. Most driers have two #6 o-ring or two #6 flare fittings that enter and exit in a line at the top of the drier. Certain Vintage BMWs and Mercedes take an unusual drier that has a #6 flare input and a #8 flare output, with the two fittings at 90 degrees to one another. Basically, any drier will work; it's just a question of size, fittings, and mounting. If you are making your own new hoses, the input and output fittings can be incorporated into the new hoses. And, as I described above, if the original drier had flare fittings, you'd be well-advised to change them to o-ring fittings, as they're far less leak-prone than flares.

Figure 175: ALWAYS replace the drier when opening a system for any reason.

If the system has an orifice tube instead of an expansion valve, it has an accumulator instead of a drier, and care must be taken to replace it with one of the same size.

Replace needed components

If you've decided you're overhauling the evaporator assembly, and updating the compressor and condenser, and using a new drier with o-ring fittings, and making new hoses to connect them all, go and do all of those things. That'll keep you busy for a few nights.

Decision time... take it in for recharge or do it all yourself?

If you've gone through the above steps, you've identified any grossly malfunctioning or leaking components and replaced them. You now presumably have a system that stands a good chance of being capable of cooling the car. You've already saved a big chunk of change. What's next? You could simply take the car in to be recharged (more accurately, evacuated, leak-tested, and recharged), and that's fine. I worked that way for years. Or you can do it yourself.

Test for small leaks

Once the system has been reassembled and any obvious leaks have been addressed, the next step is seeing if there are small leaks. The easiest way to do this is by verifying that the system will hold pressure for several hours. This time, you'll want the flow from the nitrogen bottle closed, as you don't want a constant source of pressure – that is, you'll want to pressurize the system, leave it, and see if the system holds the pressure you put into it.

Figure 176: Pressurize the system to about 120 psi for leak testing, then let it sit overnight.

Hook the nitrogen bottle back up to the center hose of the gauge set. I usually crank up the pressure to 120 psi for this pressure-holding test, but one has to be very careful, as nitrogen bottles are pressurized to thousands of pounds, which can rip apart an air conditioning system in a New York second. Close both knobs on the gauge set. Open the knob on the nitrogen bottle. Adjust the regulator to 120 psi. Slowly open both knobs on the gauges. Then close the knob on the nitrogen bottle. The gauges should now read about 120 psi. There may be some slight difference in calibration of the gauges, but that's not important. What you're looking for is change over time. Write down the reading, mark it with erasable marker or tape, or take a picture with your phone. Then, walk away for several hours, ideally until morning. Pressure varies with temperature, so the readings will naturally fall if you pressurized in the heat of the day and it cools off overnight, but if the car is sitting in the garage at a relatively constant temperature, in the morning the pressure should be the same. If it is, you have a tight, leak-free system.

If, however, it has lost a substantial portion of its pressure overnight, don't kid yourself—you have a leak. And the fact that it took overnight to lose pressure means that it is a small leak. For more information, consult the Pressure Testing and Leak Detection chapters.

Evacuate the system

If you have a system that has survived an overnight pressure test without budging, it's tight. The next step is to evacuate it – pump it down to a deep vacuum – before you recharge it. The purpose of the pump-down is to remove any moisture that might've crept in (moisture, when combined with the lubricant, can create hydrofluoric acid). Your high school chemistry tells you that lowering the pressure lowers the boiling point of a liquid. By pulling a deep vacuum, you literally cause any moisture to boil off.

To pull a vacuum, you buy or rent a vacuum pump, hook it to the center hose of the gauge set, open up the low and high pressure knobs, then run the pump for at least 90 minutes. For extra credit, after the vacuum has been pulled, you can shut all the knobs, let the system sit overnight, and verify that it holds the vacuum (though you should already know that it's tight from pressure-testing it with nitrogen). For more information, consult the Evacuation chapter.

And finally... recharge the system

It's a simplification to say that you procure the correct number of cans of the correct kind of refrigerant, connect a can tap to the center hose of the gauge set, tap one can at a time (always keeping the can upright), open the knob *for the low side only*, and let the gaseous refrigerant get sucked in while watching to make sure that the pressure doesn't climb too high, but that's basically what you do. While it's possible to do this blind with only an inexpensive low-side gauge that's part of a can tap, it is strongly advised to look at both the low and high side pressures to have

an idea of what's going on. For more information, consult the Charging chapter.

If necessary, perform further small leak detection on the charged system

If you've done a good, patient, thorough job pressure-testing the system with nitrogen prior to recharge, and let it sit overnight, or, even better, for a few days, you should have gotten it good and tight. But it is possible that it may still leak slightly. For more information, see the Leak Detection chapter.

Five short rejuvenation case studies

A few quick anecdotes may be helpful in delineating the edges of the bell curve of a/c rejuvenation. It's always best if you "do it once, do it right," and sometimes you thank your lucky stars that you do, but sometimes you get mauled by the beast of unforeseen consequences when you go into those dark caves, and other times you get lucky when you steer clear of them.

The 'Burb

I had an '84 Suburban that had never been converted to R134a. It seized its compressor while I was driving it. Because it was a large vehicle and had rear air, it had a whopping 84 ounces of R12 in it. I'd never before been faced with a dead a/c system full of refrigerant, much less filled with such a huge quantity of ozone-depleting refrigerant. I imagined an ozone hole opening up directly over my house and causing my entire family to get skin cancer. I made some calls and found a local shop who still worked with R12 and paid them to recover it.

Everything that I'd read said that, after a compressor has seized, to be sure you get any metal shavings out of the system, you need to undo every hose and flush every component. So, even though I saw no actual metal shavings when I undid the compressor hoses, that's what I started to do. Unfortunately, when I tried to undo the massively-long metal lines that ran under the car from the compressor to the rear evaporator, the end of one of the lines snapped off, destroying both the line and the rear evaporator core, which, I assure you, pegs the ruins-your-day-meter. I sucked it up and replaced the broken line and the rear evaporator core, but it made me circumspect of the risk of undoing old fittings that hadn't been disturbed in years.

Because I had opened up the system and flushed the shavings—and any old refrigerant and oil—out every hose and component, I had the opportunity to convert it to R134a. I posted the question to a Chevy forum, and the consensus was "That's a huge amount of space inside; you probably won't be happy with R134a." So I stayed with R12. It worked great. This was, however, in the mid-1990s. I'm not sure I would make the same decision now.

The Porsche 911SC

When I bought my '82 Porsche 911SC and found that it had a bad compressor, I replaced it with a rotary-style unit and a flat Porsche-specific adapter bracket that bolted to the original compressor bracket (after trying a generic Sanden adapter bracket and not having it fit correctly). I entertained the idea of replacing all the hoses, particularly since I'd read that the long hoses that run under the car tend to be leaky. Since some of the hoses run through channels in the underbody, I thought this was a perfect application for snaking the bare hose through and then crimping the ends on in place. However, when I looked at the connections between the hoses and the evaporator and condensers, saw 25 years of corrosion, recalled how I'd twisted a line off the rear evaporator in the 'Burb, and realized the odds of these connections coming off without damage were slim, I did the "if you're not prepared to battle the beast to its death, back slowly out of the cave" thing. The 911's compressor was bad but it had not seized, I was planning on sticking with R12 and mineral oil, and I didn't see any crud in the hoses, so I decided that disassembly and flushing was not strictly necessary.

The new rotary-style compressor was a Unicla, as that's what was recommended on the Pelican Parts Porsche forum, and as the market wasn't flooded by Chinese-made Sanden clones the way it is now. Like

most any new compressor, it had #10 and #8 o-ring fittings. I thought I'd try and re-use the original hoses and mate them to the new compressor with flare-to-o-ring adapters, but was surprised when I found that the York compressor I'd removed instead had two #10 flare fittings on it, so the discharge-side hose wouldn't mate to the compressor. Plus, the a/c fittings and hoses weren't standard beadlock, but more like hydraulic fittings, so I couldn't use my crimping tool to crimp on a new fitting. I found a local heavy equipment repair shop who cut the #10 end off and crimped on a new #8 fitting for me. So in this instance, I *did* get away with re-using the original hoses.

Figure 177: Unicla compressor installed in 1982 Porsche 911SC.

After compressor replacement and evacuation and recharge, the Porsche's a/c worked great, so I made a good call.

The Land Cruiser

I had a '93 Toyota Land Cruiser for a few years. When I bought it, it was cheap, partially due to my driving a hard bargain because the air conditioning was not working. The compressor seemed to be alive (the clutch worked, and the compressor wasn't seized). I pressure-tested the system and found a major leak in the condenser. My family was leaving soon on vacation and we needed to take the TLC, so I worked quickly and replaced the condenser with a used one, but when I pressure-tested the system again overnight, the system was still leaking. I isolated the leak to the evaporator assembly. When I pulled the assembly out (which, on this model, was easy), the backside of the evaporator core was oily and filthy—clear indication of it leaking. The evaporator core wasn't available as an a la carte part, only the entire assembly, and that listed at nearly $1500 from Toyota. Fortunately I was able to locate a used assembly.

Since I didn't know the history of the replacement evap assembly, and now was replacing two of the three major system components, I elected to "do it right." I flushed the system and replaced every o-ring. I wanted to add the correct amount of oil, but the only way to know how much oil is in the compressor is to take it out, turn it upside down, and drain it. I did, and found that the compressor was completely dry. The system had likely blown all its oil out the evaporator leak. If I hadn't "done it right," I probably would have burned out the compressor in short order.

Since the compressor was out, I considered converting it to R134a, which requires different oil. I sought out advice on the pros and cons of R134a conversions on forums. 8 out of 10 responses were "You live in New England? You'll be fine with R134a." The other two responses were from the Southwest, the kind of extreme heat in which I never expected to be driving the car. I converted it to R134a, and for use in New England, it was absolutely fine.

The Bavaria

The a/c on my '72 BMW Bavaria was complete and original down to its red cloth-braided hoses, but non-functional. I did a full-on rejuvenation using a new rotary-style compressor (mounted using the last Air Products Group 0151A bracket available on the planet), 16"x20" parallel-flow condenser mounted utilizing existing holes (a no-drill installation), a Spal fan plastic-tied to the condenser, and all-new hoses. I changed everything to o-ring fittings except the evaporator; the hoses plumbing it still needed flare fittings.

Figure 178: No-drill condenser installation in the '72 Bavaria.

The question was whether to yank the evaporator assembly out and dismantle and flush it. Since, like the 911SC, I was staying with R12 and mineral oil, the compressor hadn't seized, there was no evidence of contamination in the hoses, and the blower fan worked fine, I left the evaporator in place and pop-flushed it. The car now has blisteringly-cold a/c.

Figure 179: My lovely wife Maire Anne digging the cold air in the Bavaria.

The E30 325is

I had a very nice, very original '87 BMW E30 325is. When it came to me, it had a bad compressor clutch, a bad o-ring on the drier, and no refrigerant in it. I knew that I was going to sell the car soon and didn't want to go to the effort of retrofitting a parallel flow condenser, which almost certainly would've been necessary had I switched from R12 to R134a. When I pulled the compressor, I found that the lines had a black residue in them—powdery but not gooey. I first blew it out with compressed air, then flushed the lines with chemical flush.

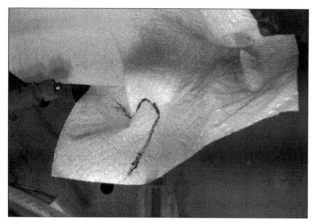

Figure 180: Powdery residue blown out of the 325i's hoses.

Because there was contamination, I had to pull out the evaporator core, flush it out, replace the expansion valve, and flush the condenser and the other hoses. Fortunately, this is a car that's late enough that the evaporator and expansion valve slide out from the right side of the console. It wasn't trivial, but it was easier than with an evaporator assembly.

I sourced a good used stock compressor, replaced the drier, pressure-tested the system, found a leak in the o-ring under one of the compressor fittings, replaced it, and charged it up with R12. It blew nice and cold. It was certainly the quickest most cost-effective path to a functioning system, but as I've said elsewhere in the book, I was surprised when an interested party declined to buy the car because it still had R12 in it.

The 2002tii

My '72 2002tii had a dealer-installed Behr a/c when I bought it, but it hadn't worked in years. I did full-on rejuvenation designed to blow as cold as humanly possible—a "Hobiedave" bracket, a Sanden 508 clone, a huge parallel-flow condenser, a big fan, all new hoses, and R12.

There was no indication that the compressor had

seized, and there was no contamination in the hoses, but I pulled the evap assembly anyway because the heater box in front of it needed to be rebuilt due to a dead motor and degraded foam on the flaps. This gave me the opportunity to remove and disassemble the evaporator assembly, replace the expansion valve, and fully flush the core. As described in the Fittings chapter, on this car I used flare-to-o-ring adapters on the male evaporator fittings, as I could install the adapters while the evap assembly was out of the car when I had the clearance to get them good and tight. This also made it much easier to get wrenches on the o-ring fittings.

Figure 181: Flare to o-ring adapters used on the evaporator fittings. Note how little clearance there is to get a holding wrench behind the adapter, and how much room there is to get wrenches on the o-ring fittings.

Folks on bmw2002faq.com reported that the brackets in the nose on which the horns mount prevent you from installing a condenser larger than 10"x18", but that if you cut the horn brackets, you can go bigger. I elected to cut the brackets and was able to install an 11"x21" condenser. I originally sourced an 11"x24" condenser, but though it may have fit, there was no way to get it through the opening. Part of my decision to cut the horn brackets was because my 2002tii is far from mint and does not have the original tii-specific "non-snorkel" nose. For a mint car with the original correct nose, I wouldn't recommend this, and probably wouldn't do it myself.

Figure 182: Right-side horn bracket on BMW 2002tii before cutting.

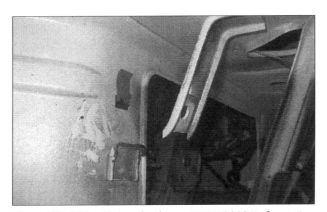

Figure 183: Right-side horn bracket on BMW 2002tii after cutting.

Note that in other 2002s, I've left the horn brackets intact but cut the bracket on the side of the condenser to get clearance.

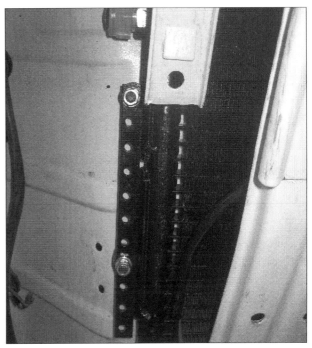

Figure 184: Oversized 11"x21" condenser fitting in gap cut in horn bracket.

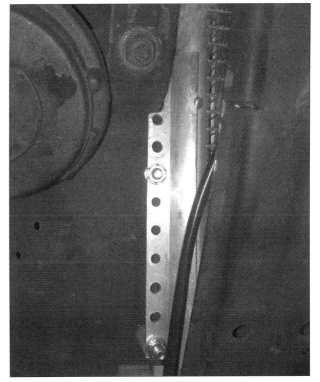

Figure 185: Horn bracket left intact but condenser bracket cut to get clearance with a 10"x19" condenser on a different 2002.

The original drier mounting location on a 2002 seemed to depend on the whim of the technician at the dealership performing the installation. Some were mounted in the engine compartment, but on other cars, the drier was shoehorned into the nose. My tii was the latter; the original drier had been mounted in the nose via a bracket that was permanently attached to the drier. Two threaded posts protruded from the end of the bracket and were attached to the nose with nuts. Further, the top of the drier was positioned exactly in front of the hole in the nose that the hose went through. In order to ease the installation and minimize the number of holes drilled in the car, I tried to source the correct replacement drier, even though that meant living with the drier's original flare fittings. When the part arrived, although it initially seemed correct, on closer examination, the bracket wasn't attached at the correct angle. Instead I sourced a generic drier with o-ring fittings, mounted it in the nose. By using a generic adjustable mounting bracket, I was able to position the drier outlet directly in front of the hole in the nose. I then fabricated a very short hose the exact length to mate the inlet of the drier to the outlet of the condenser.

Figure 187: The replacement drier with the bracket at the wrong angle.

Figure 188: A generic o-ring drier installed in the nose of the BMW 2002tii using the mounting original holes, a generic bracket, and a very short custom-fabricated hose.

Figure 186: The original drier on my 2002tii and its integrated bracket.

Rejuvenation summary

The smart, high-success rejuvenation path is to use a new or rebuilt modern rotary-style compressor and whatever bracket is needed to bolt it to the block, a new large parallel-flow condenser, and a new large cooling fan. If there's any evidence of contamination in the hoses, or if you're changing refrigerant or the kind of oil used, you have to flush the system thoroughly, which means removing the evaporator assembly, disassembling it, and flushing the core. While you're in there, you should replace the expansion valve. But if there's no evidence of contamination and you're not changing oil or refrigerant, you can try leaving the evaporator assembly in place, hoping the expansion valve is okay, and pop-flushing the lines. I strongly advise changing as many fittings as possible from flares to o-rings and making new hoses. Replace the drier, reassemble, pressure-test, evacuate and recharge, and you'll be too cool for school.

Chapter 16

The Basic Steps for A/C Retrofit

Overview

The recipe for retrofitting a system into a vintage car differs somewhat from that of resurrecting a long-dead system. The newer the car, the more challenging retrofit is, as the dashboard and under-dash area become more complex, and the connection between the under-dash a/c components and the rest of the car becomes more intertwined. Looked at from 10,000 feet, the project breaks up nicely into the following chunks.

Figure 189: An entire used a/c system for a BMW 635CSi arriving on my porch.

Decide on your overall approach – how much are you improving while retrofitting?

There are four primary approaches to retrofit.

1. Install an original system (factory or dealer-available) with no modifications.

2. Install an original evaporator assembly but make reasonable improvements to the rest of the system, such as a modern rotary-style compressor and parallel-flow condenser.

3. Roll your own, using entirely non-stock components including the evaporator assembly. As discussed in the Evaporator chapter, you can use a modern universal-fit evaporator assembly and modify or fabricate a console to fit around it, or go hole-hog and try and integrate a modern climate control box that replaces both the heater box and the evaporator assembly.

4. Buy a kit that has everything.

Most folks opt for the second option since it keeps the interior of the car looking stock but increases the odds that, after going to all that work, you come out of it with a cold car. Replacing the compressor with a smaller lighter quieter rotary-style one and updating the condenser to a newer more efficient parallel-flow unit are cost-effective, proven, and low-risk steps.

Buying a kit

Option #4 above—buying a kit—deserves a bit of ink. If you have a common enthusiast car like a vintage Mustang, the big three suppliers of parts and systems for vintage cars—Old Air Products, Vintage Air, and Nostalgic AC—likely sell a full a/c kit with all-new components for it. The kits generally include either a new modern evaporator assembly or a new modern climate control box that replaces the heater box as well. Looking at the web sites of the above three, they all appear to offer systems for a variety of vintage American cars and trucks. Vintage Air and Nostalgic AC also offer systems for the Toyota Land Cruiser FJ40, and Nostalgic AC has systems for Jeeps and some British cars (MG, Triumph, Austin, and Mini). There are also some brand and model-specific vendors. Gilmore Enterprises, for example, specializes in systems for vintage air-cooled Volkswagens.

My advice is this: Do your homework. Read reviews. Search on make-and-model-specific forums for posts from people who have used this kit on your car. Talk with the vendor. The world is full of good honest vendors selling well-engineered products at a price appropriate to keep them in business, but it is also full of people overselling their product. Remember: No one cares more about your car than you do. Be a pain in the ass. Ask tough questions like how many holes need to be drilled for the installation. If the system includes a climate control box that replaces the heater box, ask if the kit includes a block-off plate to close up the hole in the firewall. Ask how the climate control box interfaces to the existing heat and defroster sliders on the dashboard. Make them prove to you that they've solved these problems. Search through past auctions on sites like Bring a Trailer for evidence of whether or not a non-factory-looking a/c kit is a demerit to the value of an otherwise well-executed car.

When you've addressed the technical issues, ask to see photos of an installed system. This stuff can be very subjective. You may see an original console with an obviously aftermarket faceplate and aftermarket louvers in the middle, and it may simply rub you the wrong way.

Also, there's the price issue. My experience is that retrofitting a/c is not prohibitively expensive when you procure the components yourself. For a vintage BMW, I typically spend, rough round numbers, about $200 for a used original evaporator assembly and a used original console and faceplate, $100 for a new Sanden clone compressor, $100 for a bracket, $60 for a new parallel flow condenser, $100 for a new Spal condenser fan, $100 for the parts needed to build four hoses, and $20 for a drier. That's $680. Obviously there are additional odds and ends. Call it $800. In contrast, a kit from a reputable vendor that is specific to your car may cost nearly twice that. Now, if it comes with every single part, including an evaporator assembly that blows harder and colder than the stock one, and it fits perfectly, and it looks stock, and they've spent time solving problems so you don't need to, maybe that's worth it.

Note that, at the left end of the price curve, you can find generic "kits" out there for as low as $500 that include a Sanden clone compressor, a parallel flow condenser with a Brand X fan, a Brand X universal under-dash evaporator assembly, a drier, and hoses and fittings. But you get what you pay for. There's no console to surround the evaporator assembly and give it a stock look. The condenser almost certainly won't be the largest one that'll fit into the nose of your car. And these ultra-low-priced kits typically don't include a compressor bracket.

Bottom line: Understand what it is you're buying. As you'll read in the Retrofit Stories below, I thought I was buying a "kit," or something close to it, for my BMW 3.0CSi, but the seller didn't know the car nearly as well as I did, and I wound up pretty much on my own.

R12 or R134a?

As discussed in the Refrigerants and Rejuvenation chapters, other decisions branch off from this choice.

Verify that there aren't showstoppers

For example, the stock crankshaft pulley on a BMW 2002tii doesn't have a groove for the compressor belt. You need the special air-conditioned version of the pulley. You don't want to find out something like that halfway into the job. Read up on your car and plan your assault carefully.

Buy a complete a/c system out of a junked car

If at all possible, find an air-conditioned parts car and buy every interior a/c piece—the evaporator assembly, switches, relays, wiring, any duct pieces and little brackets, any special hard hose lines that are needed to cleanly route the plumbing behind the glovebox, the grommets that the hard lines go through in the firewall, and that special all-important console. Photograph the living snot out of it as you remove it—every nut, bolt, and wire. If you're buying the parts remotely, pay the seller extra if necessary to document the removal process. It's well worth it.

You don't really need the compressor, condenser, fan, hoses, receiver-drier from the engine compartment, as you'll be replacing all of that with new and improved components, but if you have them, they'll provide you with a template. It *is* helpful if you have the section of the wiring harness that plumbs the compressor and the condenser fan.

Compressor

Unless you have a car where original compressor is an integral part of the look and feel of the engine compartment, procure a rotary-style compressor and the bracket needed to mount it to the engine. The cost-effective way to do this used to be, and still pretty much is, to buy a Sanden 508 or one of its inexpensive Chinese-made clones and a mounting bracket, but as per the chapter on the compressor, the bracket issue has gotten way more complicated than it used to be. Fill the compressor with the oil that's appropriate for your choice of refrigerant. I recommend ester oil, as it works for a wide range of refrigerants. I vividly remember when doing my first retrofit (my '73 BMW 3.0CSi), bolting that shiny new compressor and bracket up to the engine, and thinking "first step is the hardest – now I'm on my way."

Condenser

Unless you want a concours-correct car, you almost certainly want to find the biggest aftermarket condenser you can physically stuff into the nose. This is especially important if, as part of the retrofit, you're converting from R12 to R134a. Unless there's a body of knowledge in an on-line forum that definitively tells you what will fit and what won't, this is an iterative process involving measuring, ordering, test-fitting, and, unless you damage the condenser, returning and re-ordering. I describe the measurement process in detail in the Condenser chapter. Most of the times I've done this, the final size was smaller than I'd estimated because unless your brain automatically performs AutoCAD clearance calculations, you can't really know where the clearance problems will be until you actually try and install a candidate unit. Sometimes the limiting factor in selecting "the biggest aftermarket condenser you can physically stuff into the nose" often isn't mounting it there, it's getting it into position. Install a suitably large electric fan as well.

Evaporator assembly

For me, this has always been by far the most time-consuming part of the process. If you're installing an original evaporator assembly out of a junked car, you'll kick yourself if you install it, install the console trim pieces around it, recharge the system, and then have trouble with the evaporator and have to take it back out. Prophylactic maintenance is the name of the game. Unless you know beyond the shadow of a doubt that the evaporator assembly was out of a car that had working a/c, and that you're going to be using the same kind of refrigerant and oil that was in it, you're strongly advised to disassemble the evaporator assembly and flush it out, and while you're

in there, you probably want to replace the expansion valve. If you can rig something up to pressure-test the core and the attached valve, do it. Feed the fan motor 12v and test it. It has to move enough air over that evaporator core to make this whole exercise worthwhile. If the motor seems anemic, you might want to have it and the squirrel cages rebuilt. At a minimum you can oil the bearings and wash the fan motor brushes down with contact cleaner. Remember that the evaporator has to allow water to drain; typically there's a small rubber hose that needs to protrude through the transmission tunnel. If your tunnel doesn't have a hole, you need to drill one. When you re-install the evaporator assembly, be sure to use cork tape around the metal hose fittings so they don't sweat and drip on the rug.

If, on the other hand, you're installing an aftermarket evaporator assembly, or going for the gold with a climate control unit that replaces both the evaporator and the heater core, you're a braver man than I, and have many fun-filled evenings of engineering and adaptation ahead. You can read up on the pros and cons in the Evaporator chapter.

Punching holes in firewall for hoses

In order for the refrigerant to reach and leave the evaporator, it has to get through hoses or hard pipes that run through the firewall. If you're lucky, the holes may already be there, covered with a panel or closed up with rubber plugs. However, on a car that's never had a/c, you may need to punch or drill new holes.

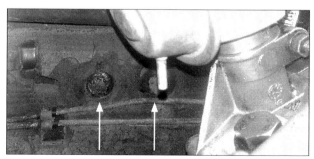

Figure 190: You got lucky: Plugged-up holes in firewall. Photo courtesy Adam Merchant.

If you're retrofitting a/c into a BMW 2002, the Behr

manual actually has a template showing you where the holes should go. It is pictured below:

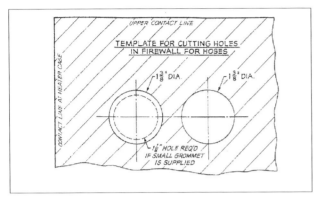

Figure 191: The instructions for where the holes go, from the original BMW Behr a/c installation instructions. Illustration courtesy Behr of America.

First, know that, if the original a/c system had hard lines running through the firewall instead of hoses, they're likely there because the clearance behind the glove box is tight enough that the bend radius of rubber hoses is too big, and hard lines with right angles are necessary. So you are strongly advised, when sourcing an original evaporator assembly, to also source any hard lines that connect to it.

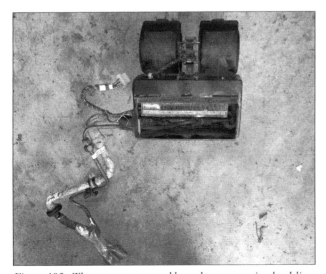

Figure 192: The evaporator assembly and accompanying hard lines for my 635CSi. You can see how specific the right angles in the hard lines are.

Second, any hole through the firewall requires a grommet both to seal it and to prevent the metal edge from cutting into the hoses. This may seem obvious, but *measure the size of the grommet, not the hose!*

Figure 193: The grommet on the large hard line for my 635CSi required a 1.5" hole.

When I retrofitted a/c into my 3.0CSi nearly 20 years ago, I was fortunate that a local acquaintance had a 3.0CS parts car from which I could take careful measurements of where the hard lines went through the firewall. The hard lines and rubber grommets had been removed, so I could use calipers to accurately measure the diameter of the holes. I used a set of Greenlee knock-out punches and the big hydraulic tool to pull the two halfs together to make the holes. These make beautiful clean cuts, and I highly recommend them, but to use them, you still need to drill pretty big pilot holes for the threaded rod that pulls the two halves of the punches together.

Figure 194: Greenlee knock-out punches and hydraulic mechanism.

My recent hole-cutting in the firewall of my '79 BMW 635CSi is described under "Retrofit Case Studies" below.

Remember to coat the newly-cut edges of the holes with zinc primer so they don't rust.

Drier mounting

Find a convenient place to mount the drier. It has to go on the liquid line between the condenser outlet and the evaporator inlet. It's typically somewhere on the right side of the engine compartment, between the nose and the firewall. If your car has an orifice tube instead of an expansion valve, it has an accumulator instead of a drier, and it must go between the evaporator outlet and the compressor inlet.

As per the Drier chapter, if your car originally had flare fittings, you can use a universal o-ring drier and make new hoses with o-ring fittings to accommodate it. If it has an accumulator, though, be careful to replace it with one of the same size.

Hose fabrication

For a from-scratch a/c retrofit, you're going to need to make all new hoses, or pay someone to make them. Install the compressor, condenser, evaporator assembly, and drier, then make the hoses. That way, you can crimp one fitting onto a length of hose, install the hose on the car, cut it to the correct length, and crimp on the other fitting. As I said above in the Flares Versus O-rings section of the Rejuvenation chapter, be aware that the a/c components on old cars used flare fittings, whereas most new components use o-rings, so if you're installing a new compressor and receiver but using an original evaporator and condenser, your new hoses will need to have flare fittings on one end and o-ring fittings on the other. And be certain that your system has charging fittings. On my first from-scratch installation, the guy fabricating the hoses for me noticed that there were no charging fittings anywhere (oops!) so he spliced them into the hoses he was making (whew!).

Figure 195: R134a charging fittings spliced into the compressor hoses.

Wiring

Wire up the system. You need to make it so that, when you turn on the a/c switch (which is generally the switch for the blower fan in the evaporator assembly), it turns on the compressor, and, via a relay, turns on the condenser fan. For a car like a BMW 2002 / E3 / E9, you may be running new wires to the fusebox, but for a newer car like an E24, the a/c control panel plugs directly into the existing climate controls. As explained in the Electrical chapter, the blower speed switch is tightly-coupled to the blower motor in the evaporator assembly. If you're buying an evap assembly out of a parts car, it's smart to buy every relay and wiring sub-harness that it touches, and to photograph it as it's removed, but if you have to wire it up from scratch, it's not that complicated. See the Electrical chapter for more information.

Console trim

Depending on the car, this can cause financial ruin. Original air-conditioned console pieces for certain cars, like the BMW 3.0CS, are unique to that car and hellishly expensive. How hard you chase them depends what price you're willing to put on originality.

The short strokes

Test for leaks, repair as necessary, then evacuate and recharge with the refrigerant of your choice (long topic there). Leak testing, evacuation, and recharging are as described in the rejuvenation chapter as well as their own separate chapters.

Two retrofit case studies

The 3.0CSi

In 1999, I retrofitted a/c into my '73 3.0CSi. I worked with a vendor who did a lot of VW retrofits, so I figured he knew about German Behr-based systems. We discussed doing an R134a-optimized system using modern components. He sent me a rotary-style compressor, bracket, a larger condenser than stock (though it was serpentine; parallel-flow condensers weren't really a thing yet), a condenser fan, a generic drier, and a universal evaporator assembly, all with o-ring fittings. The evaporator fit on the transmission hump and under the dash, and I thought that was what I wanted, but when I realized that there was no chance of it fitting inside a stock console, I changed my mind and sent it back.

I sourced the stock evaporator assembly for the a/c version of the car, and the all-important "intermediate piece" to connect it to the dashboard plumbing. I asked the vendor if there was anything that could be done to optimize the original evaporator assembly for R134a. I sent the assembly to him, and he had a custom evaporator core made for it with three passes of the cooling tubes instead of two, installed an R134a-specific expansion valve, and rebuilt the squirrel cage fan motor. I then installed the evaporator assembly in the car. Doing so without shattering the fragile plastic "intermediate piece" was very challenging.

There were no pre-existing holes in the firewall for the a/c hoses (or, in this case, hard lines). I had a friend who had a 3.0CS he was parting out, from which I took careful measurements of the hole locations. Punching the holes in the firewall was harrowing, but was ultimately achieved cleanly by using Greenlee Punches (see the section above in this chapter).

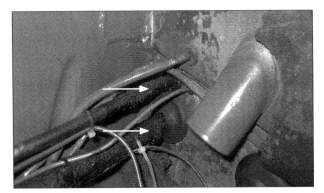

Figure 196: The hard a/c lines and grommets installed in the firewall of my 3.0CSi.

I mounted the new aftermarket condenser in the nose of the car by drilling holes, something I probably wouldn't do on a car like this again, but it didn't have the value then that it does now.

After installing the components, I took it to a local shop to have hoses made. The vendor (Harry Ellis of "Ellis The Rim Man" fame for you Bostonians) fortunately noticed that I hadn't planned for charging fittings, and spliced them into the compressor lines. I then took the car in to a local shop and had the a/c system evacuated and recharged. It blew cool but not freezing for about a week, then died. I found, somewhat painfully, that one of the fittings at the expansion valve had been over-tightened and had cracked the flare fitting on one of the hard pipes (fortunately a replaceable part). Another cycle of evacuation, recharge, month of performance, death, leak test, repair later, and it finally functioned for the long haul. But each time I pulled the evap assembly out and re-installed it, the cracks in the fragile plastic "intermediate piece" widened.

The R134a-based system worked... okay, but not great. I had to run it for a while before it would blow cold. Once it did, it cooled the cabin down, provided that the ambient temperature wasn't over 90 degrees and the humidity wasn't too high.

As per the chapter on "Other Things That Heat Up the Interior," I instituted several rounds of improvements. I installed a cut-off valve on the heater core so it wouldn't be plumbed with hot water. I devised a way of blocking off the flow of hot outside air into the heater box (I should've rebuilt the heater box before the evap assembly was installed, but I didn't know that at the time). I tinted the windows. None of it made a big difference. A/c performance continued to be okay, but not great. In particular, there seemed to be little or no benefit from the custom triple-pass evaporator core.

Since the original a/c-specific console and faceplate pieces were hellishly expensive, I just let the evaporator assembly sit bare on the transmission tunnel for several years. Then I adapted the original non-a/c console by cutting holes in the sides for the squirrel cages and screwing on some slotted side covers from a different BMW, and left the front open. Finally I found original a/c console pieces from a parts car that were in horrible shape, and paid an upholstery shop to recover them. Then I paid more than I should've on eBay for the E9-specific console faceplate, only to find out that the piece I bought was for a Bavaria and not an E9. Shame on me. The faceplate is in the car to this day, but it doesn't fit correctly; it puts the radio laughably low in the console.

Figure 197: The most expensive part of the a/c retrofit in my 3.0CSi was the cosmetic part—the console and related trim.

Most recently, in an attempt to increase the a/c performance from adequate to cracking, I removed the serpentine condenser and replaced it with a parallel-flow condenser, as I'd done in my other cars. It seemed to make some difference, but not a dramatic one. I believe that what I'm feeling is the difference between the R134a in this car and the R12

in my 2002tii and my Bavaria, both of which have a/c systems so cold that I could use them to store meat in.

The Euro 635CSi

My most recent a/c project was the from-scratch installation into a '79 Euro BMW 635CSi. I loved the Polaris-black-sport-interior-black-stripes scheme of the car, and the price was right, but I almost didn't buy it because of its lack of air. I caved, bought it, and soon took the car on a 2200-mile road trip to and from Chattanooga. After the last few hundred miles nearly heat-stroked me, I decided never again, and embarked on the retrofit.

Figure 198: My '79 Euro 635CSi, the car for which I ignored my own advice and bought it even though it didn't have air.

I was incredibly fortunate to find someone parting out the exact same car, right down to the year and Euro version. He sold me every component, nut, bolt, wire, and connector in the interior, as well as the wiring harness that went through the firewall, photographing it all during the disassembly. It was a godsend.

For the compressor, I used a Sanden 508 clone and mounted it using a modified wing-cell bracket and a pair of adapter brackets (see the BMW-specific section of the Compressor chapter). It worked, but I don't think I'd do it again; I'd be more likely to source a rebuilt wing-cell compressor and bolt it right on.

For the condenser, I used a 16"x19", short-drop fittings, and a low-profile Spal fan held on by the plastic tie kit.

For the drier, I surprised myself by using a new version of the original oddball part with #6 and #8 flare fittings, one of them pointing downward. I did this because the original flare drier mounted directly to the hard compressor inlet line, thus eliminating one hose, and because mounting the drier anywhere other than the original location either interfered with the air cleaner and washer bottle or brought it uncomfortably close to the exhaust manifold.

The cutting of holes through the firewall was a bit of an adventure. In this big web-enabled world, I assumed that I could find a pic showing where the hard a/c lines went through the firewall on the car. I looked at every photograph I could find online of the engine compartment, and could see that the two hard metal a/c lines emerged from the firewall at the right-hand corner, just to the left of the inner fender. However, owning to clearance issues, you can't easily get a drill into that corner; you need to drill from the passenger compartment side. Thus, I needed photographs from under the glove compartment. To my surprise, I could find none online, and the fellow who sold me the system no longer had the hulk of the parts car from which the parts originally came.

Finally, I found an online acquaintance with the same car. By doing the iPhone Facetime thing, he showed me where the hard lines went through his firewall above the glove box. We used the glove box hinge's second screw hole from the right as a fixed point for measurements of the holes' locations.

Despite the obvious trepidation one has about drilling holes in the firewall of a car, the placement of the holes does not need to be millimeter-exact. If the car uses hard lines, copper pipes can be bent. Plus, there's a good-sized grommet between the pipe and the hole that offers a fair amount of play. If they're rubber hoses, you're going to make new ones and cut them to length anyway. The thing to do is drill a tiny test hole with a very small drill bit, secure in the knowledge that, since the final holes for the grommets are probably at least an inch big, as long as any test holes are inside that diameter, you can drill as many of them as you want, choose one as a pilot hole, and when the final large holes are punched, all

traces of the tiny test holes will be wiped from the face of the Earth.

Once I marked and drilled the first test hole at the measurement point for the larger of the two hard lines, the area where the two pipes needed to come through the firewall was obvious, as it was bounded on the right by the inner fender wall, on the left by the brake lines, and on top by the ceiling of the firewall. It's just that you have to drill from inside and you don't have x-ray specs, so in order to get a reference point mapping the outside to the inside, you need that first little test hole.

Figure 199: Marking the position of the first test hole in the firewall of the 635CSi.

I then adjusted the location slightly, drilling a few additional test holes to move it away from the right inner fender and up slightly. In the picture below, with the firewall insulation cut away, the general area where the two holes need to go is obvious.

Figure 200: Hole location with firewall insulation pulled away.

I began to ready the Greenlee knock-out punch. Each sized punch has an inner and an outer cup, pulled together by a pump-driven actuator to punch the hole. To use it, I'd need to widen the tiny test hole into a ½" pilot hole big enough to receive the punch's threaded rod. Before I did this, though, I first began to test-fit the two halves of the punch both in the engine compartment and inside the car.

I found a problem. The outer shell of the punch hit the bracket that holds the glovebox hinge. The bracket is welded to the inside of the firewall, so there's no easy way to take it off to get clearance for the punch. I looked at reversing the punch and putting the smaller inner shell inside the car and the larger one in the engine compartment, but the thicker part of the punch came very close to hitting the inner fender wall. Suddenly, there appeared to be no easy way to use the punch. I needed to use a hole saw instead, and was very glad that I hadn't drilled the monstrously large ½" pilot holes required for the punch, as they would've made it impossible to precisely position a hole saw that needed a much smaller pilot hole.

I found an old dull 1.5" hole wood saw in the basement, test-fit it inside the car, and found that, if I moved the pilot hole upward slightly and angled the drill downward, there was just enough room to fit the hole saw above the hinge bracket. I did some quick reading online, found that Milwaukee "Hole Dozer" saws cut metal and are available inexpensively at Home Depot, and ran to a nearby store and bought the two I needed.

Figure 201: Using a hole saw that just clears the glovebox bracket.

They say "measure twice, cut once." This was more like "Measure a bazzion times, drill six test holes, and

then pray that you cut once," but the cutting part was done quickly.

Figure 202: The freshly-cut holes.

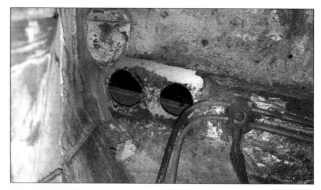

Figure 203: The same, as viewed from the engine compartment.

Placing the evap assembly on the hump was a bit more alignment-fussy than in other cars, but I got it in the ball park.

Electrically, the integration was much more involved than any other a/c work I've done, and I still haven't polished it off. I'd just installed the evaporator assembly, and then realized that it had no controls hanging off it. No temperature control. No fan speed control. Nothing. How do you control it? How do you even turn the air conditioning on and off? What was I missing, both in parts and in understanding?

I looked in the parts the seller had sent me, and saw that there was a heater control panel. I'd looked at it once before, but assumed that it had just been thrown in there for completeness and I didn't need it. This time, I examined things more closely. There was no air conditioning button on it like there is in an E30 or an E28. From the front, it looked just like the one that was in the car, except that it had blue and red swoopy symbols around the temperature knob, whereas the one in the car was all blackface.

But then I turned the heater control panel over, and saw that, on the back, it had a box with a metal thermocouple probe that clearly was supposed to snake inside the evaporator assembly. This obviously was the a/c temperature sensor and switch. There were also two relays on the back of the panel. And, on close examination, I saw that there was a microswitch on the temperature knob that was tripped closed when the knob was turned into the cold (blue) region.

Figure 204: Original (left) and a/c (right) climate control panels from the front...

Figure 205: ...and back.

This wasn't a heater control panel: *It was a heat and a/c control panel.* It was clear that I was mistaken in thinking that the heat and a/c in the 635CSi were "completely separate systems." Instead, the compressor's turn-on and the evaporator's temperature and fan speed were controlled by this panel. I had to pull out my existing panel (which actually *was* a heater control panel) and install this new one.

It actually wasn't too bad. I yanked the old panel out and test-fit the a/c-equipped one, plugging it into the car's wiring harness and mating its additional connector to the one coming out of the evaporator assembly. I re-connected the 635CSi's battery for the first time in months, and to my delight, the panel did what it was supposed to. With the temperature knob in the red, the fan speed control governed the fan in the heater box, but when you turned the knob into the blue range, the relay switched fan speed control to the fan in the evaporator assembly. Cool.

Initially I couldn't see how the compressor and the condenser fan are turned on. That turned out to require a section of wiring harness that snakes from the panel into the engine compartment. Fortunately, the seller had extricated the harness from where it goes from the fuse box, wraps clear around the nose of the car, runs along the right inner fender, through the firewall, and into the passenger compartment. Unfortunately, none of the connectors on it were labeled.

The typical action for such things is to find a wiring diagram, but that's less helpful than you'd think. Part of my tirade against wiring diagrams (yes, I who wrote an electrical book actively despise them) is typified by the fact that I located a wiring diagram for a 1980 633CSi, which is probably close enough to my Euro '79 635 to be useful, and while it shows the surprisingly torturous path that 12 volts takes to the compressor, and shows four relays being part of the heat and a/c system, it doesn't list where the connectors or relays are located in the car, or what color or size the connectors are. Initially, looking at the a/c wiring harness, it wasn't even clear to me which end went inside the car and which went under the hood.

Eventually I noticed that the harness had a one-prong male spade connector inside a plastic sleeve, exactly the kind of connector that the compressor typically plugs into. I also noticed a small two-prong connector on the harness. I then looked under the dashboard, and to my delight, located a small two-prong connector on the wiring on the back of the climate control panel that mated with the one on the harness. I turned the temperature knob past zero, checked for voltage on this connector, and...

taDA. This was apparently how the compressor got switched on. I used the multimeter to test continuity of wires in the harness, and determined that the male spade connector went to one wire on the little two-prong connector. I then plugged the connector on the wiring harness into it and repeated the test, checking for voltage at the spade lug inside the plastic sleeve, and… taDA a second time. I snaked one end of the wiring harness through the grommet in the firewall where one of the hoses went through. The compressor was now wired, though most of the length of the new harness was simply dangling over the side of the engine compartment.

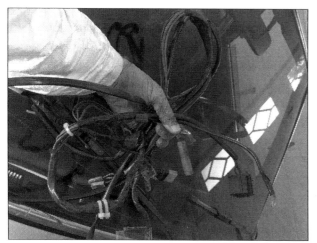

Figure 206: Trying to figure out the connectors on the a/c wiring harness.

Next came figuring out the condenser fan wiring. I began by trying to decipher what the other eight or so connectors on the harness were. I cross-checked them with the wiring diagram, and figured out most of them by process of elimination. But some things were baffling. My car appeared to have a missing relay. And, unfortunately, it looked like, on the new a/c harness, the wires that connected it to the fusebox had been cut in order to get it out of the car from which it was taken.

I slowly realized that I was in uncharged territory. Unlike any other car I'd ever retrofitted air into, the 635CSi already had an auxiliary cooling fan that was turned on via a temperature switch connected to the radiator, or at least was supposed to be. The original

fan was dead. I'd thrown it away and installed a new Spal fan on the condenser, but I hadn't actually thought about how to get the Spal working as both an a/c condenser fan and as an auxiliary cooling fan.

I began by simply wiring the Spal fan to the connector that went to the original aux fan. I'd read that you can get the aux fan to turn on by removing the two connectors to the temperature switch on the bottom of the radiator and jumpering across them together to bypass the switch. I did, and nothing happened. So, it seemed that in order to get the condenser fan working, I first needed to trouble-shoot the original wiring to use it as an aux cooling fan.

It didn't take long to realize that there were numerous problems. I found references online to the fuse for the aux fan being in a small two-fuse box that was supposed to be located above the battery. This was missing on my car, though I saw the holes where it should've been, and found the connector that presumably originally fed it dangling under the battery. I could not locate the output connector. I was aware that my 635CSi had been hit in the front at some point in the distant past. It was looking increasingly likely that the wiring and the aux fan were never fully reconnected after the accident and the bodywork.

So, I had three choices. I could ignore the a/c condenser fan issue for now and keep trying to get the new Spal working as an aux cooling fan. Or I could jump straight to trying to integrate the a/c wiring harness, even though the portion to the fuse box appeared to have been cut and a relay appeared to be missing. Or I could go full Hack Mechanic on its ass, ignore every connector on the a/c wiring harness except the one I had successfully powering the compressor, and simply wire the Spal fan, via a relay, to a switch on the dashboard, allowing me to manually turn it on for a/c, or auxiliary cooling, or both.

Any guesses which option I selected?

In addition to having bought the Spal fan, I'd bought the proper two-pin Molex connector that mates to it, and a Spal relay kit. I usually make these connectors myself and use generic relays, but I'd found an open box Spal kit on eBay for a good price.

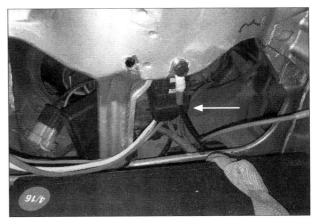

Figure 208: The installed aux fan relay.

I simply wrapped up the unused length of the a/c wiring harness (which was most of it) into a coil and zip-tied it in place beneath the washer bottle at the lower right corner of the engine compartment. At some point, if I have a slow week and find someone with an early E12-based 635CSi like mine that I can poke around in, I may resurrect the idea of using the a/c harness. But at least I got the aux fan working.

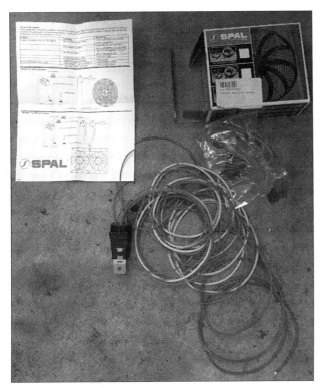

Figure 207: Spal relay and harness.

I mounted the relay inside the nose, connected the high-current wire to the battery via a fuse, and ran the thin low-current wires inside the car.

I looked at the dashboard to see where I might mount a switch, saw that there was a factory pull switch for non-existent fog lights, found that there were even wires running from there into the engine compartment, and totally took it as a sign. I had it all wired up in about an hour. It was a great rush pulling the factory fog light switch and hearing the Spal fan gloriously go whoooooooosh.

Retrofit summary

For most folks, sourcing an original evaporator assembly and console, a modern rotary-style compressor and the proper bracket to mount it to the engine, a big new parallel-flow condenser and fan, and newly-fabricated hoses is a good path to retrofitted a/c. If you can buy every a/c component out of a parts car, do it (and photograph the removal), but you'll likely wind up only using the evaporator, console, switches, and some wiring bits. The newer the car, the more involved the retrofit is, particularly from the electrical end. If you have a car where a modern aftermarket climate control box is offered as part of a bolt-in kit, you might consider it, but if you have to do your own adaptation, be aware that it's a lot of work, and will likely change the look of the interior away from stock, which will likely affect the value of the car.

Don't let anyone tell you not to bother with retrofitting a/c into a vintage car. Conditioning my 3.0CSi and 635CSi were great projects. During the summer, it makes the difference between my driving the cars versus leaving them parked. And when someone yells "Hey! Cool car!" I think, buddy, you don't know the half of it.

Chapter 17

Making and Installing Hoses

Overview

As I've repeated until you're probably sick of hearing it, if you're going to all of the work to rejuvenate an old a/c system, you'd be smart to replace every hose to ensure that the resulting system is clean and tight. The hoses and fittings are cheap. They can be bought from any number of places including NAPA, web sites such as coldhose.com, and eBay. Hose is typically about three bucks a foot, and fittings typically cost between three and ten dollars each. So in materials, you're usually talking less than twenty bucks a hose. You *do* need a crimping tool, and they're pricey; see below.

Buying the hose-crimping tool

All you need in order to turn bulk hose and fittings into a ready-to-install hose is a crimping tool. If you plan to do this kind of a/c work more than once, you should just buy the tool. "The tool" is the Mastercool 71500 Hydra-Krimp, a handheld hydraulic device that crimps beadlock fittings onto hoses. It comes with a set of swappable dies for the different-sized fittings and hoses. Unfortunately, its list price is big money—over six hundred bucks.

You can buy its smaller companion, the Mastercool 71550, for closer to $150 instead. However, the 71550 is just the crimping portion without the hydraulic hand-held assembly. This requires you to hold the tool in a bench vise and tighten the crimping jaws down onto the fitting with a wrench. It's better than nothing, but unfortunately it removes a big part of the utility of the 71500, which is that you can crimp the fitting on one end on a hose, install that end in the car, and then, in situ, measure the exact length the hose needs to be to reach the other end, cut it, and crimp the other end on right there in the car.

Due to the double-edged sword of Far East manufacturing, Chinese-made knockoffs of the 71500 Hydra-Krimp are, as of this writing, available on eBay for about $200, aping the same form factor and even using the same color crimping dies as the Mastercool. I am not making a recommendation either way. I have a used Mastercool 71500 that I bought years back on eBay for about half of the new

cost. I love owning and using it. But I've bought other Chinese-made knock-offs and had them work fine with my occasional non-professional work load.

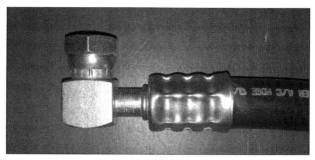

Figure 209: A newly-crimped hose fitting.

Figure 210: The essential but pricey Mastercool Hydra-Krimp 71500.

Buying hoses instead of making them

The website coldhose.com (and others) lets you click-and-build custom hoses at pretty appealing prices. As of this writing, a 24" #10 hose with standard o-ring fittings at both ends from coldhose is $35 plus about $10 shipping. The costs increase with the hose length and the selection of certain fittings. If all that you need is one hose, and if you're never going to do this kind of work again, this path may make sense. Be aware, though, that it's pretty easy to misjudge which fitting is best, or the length of the hose, or the "clocking" of the fittings (the angle that the two fittings make relative to one another). The best way to get this stuff right is to make the hoses yourself while standing right next to the car, test-fitting one end, then cutting the hose to length and crimping on the other end.

Make a table listing the a/c fittings

As you're preparing to make hoses, or to have them made, it's best to be organized and make a table of the fittings on each component, and from there determine the fittings needed for each hose. Geek alert, I do this in Excel. Since I just fabricated hoses for my '79 635CSi, I'll use it as an example.

As I've mentioned, the original a/c systems in vintage BMWs are a bit unusual in several ways. My '73 Bavaria had a drier that had two #8 flare fittings instead of the usual #6, and they were both facing in the same direction. This '79 635CSi had a drier which had a #6 flare input that faced downward, and a #8 flare output, feeding a #8 flare input to the evaporator.

Further, the original drier on this car was directly connected to the hard input line to the evaporator with no hose between them. That meant that I had a choice: I could try to source an original drier with #6 / #8 flare fittings, and connect its output directly to the hard evaporator input line. Or, as I've recommended elsewhere, I could use a generic drier with #6 o-ring fittings, and fabricate a hose with a "step-down" fitting to connect its output to the #8-sized flare on the evaporator input line.

The drier can be mounted anywhere between the condenser output and the evaporator input. Its location is thus typically either in the nose of the car, or along the right inner fender wall, or up against the firewall. In my case, when doing this in my 635CSi, putting the drier on the inner fender wall made it uncomfortably close to the exhaust, so the best location for the drier was its original location, up high near the firewall, directly connected to the hard line to the evaporator. As such, I took the somewhat unusual step of not using a generic drier with o-ring fittings and instead using an original drier with #6 input and #8 output flares. That's reflected in the table below. Also reflected in the table is the fact that the evaporator has hard lines with flare fittings on

both ends, and you can't really do much about that.

Below is what the table would look like for most cars with standard components and fittings:

Fittings By Component, Most Cars	
New Compressor	
Input	#10 o-ring
Output	#8 o-ring
New Condenser	
Input	#8 o-ring
Output	#6 o-ring
New Drier	
Input	#6 o-ring
Output	#6 o-ring
Standard Evaporator	
Input	#6 o-ring or flare
Output	#10 o-ring or flare

And below is what it looked like for my BMW 635CSi:

Fittings By Component, Early BMW 635CSi	
New Compressor	
Input	#10 o-ring
Output	#8 o-ring
New Condenser	
Input	#8 o-ring
Output	#6 o-ring
Weird Drier	
Input	#6 flare
Output	#8 flare
Weird Evaporator (Hard Lines)	
Input	#8 female flare
Output	#10 female flare

Now that you've listed the fittings component by component, you need to know how these components are connected. Every automotive a/c system with an expansion valve I'm aware of is plumbed as follows:

- The compressor discharge hose goes to the inlet at the top of the condenser.

- The hose from the outlet at the bottom of the condenser goes to the drier inlet.

- The drier discharge hose goes to the evaporator inlet.

- The evaporator discharge hose goes to the compressor inlet (the suction side).

The interconnect diagram for a standard expansion valve system is on page 16. Note that if the system has an orifice tube instead of an expansion valve, an accumulator replaces the drier, and it's located between the evaporator outlet and the compressor inlet.

You see that, for a standard a/c system, you need to fabricate four hoses. So rather than being component-centric like in the tables above, you need to be hose-centric. Double geek alert, I actually do this in a linked table in Excel to make sure I'm not screwing things up. Below is what it would look like for most cars with standard components and fittings. Note that there's an added row for the fitting angles.

Fittings By Hose, Most Cars				
	#1	**#2**	**#3**	**#4**
from	compressor discharge	condenser out (bottom)	drier out	evaporator out
to	condenser in (top)	drier in	evaporator in	compressor suction
hose size	#8	#6	#6	#10
input	#8 o-ring	#6 o-ring	#6 o-ring	#10 o-ring
angle	90	90	straight	Straight
output	#8 o-ring	#6 o-ring	#6 o-ring	#10 o-ring
angle	90	straight	straight	90

The list below is for my BMW 635CSi with its unusual drier, and evaporator inlet hard line connected directly to the drier. Because of this, there was no #3 hose.

Fittings By Hose, Early BMW 635CSi				
	#1	**#2**	**#3 (not used)**	**#4**
from	compressor discharge	condenser out (bottom)	drier out	evaporator out
to	condenser in (top)	drier in	evaporator in	compressor suction
hose size	#8	#6	#8	#10
input	#8 o-ring	#6 o-ring	hard-connected	#10 male flare
angle	90	90 short drop	hard-connected	straight
output	#8 o-ring	#6 flare	hard-connected	#10 o-ring
angle	90 short drop	45	hard-connected	90

Determine the necessary angles for the fittings

The other thing you need to suss out before ordering fittings is what angles you need for each. Beadlock fittings come in straight, 45 degree, and 90 degree versions. On the condenser, unless the opening for the hose to pass from the nose into the engine compartment is directly in front of the fitting, you usually want fitting angles of 90 degrees, often configured as "short drop" fittings in order to maximize clearance (I described these in the chapter on the condenser). The fittings for the drier are usually straight or 45 degrees. Compressor fittings are usually 45 or 90 degrees so the hoses can curve away from the engine. Judge as best as you can by eyeballing each component, and when in doubt, simply order any and all of the fittings you think might work, and try them out. They're cheap.

Charging ports

You also need to deal with the issue of charging ports (the places where the gauge set attaches, enabling you to pressure-test, evacuate, and charge the system). If you're not going to use the charging ports on the compressor, or if the compressor doesn't have them, you can splice charging ports into the hoses on the low and high pressure sides, or use compressor hose fittings that have charging ports built in. On my 635CSi, I tried the latter, but found that there wasn't sufficient clearance to use them. In the photo below, you can see the top of the charging port nearly hitting the block.

Figure 211: Test-fitting a compressor fitting with integrated service port on the 635CSi. In this case, there wasn't enough clearance because the service port hit the engine block.

Because of this, I elected to simply use the ¼" 7/16-20 SAE charging ports already in place on the back of the compressor. The downside is that they're quite inconvenient to reach—you pretty much have to jack up the car and connect the gauge set from underneath—but once the system is pressure-tested and recharged, you don't need to access them again unless something goes wrong.

Also, keep in mind that, by EPA regulation, the charging ports are supposed to have fittings on them that match the refrigerant. The ¼" 7/16-20 SAE fittings on the back of many compressors are for R12, not R134a, and because the fittings are so close together, you can't screw 13mm and 16mm

R134a charging port adapters onto them and have the charging hoses fit (see the Fittings chapter). If it's your car, you can do whatever you want, but if you sell the car, the charging ports really should match the refrigerant. So if you do this with R134a, at least put a tag somewhere on a hose clearly labeling the refrigerant in the system.

Make the damn hoses already!

When your hoses and fittings arrive, before you begin fabrication, it's important to test-fit every fitting onto the place it's supposed to go. Sometimes you don't have the clearance you thought you did, as was the case with the charging ports on my compressor hoses. And sometimes you simply get a bad fitting, with threads that don't mesh with those on the component. Best to find these things out before you crimp the fittings onto hoses.

I usually fabricate the hoses in the order listed above. On my 635CSi, I first crimped the short-drop fitting for the top of the condenser onto a more-than-long-enough piece of hose, then test-fit the fitting end in place. Since hose is usually shipped coiled, it has a natural bend direction. It's always wise to position the fitting to use the bend direction to your advantage, as I've done in the photo below. Here, the other end of the hose has to pass through a channel that's to the left of the hose fitting, so I'm taking advantage of the natural set to the hose.

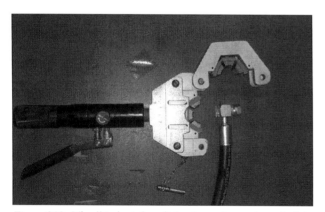

Figure 212: The #8 short-drop fitting inserted onto the end of the #8 hose, taking advantage of its natural bend. The Hydra-Krimp is ready with the #8 crimping die.

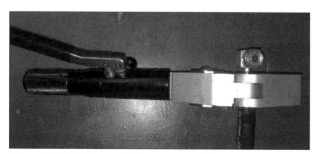

Figure 213: Nothing to do but squeeze until it stops.

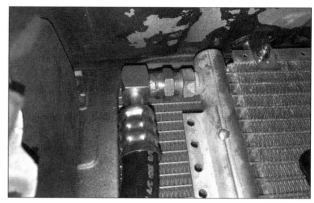

Figure 214: Test-fitting the crimped fitting onto the condenser.

I passed the hose through the nose and into the engine compartment, hand-tightened the other fitting onto the compressor, cut the hose to length, inserted the hose into the fitting, marked both so I could crimp the fitting on in the "clocked" orientation most favorable to the bend in the hose, then removed the fitting from the compressor and used the Hydra-Krimp to crimp the fitting in place on the hose. Being able to do this with the hose in place is a huge benefit of having a tool like the Hydra-Krimp as opposed to a crimper that needs to be set in a table vise.

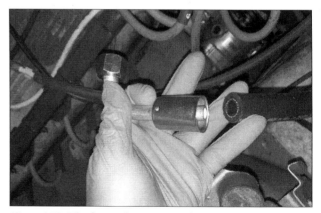

Figure 215: The fitting about to go on the cut-to-length hose.

Figure 216: Marking the hose and fitting to get the orientation right.

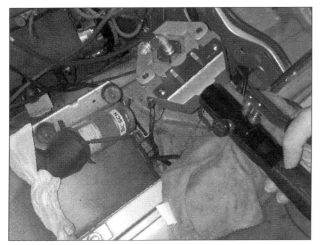

Figure 217: Using the Hydra-Krimp to crimp on a fitting with the hose in place. Note the towel to prevent the fender from getting scratched.

Figure 218: Ta-da!

Above, I showed the fabrication of a single hose. In general there are four. In the case of my 635CSi, there were only three, since the drier was connected

directly to the hard evaporator inlet pipe. As with many things, the majority of the work is in the preparation; it took less than an hour to actually fabricate and test-fit the three hoses.

Final attachment—Nylog, o-rings, and crush washers

With the hoses fabricated, you then attach them to the fittings for real. This involves coating all threads and o-rings with Nylog sealant, and, if any of the hoses have flare fittings, using copper flare washers, also coated with Nylog.

Finally, tighten everything down. With o-ring fittings, the o-ring is providing the sealing, so you don't need to tighten them down with a dying strain. With flare fittings, though, it's the metal-to-metal surface that's doing the sealing, and you sometimes need to really crank down on them to get the sealing faces mated up.

It is enormously satisfying getting the hoses installed. Reaching this point is a huge milestone. It means that all the heavy lifting is done, the major components are installed and interconnected, and there's just electrical connections, pressure-testing, evacuation, and charging standing between you and a cold car. The only thing more satisfying is the final blowing of cold air.

Figure 219: Both newly-crimped compressor hoses.

Chapter 18

Flushing the System

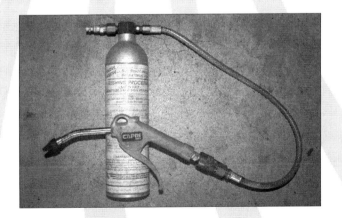

Overview

Air conditioning systems need to be scrupulously clean inside in order to function. Even the smallest amount of contamination can clog the expansion valve or orifice tube and prevent the refrigerant from expanding into the evaporator and cooling. Flushing is the process of blowing a chemical wash through the a/c hoses, pipes, and major components (condenser and evaporator) to remove debris, residue, old oil, and internal corrosion.

When do you need to flush a system?

If a system was left open (for example, if the compressor was removed and the hoses were left hanging), or if the compressor seized and threw metal shavings into the system, or if the refrigerant is being changed and, along with that change, there's a required change in the kind of oil used, then the system needs to be flushed. If none of these things are the case but, when you remove a hose, you see powdery residue or oily goo, the system must be flushed too.

Another reason to flush the system is that, with the different choices of refrigerants and oils, you may not be absolutely sure what kind of oil is in there, or how much. The only way to be certain is to flush it and start from scratch, refilling it with the correct amount of the correct kind of oil.

If, on the other hand, the system has remained closed, didn't suffer catastrophic failure (e.g., seized compressor), and if neither the refrigerant nor the type of oil are being changed, then it may not need to be flushed. If, in particular, you know that the system had been working (specifically, that the expansion valve wasn't clogged), and when you open it up, you find no evidence of contamination, and you're only, say, upgrading to a parallel flow condenser, you're probably fine not flushing it.

Be aware that there is risk in disassembling an old system, taking apart fittings that have been mated for 40 years, to flush it. In particular, if the fittings are one metal (say, steel) and the components are another (say, aluminum), you get corrosion of dissimilar metals creating a death grip. You need to trade off the risk of taking things apart so you can flush against the risk that the system is full of crap and the a/c will fail if you don't flush. Read the "Rejuvenation Case Studies" section of the Rejuvenation chapter to see where I got it right and wrong.

But err on the side of flushing.

What you do and don't flush

- To be clear, you don't actually "flush the system." You flush components of the system.

- You shouldn't flush through a drier or an accumulator; you should just replace it.

- You shouldn't ever try to flush a compressor; you just turn it upside down and drain it as thoroughly as possible into a coffee filter. If nasty stuff comes out of it, you'd be wise to replace it.

So that leaves the condenser, the evaporator, and the hoses.

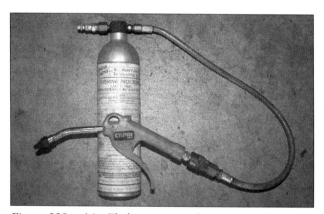

Figure 220: A/c Flush canister and standard rubber-tipped air nozzle.

How to flush

For each of those, flushing is performed either by using pressurized cans of a/c flush, or, better still, by filling an a/c flush canister with the appropriate flushing chemical or a volatile compound such as mineral spirits, putting it in line with an air compressor, connecting a standard air nozzle with a rubber tip, and blasting the chemical through sections of the system. For example, you can undo the hoses coming from the condenser to the drier and from the condenser to the compressor, put the flush nozzle in the end of the condenser input hose, put the end of the condenser output hose in a catch receptacle like a wide-mouthed bottle, and flush through the condenser and out the other hose. Be certain to wear gloves and goggles whenever flushing.

However, if an evaporator assembly has an expansion valve in it, you can't flush through the assembly because the expansion valve stops the flow. You can, however, "pop flush" an evaporator assembly, where you press the rubber tip of the nozzle into the inlet hose and the pressure build up and pop the flush nozzle off, then do the same thing on the outlet side. This is really, really messy to do, as the flushing chemical sprays absolutely everywhere. *Never* pop-flush without wearing goggles. If you have any concern about damage to paint, under-hood components, or other items inside your garage, don't do it, and remove the evaporator assembly, disassemble it, and flush the evaporator core alone instead.

Note that, when you disconnect hoses, if you see black oily tarry stuff in any of the components, do-it-yourself flushing as described above is unlikely to get it all out. There was a problem, mostly associated with Ford products in the 1990s, referred to as "The Black Death," where the Teflon rings in the compressor would fail, get pulverized into a fine dust, be combined with hot liquefied refrigerant, and get baked onto the inside of the system. If you see this, you'd be advised to consult a professional, as they have professional-grade flushing machines. However, even those machines might not be able to remove all of the goo, and the only sure path to success might be to replace literally every a/c component and hose that refrigerant passes through.

Note also that, if the car already has a parallel-flow condenser, and if there's any contamination found in any of the hoses, you're best advised to replace the condenser, as the tiny passageways in a parallel-flow condenser are easily clogged and resist cleaning by flushing.

Flush away!

Chapter 19

Pressure-Testing
the System for Leaks

Overview

Along with ensuring that the internals of an a/c system are clean, leak-testing a system is quite possibly the most important part of the a/c repair, rejuvenation, or retrofitting process. If you are repairing a system, the most common reason for repair is that the system has no refrigerant in it, meaning it leaked out, so you want to be sure that that doesn't happen again. And if you are upgrading or performing a from-scratch installation, after going to all that work, you want the system to be tight and leak-free. In either case, I strongly advise that you prophylactically leak-test the system by pressure-testing it with nitrogen. Get it right, and you're just an evacuation and a recharge away from having a car that reliably gets cold for years. Get it wrong, and you may be chasing leaks for months.

There are two schools of thought on leakage. The first is the mantra that I've repeated throughout this book—that refrigerant is not a normal use-it-up commodity like oil or brake pads, and thus if an a/c system isn't cooling because its refrigerant is low or empty, it means the refrigerant has leaked out, which means that the system is, in a sense, broken. It has a leak that must be found and fixed. Most of the time, when someone says it "just needs a recharge," they're either tragically mistaken or lying through their damned teeth.

But the other school of thought is that all a/c systems leak a certain amount, or start to leak a certain amount at a certain age, and it's just a question of how much they leak and how quickly it affects performance. My "it never just needs a recharge and anyone who says it does is lying scum" rants notwithstanding, I'll admit that I've bought cars that have had non-functional a/c due to being empty of refrigerant, pressure-tested them with nitrogen, and had them sit overnight and not budge the needle on the gauges, and then, once recharged, I never got a chirp out of the sniffer, and did not need to recharge them again during a year of ownership. If they had a leak (and they must have), it was a very small slow one.

Going a step further, I will even admit that part of the reason I'm moving away from using R12, even though I love how well it cools, is the knowledge that, no matter how tight I get a system, if I charge it with R12, the odds are that, in the next 20 years, the R12 will end up in the atmosphere. Sigh.

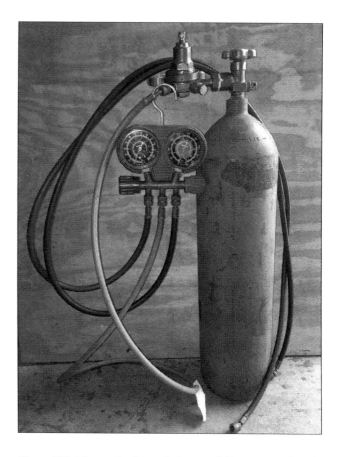

Figure 221: Nitrogen bottle attached to manifold gauge set. Photo for reference only. Any pressurized gas bottle should be chained to wall or in tip-resistant cart.

To be clear, when I say "pressure-testing the system for leaks," I'm talking about making sure that the system is tight by pumping it full of nitrogen or some other inert gas before you evacuate it and charge it with refrigerant. Once it's charged, if it seems like it's leaking, there are additional leak detection tools such as chemical sniffers and dye. That's an overlapping but separate issue. It's really best to do this prophylactically (which many of my Facebook followers will tell you is my favorite word :^). That having been said, I do usually use pre-mixed oil and dye and add it to the compressor at assembly time so it is already in the system. That way, if a new leak develops down the road, the dye is already in there and will make leak detection and repair easier.

Why pressure-testing is better than vacuum testing

There are folks who say that pressurizing the system isn't necessary at all, and that, instead, you can find out if it's leaking when you perform the necessary evacuation, which uses a vacuum pump to draw a deep vacuum and boil off any moisture. Doing it that way is better than nothing, but pressure-testing as I describe is simply superior. Here's why.

From a practical standpoint, leaks fall into three broad categories:

1. Leaks that are so large that the system won't hold pressure at all, or for more than a few seconds. In this case, the leak should be so loud that you can find it by simply listening while also feeling for it with your hands.

2. Medium-sized leaks that you may be able to hear and feel when the system is under pressure, but may require the use of soap solution to be found.

3. Small silent leaks that can only be found with a leak-detection aid, be it soap solution or something else.

In all three cases, pressurizing works better than vacuum-testing because you can leave the pressure in the gas bottle turned on, which generates the evidence of the leak. In contrast, when you hook up the vacuum pump, it only draws the vacuum while the pump is running, and the pump is loud, making it impossible to localize the leak by ear. If you shut it off, the vacuum quickly goes away, and so does the audible indication of the leak. Plus, you can't feel a vacuum leak with your hands as easily as an under-pressure leak. Plus, you really don't want to spray soapy solution when the system is under vacuum. The last thing you want is soap and water drawn into the system.

Put another way, pressure-testing the system provides both leak testing and a means of leak detection. Vacuum-testing does not, or doesn't do it as well.

To be sure, you can pull a vacuum, wait overnight, and see if the needle on the gauge has moved. That's fine, but it's just not as accurate as pressurizing. Here's why.

When you pull a vacuum, you're drawing the system down as close to 30 inHg (inches of mercury) as possible in order to boil off any moisture in the system. This utilizes the small negative part of the display scale on the blue pressure gauge as shown below. Because the range on the gauge between 30 inHg and zero is so small—less than an inch on the scale—a small drop in vacuum is difficult to see on the gauge. In contrast, when you put the system under 120 psi of pressure, you're using the full range of the blue gauge, which makes it easy to see a small drop in pressure.

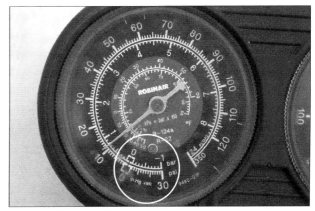

Figure 222: Low-side (blue) gauge showing how much larger the 0 to 120 psi scale is than the 0 to 30 inHg scale.

How to pressure-test

With that said, to pressure-test an a/c system, you need to buy or rent a nitrogen bottle and a regulator from a welding supply or other store. Nitrogen is used for pressure testing because it's a dry gas. Since moisture is absorbed by both PAG oil and ester oil and reacts with R134a refrigerant to produce hydrofluoric acid, you really don't want to run the risk of introducing moisture into the system. Some folks pressure-test using a standard shop air compressor with an in-line moisture separator, but I've never wanted to run the risk. I've read that some folks pressurize with a mix of CO_2 and a gas like argon and then use a chemical sniffer to check for leaks, but I've always just used nitrogen. You also need a ¼" NPT to ¼" flare adapter to connect the regulator on the bottle to a standard a/c manifold gauge set.

Figure 223: 1/4" NPT to 1/4" 7/16-20 SAE adapter.

Once you have the necessary pieces, you use the yellow hose to connect the tank output to the gauge set, and connect the red (high pressure) and blue (low pressure) hoses to the charging fittings on your a/c system. If for some reason you can only access one of the fittings but not both, that's fine; the pressure will very quickly equalize on both sides of the system.

What you want to do is adjust the regulator to supply about 120 psi of pressure. It doesn't matter if the pressure reads exactly 120 psi; in this first step, you're just checking for large leaks. The main thing is to be sure that the regulator isn't set to deliver hundreds of psi that can blow up the a/c system.

Close the knobs on the gauge set (screw them in clockwise). Close the regulator on the nitrogen bottle by unscrewing the T-handle all the way. Open the valve on the top of the nitrogen bottle. Then screw in the regulator until the gauge on the regulator reads about 120 psi.

Now slowly open both knobs on the gauge set to allow the nitrogen to flow into the low and high pressure sides of the system. Watch the manifold gauge set, and listen. With the knobs on the gauge set open, there will be a continuous source of nitrogen from the bottle coming into the system.

Figure 224: Pressurizing the system with nitrogen to about 120 psi, which is the maximum reading on the low-pressure gauge psi.

Often, the first time you do this with a newly-assembled a/c system, you'll hear nitrogen hissing and see the pressure on the gauges unable to hold 120 psi. This is clear evidence of a leak so major that you should be able to localize with your ears and your hands. Most of the time, a leak of this size will be coming from where a hose fitting is attached to a connection on one of the major components (the compressor, condenser, evaporator, or drier), or from an improperly-crimped hose. Check and re-tighten as necessary. Don't forget to check the connections to the gauge set itself, as they can certainly be a source of leaks.

If the system passes the gross leak test, you next look for medium-sized leaks. Re-check the pressure reading on your gauges. Again, you want it to be near the full-range reading on the blue gauge, which is usually 120 psi. It doesn't need to be exact, but when it's in the ball park, close both of the knobs on the gauge set and the big knob on the nitrogen bottle, and record what the pressure is on the blue gauge. You can mark the reading with a piece of tape, or write the number down, or take a picture with your phone.

Next, leave the knobs on the gauge set closed, and wait. With the knobs closed, no new nitrogen will flow into the system, so you're testing to see if it holds the 120 (or so) psi that you've shot in there.

Re-check the gauge at regular intervals. If, after five minutes, the reading has dropped, you have a leak you need to locate, but if it looks stable, continue to let it sit. I let it sit for, at a *minimum*, overnight before declaring the system tight. *This is one of the reasons you can do this better than a shop—you have all the time in the world, whereas they will want the car in and out.* The readings may drop if the temperature in your garage falls, but it should rebound as the temperature goes back up. If the pressure reading steadily drifts down overnight, and *still* steadily drifts down as the sun warms your garage the next day, you have a leak, and if you're trying to convince yourself otherwise, you're in denial.

Figure 225: Big Blu leak-detecting soap solution—WAAAAAY better than dish soap and water.

If the gauges show you have a leak, use a soapy leak detecting solution such as Big Blu from Refrigerant Technologies. These purpose-built solutions are way better at showing up small leaks than dishwasher soap and water. Personally speaking, I think Big Blu is the balls. Soapy water may work fine for large and medium-sized leaks, but for tiny leaks, with Big Blu, although the bubbles may take hours to accumulate, when they do, they are often plainly visible because they look like small clusters of insect eggs.

Spray the leak-detection fluid on all of the hose-to-component connections where leaks are most likely to occur. As I've said, flare fittings sometimes require a lot of torque to get them to seal.

The picture below was taken after replacing the condenser on my 3.0CSi. I did a routine pressure-test, and found that the system was leaking. To my surprise, it turned out a leak was coming from the tube-to-collar joint in the 19-year-old crimped-on hose fitting itself, not from its connection to the drier. I made a new hose.

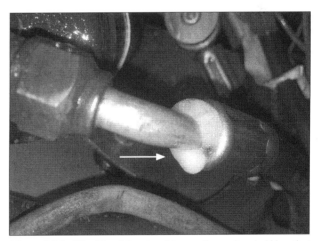

Figure 226: Big Blu doing its thing and growing bubbles that "cocoon" over a period of several hours to help locate a tiny leak.

If you've examined all of the connections thoroughly and haven't found the source of the leak, you'll need to spray the soap solution on the components themselves. It *is* possible for compressors, even new ones, to leak at the shaft seal behind the pulley or at the head plate, and for condensers, even new ones, to leak where the tubes are joined. If you *still* can't find the source of the leak, it's possible it's inside the evaporator assembly, in which case you'll cry and wish you had followed my advice in the Evaporator chapter to pressure-test it with nitrogen before it went in the car, probably in that order.

Note that you *can* crank the pressure up higher

than 120 psi, but be careful. When the a/c system is running, the components conspire to keep the high-side and low-side pressures separate. The high-side pressure may reach 300 psi on a very hot day, but on the low side that runs from the expansion valve output to the evaporator to the compressor inlet, when the system is running correctly, the pressure is usually in the 20 to 40 psi range. In contrast, during this kind of pressure testing, the pressure is equalized in both the high and low sides of the system. I've always had concerns that evaporators might not be designed to take the kind of pressures that condensers do, and as such, I don't ever test at pressures above 150 psi. 120 psi works well, since, as I said, it maximizes the use of the scale on the blue gauge.

Pressure-testing summary

Pressure-testing with nitrogen works way better than evacuating the system and seeing if it holds the vacuum. Do this and get it right, and you're likely to have a tight system.

Chapter 20

Evacuating the System

Overview

If you are simply topping off a system (adding a small amount of refrigerant to an already functioning system), you don't need to evacuate it first, but if you are recharging a system that was opened up to replace a component and is now empty, you must evacuate it—pump it down with a vacuum pump. Here's why.

The refrigerant lubricants PAG oil (used exclusively for R134a systems) and ester, or POE, oil (used for both R12 and R134a) both are hygroscopic, meaning that they absorb water, and the water reacts with the refrigerant to form hydrofluoric acid which corrode the components. It is imperative that any moisture is removed before refrigerant is added and the system is sealed up, hopefully for years.

The way that moisture is removed is to turn it to a vapor and then suck it out. The vacuum pump serves both of these purposes. You may recall from chemistry or physics class that the boiling point of a liquid drops as the pressure drops. You also may have experienced firsthand from hiking and backpacking that water boils faster at a higher altitude. It's not the altitude itself that makes the difference. It's that atmospheric pressure is lower at a higher altitude, and with the lower pressure comes boiling at a lower temperature.

The idea behind evacuation is that, by connecting a vacuum pump to the a/c system and drawing a deep vacuum, you lower the pressure of the system to the point where water boils at room temperature. In this way, any water left inside turns to vapor and is sucked out by the pump.

To evacuate the system, you need a vacuum pump that's made for the task. Don't buy one of the $20 pumps that you connect to an air compressor and that draws a vacuum via the Venturi principle. They don't draw a deep enough vacuum to reliably boil off all the moisture. Buy one of the electric pumps. These days, most of them are Chinese-made and thus inexpensive (between $50 and $100). I have an old Robinair pump that's been with me for 20 years.

Connecting the pump

You need to connect the pump to a manifold gauge set via the yellow hose. In theory, you could connect the pump directly to either the low or high side fitting, but in practice, you need the gauge set for three reasons. First, when you shut off the pump, you need to disconnect it and not have humid air rush back in, so you need a valve you can close between the pump and the car. The knobs on the gauge set provide this capability. Second, it's best that the system is under vacuum when you begin to charge it. That way, the first influx of refrigerant is drawn directly into the vacuum instead of some amount of air, even dry air, still being inside. Third, after evacuating the system, the next thing you do is recharge it, and it's best to do that through the yellow hose of the manifold gauge set as well.

Figure 227: Vacuum pump connected to manifold gauge set via yellow hose.

As a related aside, it's sometimes said that it's unhealthy for an a/c system to sit uncharged. The concern here is that moisture can get into the system and be absorbed by the refrigerant oil, leaving it lying in wait to form hydrofluoric acid when the system is charged with refrigerant. It is true that if you assemble a new system, have the compressor filled with oil, and attach the hoses to new components, unless you live in the desert, the ambient air inside those components has some amount of moisture in it. The way that I've handled this is that if I assemble a new system but for some reason don't plan to charge it immediately, I'll pressure-test it with nitrogen, which is a dry gas (it doesn't have moisture in it). Prior to pressure-testing, I'll undo the red or blue line from the manifold gauge set and use the nitrogen to purge the system of the air that's in it. Then I'll pressure-test the system and leave it full of nitrogen. This has always addressed any concerns I've had.

Figure 228: My old Robinair vacuum pump that's sucked the moisture out of many an a/c system.

Evacuating the system

First, close both knobs on the gauge set (rotate them clockwise), then connect the red and blue charging hoses to the car, with the blue hose connected to the low-pressure side and the red one to the high-pressure side. As I've explained elsewhere, if you have an R134a system, the charging fittings are different for the low and high sides so you can't accidentally switch them, but on old R12 systems, the low and high side fittings may be the same. The blue low-side fitting is on the suction line between the evaporator and the compressor. The red high-side fitting is on the discharge line that the receiver-drier is on, between the condenser and the evaporator.

Next, connect the yellow hose from the center of the manifold to the vacuum pump. As per the Fittings chapter, the fitting on the end of the yellow hose on the gauge set can be either a ¼" 7/16-20 SAE fitting or a ½"-16 ACME fitting. The fitting on the vacuum pump can be either of these as well. You'll need to check which you have on your hose and on your pump. There are adapters that convert between them.

Turn on the vacuum pump. If the pump has a valve on it (some do, some don't), open it to begin to draw a vacuum through the yellow hose. Then gradually open both the red and blue knobs on the gauge set (turn them counter-clockwise). As per the description in the Manifold Gauges chapter, this connects the yellow hose to the red and blue hoses, which in turn are connected through the charging fittings. Note that you only open the red knob for pressure-testing and evacuation, never for charging.

With the pump running and the knobs open, you should immediately see the readings on both gauges drop. The high-pressure gauge will go to zero and stop there, but the low-pressure gauge has a negative zone on it beyond zero.

The rule of thumb is to draw a vacuum for 90 minutes and to get the system down as close as possible to 29 inHg (inches of mercury). Don't worry about the exact reading on the gauge; very few DIY-quality gauges read accurately in the deep vacuum section.

After 90 minutes, close both of the knobs on the gauge set (turn them clockwise), then close the valve on the pump if there is one, then shut the pump off. Look at the low-pressure gauge. Its reading should stay steady. Again, it doesn't matter if it says exactly 29 inHG or not, but if it starts slowly dropping toward zero, you have a leak. It could be in the gauge hoses or the charging fittings, but it also could be in the a/c system itself.

As per the Pressure Testing chapter, leak-testing with pressurized nitrogen is a much better way to test the system for leaks than vacuum testing, so looking at the vacuum gauge should be a final sanity-check that the system is tight, not a primary test. So if you have pressure-tested with nitrogen overnight and already determined the system is tight, you're done evacuating. If you haven't pressure-tested with nitrogen, it's best to either mark the gauge with tape or take a picture of it, then let the system sit overnight to verify that it's holding vacuum.

Only one thing left to do... charge!

Chapter 21

Charging the System

Overview

In a sense, the entire book has led to this chapter. Whether you installed an a/c system from scratch into a car that didn't have one, or resurrected one that had been dead for decades, or replaced a single component, you presumably battled the beasts you encountered along the way, kicked their asses, gotten everything clean and tight, then pressure-tested and evacuated the system.

It's charging time. If you want to pretend you're a black rhino, go ahead. You've earned it. Personally, I prefer putting four fingers on each hand above my head and making moose noises. Hey; it's New England.

Figure 229: R134a can hooked to manifold gauge set via yellow hose with ½"-16 ACME fitting on one end, manifold gauge set connected to car, ready for charging. Picture is for reference only. Don't put a can of refrigerant on a hot engine.

Should you put dye in the system? (hint: YES)

If you've followed the steps that I've laid out and pressure-tested the system with nitrogen and let it sit overnight (or more), the system should be good and tight, but even so, a leak may develop later. If you haven't already used oil with dye already pre-mixed, you might consider adding dye right now. Make sure you buy dye that mixes with whatever oil you have in the system. The dye, along with a UV light and glasses, can help you to find a leak if one develops.

Figure 230: It's smart to add dye prior to charging in case a leak develops later.

How much refrigerant to add

Ah, that's the question. There are eight ways to charge a system with refrigerant. Well, that's not true. There's pretty much one way to charge it. But there are eight ways to judge how much refrigerant to add and know when it's full. They are:

1. Charging by weight
2. Charging by number of cans (by volume, sort of)
3. Charging until the suction line sweats
4. Charging until the vent temperature thermometer is right
5. Charging by temperature-pressure rules of thumb
6. Charging using a temperature-pressure table
7. Charging by watching the sight glass (R12 only)
8. Paying a professional to do it

Often, a combination of the first seven is employed.

Charging by weight

If you have a completely stock a/c system running its original refrigerant, you can charge it by weight. That is, if the owner's manual or the sticker under the hood says it takes 24 ounces of R134a, you shoot in 24 ounces of R134a, done. Well, almost. As you'll read below, you may need to take several ounces into consideration due to losses delivering the charge in the cans through the refrigerant hoses. But this is how a professional with a refrigeration scale does it.

Charging by number of cans (by volume, sort of)

Because very few do-it-yourselfers have a 30lb canister of R134a and a refrigerant scale, most people wind up charging by volume—that is, by shooting in a certain number of small cans. The less-expensive 12oz cans of R134a are the bare cans that require a can tap. The 14oz, 18oz, and 22oz cans are generally the more expensive ones that have an integrated shut-off valve, charging hose and gauge. So, again, if the spec is 24 ounces of R134a, you go and buy yourself two 12oz cans, shoot both of them in, and you should be good. Or if the spec is 26oz, you shoot in one 12 and one 14oz can. Sort of.

Figure 231: So, your car needs 24oz of R134a, you shoot in two 12oz cans and you're good, right? Sort of. Read on.

Two ounces for the hoses, one ounce for the can

My wife's grandmother, when making tea, used to put in "a teaspoon for the pot." In that spirit, there's a very interesting technical tip from 4 Seasons, who sells a variety of air conditioning parts and tools. According to 4 Seasons, during a charging session, an average of two ounces of refrigerant is retained by the manifold gauge set and the charging hoses. In addition, owing to the fact that, because the can is pushing against the pressure on the low side of the system, the can never completely empties, and you should assume that the actual amount of the can emptied is short by one ounce. Thus, if you shoot in three 12oz cans, the total effective amount introduced isn't 36 ounces, but 31 ounces (36 less a total of two ounces for the hoses,

and one ounce for each of the three cans).

Note that, according to 4 Seasons, with R134a, the accuracy one should endeavor to reach with R134a is to charge it to within +/- 2oz of spec. Thus, the "two ounces for the hoses and one for each can" is significant.

The problem with fractional cans

Even when factoring in 2oz for the hoses and 1oz for each can, the problem comes where the system calls for an amount of refrigerant that cannot easily be made up of integral numbers of cans of various sizes. What you do in practice is estimate, trying to judge when a can is half or a quarter full by sloshing it, and also looking at the pressures, the vent temp, and the sweating of the suction line (below). When dealing with fractional cans, the R134a cans with the integrated valve, gauge, and charging hose that I've ridiculed are actually a big plus, because the valve can be closed and the partially-full can stored for later use.

The problem with bare cans of R12

But if you're using NOS small cans of R12, and the system doesn't take an integral number of cans, you have a bit of a problem. R12 cans were never made in the handy form factor of the charge-ready R134a cans with a hose and a shut-off valve, so once the can is tapped, it's no longer sealed. On both the R134a and the R12 top-taps, that top-piercing needle has no rubber seal and is not intended to be a shut-off valve to store gas in the can, but the problem is worse on those old R12 top-taps with the semicircular clamp that swings over the ridge on the top of the can and the T-handle that drives the needle into the top. They're very leak-prone even under the best of circumstances.

Fortunately, unlike the top-taps, most of the newer side can taps have a valve core in them, so you can, in theory, unscrew the hose (quickly, with "de minimus" refrigerant loss) and leave the side-tap in place. The least expensive side-taps are around ten bucks, so with the cost of NOS small cans of Freon around $25 to $30, it makes economic sense to do this. Even still, the side-tap is simply a piercing tube surrounded by a rubber seal; it's not like a high-pressure cylinder with pipe fittings and Teflon tape. Over time, it is likely to leak.

As I've said repeatedly, I cannot stress strongly enough that R12 is a nasty ozone-depleting agent, and releasing it into the environment is not only illegal and can get you a fine of tens of thousands of dollars, it is highly unethical, and as a reader of this book, I task you to take whatever actions are necessary to prevent its release into the environment. It's things like this that add to the steady drumbeat of reasons why I'm moving away from using R12 in my vintage cars, even though it works the balls.

Fortunately, according to 4 Seasons, R12 systems are more forgiving than R134a systems in terms of charging volume—they can reportedly be as much as half a pound shy or over without adversely affecting system performance. A "can" of R12 is 12 or 14 ounces, so if you can get the R12 refrigerant volume calibrated to within ½ a can of a full can, you may be good.

What if you don't know what the refrigerant weight should be?

If you have a system that's no longer running the original refrigerant, it's more complicated, because neither the original weight nor the volume are likely to be known exactly. If it's a straight conversation from R12 to R134a, the rule of thumb for R134a is to use 80% of the Freon weight, but that's just an estimate.

But if you have a modified system that's no longer running the original refrigerant, really, who the hell knows what the refrigerant weight is "supposed" to be? I and others repeat the mantra "install the largest parallel flow condenser that'll fit into the nose" without giving any advice on how that affects refrigerant weight. I have searched online and not found a reference or a rule of thumb.

What I do when charging my modified systems is combine most of the methods listed below.

Charging until the suction line sweats

The way I was taught to do it with the highly non-stock a/c on my BMW 3.0CSi is to look at the suction line (the one from the condenser outlet to the compressor inlet) and charge the system until the line begins to sweat—that is, until the metal connector on the line that's close to where it emerges from the firewall line is cold enough that condensation begins to form on it. This works well unless you live in a desert environment where the ambient air lacks the moisture to condense out on the line.

Figure 232: Condensation, or sweating, on the fitting on the suction line (left) as it emerges from the firewall is a good indication that the system is charged. Photo courtesy Gary York.

Charging until the vent temperature thermometer is right

Another way to charge the a/c is to use a vent temperature thermometer and charge the system until the vent temp looks good, then stop. "Good" can mean, for R12, 32 to 40 degrees, or for R134a, mid 40s, or, for either, no longer dropping as you're adding refrigerant.

Figure 233: When the vent temperature gauge stops dropping, you're probably done. This one isn't.

Charging by temperature-pressure rules of thumb

If you look online, you can find the following temperature-pressure rules of thumb for charging:

- For an R12 system, the high-side pressure should be about equal to 1.8 to 2.1 times ambient temperature in °F.

- For an R12 system on a hot humid day, the high-side pressure should be about equal to the ambient temperature in °F plus 100 psi.

- For an R134a system, the high side pressure should be about equal to 2.2 to 2.5 times the ambient temperature in °F.

- On a system with an orifice tube, when fully charged, the evaporator inlet and outlet should be within about a degree of each other.

I don't use these, but some folks may find them useful.

Charging using a temperature-pressure chart

Most manifold gauge sets comes with a little laminated foldable pressure-temperature pamphlet that lists the correspondence between refrigerant temperature and pressure for different refrigerants. It's often held in mounting tabs on the back of the gauge set. Note, though, that this isn't terribly helpful for charging (though you use it to calculate superheat and subcooling; see the Troubleshooting section).

Instead, most DIYers want to know what the high and low pressure gauge readings should be as a function of ambient (outside) temperature. You can find such charging tables online. They're different for R12 and R134a. The R134a charging table below is courtesy of Mastercool and is widely reproduced online. Note the sharp increase in high-side pressure at 85°.

R134a Temperature Pressure Chart		
Ambient Temp (°F)	Low Side Gauge (psi)	High Side Gauge (psi)
65°	25-35	135-155
70°	35-40	145-160
75°	35-45	150-170
80°	40-50	175-210
85°	45-55	225-250
90°	45-55	250-270
95°	50-55	275-300
100°	50-55	315-325
105°	50-55	340-345

For example, if you're using R134a, and charging the system at 90°F, according to this table, the low side should be 45 to 55 psi, and the high side should be 250 to 270psi. Note that the table should be used as a guideline only, and that the pressure readings will change with changing humidity. I very rarely see low-side readings as high as they are in this table; they're usually about 30 psi, even in hot weather. 'Course, I don't live in Florida.

As a DIY-er, you almost always combine the pressure readings in the table with the other methods. For example, if the ambient temperature is 90°, and you've shot in the specified amount of R134, and the high-side pressure is 250 psi, and the vent temperature is 34° (you wish :^), and the suction line is beginning to sweat, there's every indication that the system has adequate refrigerant in it, and adding more risks overcharging, so stop! Conversely, if the vent temperatures aren't cold, the suction line isn't sweating, and the high-side pressure isn't even close

R12 and R134a Temperatures And Pressures

Relative Humidity (%)	Outside Air Temp (°F)	R12 Discharge Temp (°F)	R12 Low Pressure (psi)	R12 High Pressure (psi)	R134a Discharge Temp (°F)	R134a Low Pressure (psi)	R134a High Pressure (psi)
20	70	44	24	143	44	9	69
	80	44	31	192	44	24	85
	90	50	45	232	47	40	136
	100	59	47	270	53	50	231
	110	66	57	320	64	58	308
30	70	44	23	154	44	10	80
	80	44	35	203	44	28	110
	90	54	47	239	48	42	168
	100	63	50	283	59	54	253
	110	74	60	334	69	62	328
40	70	44	34	170	45	12	93
	80	50	40	216	50	32	149
	90	58	48	246	56	46	212
	100	67	53	291	64	57	264
	110	77	63	350	74	67	348
50	70	46	37	178	45	14	102
	80	55	43	223	51	36	164
	90	61	50	252	59	54	229
	100	71	58	312	70	67	329
	110	84	66	365	80	76	368
60	70	47	40	187	45	18	133
	80	55	49	230	53	39	191
	90	64	54	266	62	57	249
	100	75	60	318	72	72	310
	110	86	68	383	83	80	384
70	70	47	41	228	46	19	168
	80	56	50	257	56	42	215
	90	66	56	278	67	61	260
	100	78	63	33	77	75	321
	110	91	72	402	87	87	390
80	70	47	43	247	46	21	178
	80	57	53	268	57	47	218
	90	69	62	287	69	67	267
	100	82	70	340	78	80	331
	110	95	76	438	90	89	405
90	70	48	44	258	46	33	183
	80	60	55	286	59	54	223
	90	72	63	307	71	69	274
	100	85	72	350	84	84	345
	110	101	80	462	87	94	424

to the low end of the range in the table, the system is likely still undercharged.

A second table below lists both R134a and R12 ambient temperatures and pressures, and also includes ambient humidity and the expected discharge temps. I cannot find the original source, but the table is widely reproduced online. Like the first table, it is included for reference only. Note the spectacularly high high-side pressures in the upper ends of the temperature and humidity scales. If I saw 400 psi pressures, I'd probably run out of my garage for fear of getting impaled by a piece of my condenser.

Charging by watching the sight glass (R12 only)

A fully-charged a/c system should have the receiver-drier (if it has one) completely full of liquid refrigerant, with liquid refrigerant continuing up the liquid line (why do you think it's called the liquid line?) to the evaporator outlet. For this reason, on vintage cars running R12, there's often a small clear sight glass the size of a pencil eraser at the top of the receiver-drier. A method of charging an R12 system is, or used to be, to add R12 until the sight glass runs clear—until only liquid flows without the presence of bubbles. This may still be valid with R12, but it is not a reliable metric for cars with R134a, and should not be used.

Figure 234: Some driers have a sight glass, but with R134a, it's not a reliable charging indicator.

Paying a professional to do it

If you're uncomfortable with all of this, you can find

a reputable a/c specialty shop (which is probably *not* one of the ones advertising "A/C Service $79"), quiz them on exactly how they would do what you want them to do (e.g., optimally charge a custom system), have them carefully charge the system to the point where they think it's right, then have them tell you what the weight was of the refrigerant charge they used so you can try to do it yourself in the future. There's no shame in this at all. And, if you've done all the rest of the a/c work yourself and are bringing them a clean, tight system, it shouldn't be too expensive.

ENOUGH! Charge the damned thing already!

The actual mechanics of charging an a/c system aren't complicated, but they do require care and understanding.

As I've said repeatedly, when charging up a system, you should use a manifold gauge set. If you're using R134a, you *can* buy those cans with an integrated hose, charging fitting, and gauge, and connect them directly to the low side, but using a manifold gauge set is vastly preferred, as you can see what both the low and high pressure sides of the system are doing.

Connect the gauges

First, close both knobs on the gauge set (rotate them clockwise), then connect both charging fittings on the gauge set's hoses to the car, with the blue hose connected to the low-pressure side and the red one to the high-pressure side. Wear gloves and googles. Take the caps off the charging fittings and clean the fittings with a paper towel before connecting the charging hoses. If you have an R134a system, the charging fittings are different for the low and high sides so you can't accidentally switch them, but on old R12 systems, the low and high side fittings may be the same. The blue low-side fitting is on the suction line between the evaporator and the compressor. The red high-side fitting is on the discharge line that the receiver-drier is on, between the condenser and the evaporator. If you accidentally connect a can of refrigerant to the high side instead of the low side, it can blow up the can and injure or kill you, so if you don't understand these terms and are at all confused about the fittings on your car, don't try to charge it up. Have a professional do it. For more information, see the Fittings and Using Manifold Gauges chapters.

Figure 235: R12 gauge hoses directly connected to ¼ 7/16-20 SAE service ports on back of compressor (blue goes to suction side, red goes to discharge side).

Figure 236: R134a gauge fittings hooked up to 13mm and 16mm charging ports.

Start the car, turn the a/c and fan on full, close the windows, and run the engine at about 1500 rpm. If you have one of those big shop fans, aim it at the condenser in the nose of the car, as you want to simulate the air flow you'll have while driving that helps the condenser to dump heat. Put a vent temp thermometer in the main dashboard vent.

Tap the can

Then connect the yellow hose—the one that goes to the center of the manifold gauge set—to the can of refrigerant. Wear gloves and eye protection, and if

you're not comfortable with it, don't do it at all. You may have heard me when I've said, over and over, "a liquid cools when boils, turns to gas, and expands," but you probably don't understand that if you get liquid refrigerant on your hands while undoing a hose fitting, it is going to boil and cool so quickly that it will literally give you instant frostbite.

Unless you have one of those recharge-ready cans of R134a that has a hose and a valve built in, you need a can tap (top or side) to pierce the can. As described in the Fittings chapter, if you're using R134a, the threads on the top of the can, on the top-tap, and at the end of the yellow hose are all ½"-16 ACME and will all seamlessly connect. If you're doing more, uh, creative things with gauges, refrigerants, and taps, some of the fittings may be ½"-16 ACME and some may be ¼" 7/16-20 SAE, requiring an adapter.

Figure 237: Yellow hose connected to top tap used on can of R134a. Keep the can upright at all times.

Connect the yellow hose to the tap, then tap the can. Keep the can of refrigerant upright at all times. Note that if you're using a side tap, "upright" means that the side tap is pointing up. Don't follow the things you might read online that say you can save time by shooting the first can in upside down. The can is full of liquid. You're shooting refrigerant into the a/c system, which has a compressor. Liquid is not compressible. You need to be shooting in gaseous refrigerant, not liquid refrigerant. So keep the can upright so the gaseous refrigerant slowly wafts in from the top of the can.

Purge the yellow line

Next, purge any humid air from the yellow line by—with gloves and goggles on—slowly unscrewing the yellow line from the center of the manifold gauge set until, for a brief instant, gaseous refrigerant escapes from it. As soon as there is a small release, tighten the yellow line. This is a "de minimus" refrigerant release that is allowable under the EPA regulations.

Let the gaseous refrigerant in

Slowly open the blue knob *and only the blue knob – never, under any circumstances, open up the red knob while charging an a/c system.* You only want to introduce the refrigerant on the low-pressure side of the system, always always always.

Watch the blue low pressure gauge. The pressure should start to rise almost instantly after the tapped can is introduced into the system by opening up the blue knob.

Use the blue knob to control the rate at which the gas is drawn in so the low-side pressure stays at about 30 psi or less. It'll want to go considerably higher as the refrigerant is initially drawn in. Don't let it; close the blue knob slightly to keep the pressure at 30 psi or less. Eventually the pressure will stabilize and you'll be able to open the blue knob all the way and not have the pressure rise much above 30 psi. It also may go higher if the ambient temperature and humidity are high, but the point is that you want the system and the temperature to dictate the pressure, not the inrush of refrigerant vapor.

The process of charging *is* slow. It may take 10 or 20 minutes for the liquid inside each can to completely vaporize and be drawn into the system. You can speed the process up by warming the can. The safest way to do that is by putting the upright can of refrigerant in a bowl of warm (not hot) water. *Do not put the can in hot water or set it down on the hot engine!* Doing so runs the risk of causing the can to burst, which could cause injury or death. When the can is no longer cold and no longer sloshes, it's empty.

Most recent a/c systems have a cutoff switch that prevents the compressor from engaging if the pressure

is too low or too high. Vintage systems may or may not have a cutoff switch. If there is one, usually the drawing in of the refrigerant vapor is enough to raise the low pressure side above the cutoff, but sometimes it's necessary to disconnect the wires from the temperature switch and jumper across them in order to get the system to draw in its first breaths.

Watch the gauges

If you see the low pressure reading settle at about 30psi or less, and the high pressure reading gradually rise as the refrigerant goes in, then the system is working—the compressor is doing its compression thing, and there aren't any obvious system blockages like a clogged expansion valve. If your car has an orifice tube, an accumulator, and a clutch cycling valve, you'll likely hear the compressor cycle on and off, which will cause the high reading to fall and the low reading to rise, and then return to where they were. That's normal.

Figure 238: Gauges coming up to pressure.

Watch the vent temperature and the suction line

As I've said, even if you're charging to weight or to volume, it's still smart to watch the vent temperature and check for sweating on the suction line. If the suction line is sweating and you're seeing cold vent temperatures, you may well be done.

If you need to shoot in more than one can—and you

almost always do—fully close the blue knob before disconnecting the empty can (the red knob should always be closed when charging), connecting the next one, and briefly purging the yellow line again.

Since you really don't want to overcharge the system, it's smart to take the car for a drive and see how the a/c feels. If you have good R134a charging fittings with the knobs on them that depress the valve cores, you can unscrew them and pop the fittings off without losing refrigerant, but on an R12 system, there's always refrigerant loss when you unscrew ¼" 7/16-20 SAE charging fittings, so you want to leave the gauge hoses connected until you're sure you're done charging. With care, I've sometimes been able to drive the car with the manifold gauges still attached to the charging fittings and everything, including the can of refrigerant, stowed carefully and secured in the engine compartment. If you try this, be absolutely certain everything is well-secured and can't touch any hot engine components. If you're uncertain this can be done safely, don't do it.

Disconnect the charging fittings

When you think you're done charging, close the blue knob by turning it clockwise. Undo the charging fittings. Wear gloves and goggles. If you have high-quality R134a charging hoses with knobs to depress the valve cores, turn the knobs counter-clockwise to lift the plungers, then lift the collars to undo the charging fittings. The beauty of the knobs is that this disconnection occurs with zero refrigerant loss. If you have R134a hoses without the knobs, there is some amount of "de minimus" loss as you lift the collar and the fitting snaps off while the valve core is still depressed, but it is small and stops quickly.

Unfortunately, if you have screw-on R12 fittings, even the "de minimus" loss can be non-trivial as you unscrew the fittings and the rubber seals lift before the posts no longer depress the valve cores. I cringe every time it happens. Be certain you're wearing gloves and goggles, and unscrew the fittings as quickly as possible.

Whichever fittings you have, screw the caps back on

them when you're done charging. The caps are an integral part of the system, both in terms of seal and cleanliness.

Figure 239: Put those caps back on the charging fittings when you're done.

Charging summary

Start with a clean, tight, evacuated system, carefully shoot in refrigerant until the suction line sweats, the vent temp is about right, and the pressures are in the ball park, and you're probably good.

I have to tell you – recharging is the dessert at the end of the meal, the sex at the end of the date. When you feel that air start to blow cold, it's a rush, and when you button it all up and drive the now-cold car in the heat, it's bliss. No other automotive repair, not new shocks, struts, and springs, not a five-speed in a vintage car, not even a replacement engine, comes close.

Chapter 22

Leak Detection

Overview

We've already discussed pressurizing the uncharged system with nitrogen in order to prophylactically leak-test it. We talked about how there are three classes of leaks: Those that are so huge you can't help but hear them hissing out; those that are small enough that you might hear them hissing out but might need to use soap solution, and those that are so small the *only* way to find them is using soap solution.

Pressure-test first!

If you were a good doobie (I'm dating myself again. First, Erector Sets, now Romper Room. Next, a misty-eyed reference to mechanical coin banks.), you *did* pressure-test the system as I described, and let it sit overnight. This *should* result in a system that's pretty tight, and *should* to a large degree inoculate you against having to chase leaks. However, it is possible for small leaks to develop, and if you already pressure-tested and the system is already charged, any leaks are probably of the last class, meaning that they may not be easy to find.

The three weapons deployed against leaks in a charged system are soap solution, chemical sniffers, and dye.

Soap solution

Soap solution is the same stuff we used in the pressure testing chapter, and is used in the same way after charging as it is during pressure-testing. As pictured above, bubbles form at the source of leaks. Purpose-built products such as Big Blu from Refrigerant Technologies work far better than dish soap and water, particularly for very small leaks. First spray every joint and connection. If that's not productive, spray every hose and surface. Letting the soap solution sit overnight and looking in the morning for "cocooned" groups of bubbles is often necessary to find very small leaks.

Chemical sniffers

If soap solution is not productive, the next weapon is chemical sniffers. These work by directly detecting the presence of refrigerants and alert you with an audible tone, a flashing light, or both. As with soap solution, you typically probe first around every connection and joint, then along flat surfaces. I have a Yokagawa leak detector and it works great. I've used it to find pinhole leaks in hoses that I hadn't sprayed directly with soap solution. Newer hand-held battery-operated units are now available on Amazon for very short money.

Figure 240: Soap solution being used to find leaks on the compressor of a 1987 BMW 325is. Here, bubbles were coming from both the o-ring at the #10 hose fitting, as well as from o-rings underneath the plates both threaded fittings are attached to.

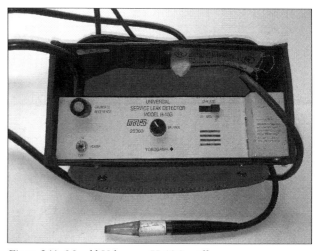

Figure 241: My old Yokagawa H-10G sniffer.

Dye

Fluorescent dye is inexpensive and can either be purchased in liquid form and mixed with the oil prior to system assembly, or introduced as pre-mixed oil and dye and used to fill the compressor. If the system has already been charged, dye can be mixed with oil and added with an oil injection tool. Then the a/c is turned on to distribute the dye through the system and an ultraviolet light and a pair of special glasses are used to hunt for the dye. Personally, I'm not a big fan of dye—it's messy, it's difficult to distinguish old dye from that which is from a fresh leak, and prophylactically conducting leak testing by pressurizing the system with nitrogen during the assembly process usually renders dye unnecessary—but sometimes you need to throw every tool you have at the problem.

I *do* typically use pre-mixed oil and dye to fill the compressor, because… why not? That way, if a leak develops later, the dye is already in there. My friend and pro Terry Sayther reports that his shop is a big fan of prophylactically using dye. "We add dye to every a/c system we work on. It's a major benefit to the customer. That way, when the car comes back, we can see the leaks, even small ones."

Figure 242: A little bottle of dye to mix with mineral oil for R12, a bottle of pre-mixed dye and PAG oil for R134a, and the UV light and glasses.

If the system is leaking from inside the evaporator assembly, you're probably not going to hear it hissing, and you can't spray soapy water in places you can't reach or look for dye in places you can't see. If the system has dye in it and it's leaking a *lot,* you may see dye coming out the evaporator drain hole. But sometimes the only way to diagnose an evaporator leak it is to use a chemical sniffer in the vicinity of the under dash. If you slowly bring the sniffer inside the car, then down at the footwells, then up near the evaporator, then inside the opening to the evaporator assembly where the pipes emerge, and it wigs out and does the *DANGER WILL ROBINSON* thing, you've got some work ahead of you. In a newer car such as an E30 or E36 3-Series BMW, replacing the evaporator isn't too bad, as the evaporator core and expansion valve slide out from behind a panel. But if you have an older car like a 2002 or a 3.0CS where the evaporator core is inside an evaporator assembly, just drink yourself into a stupor for a few days because it's simply going to suck.

Because it's illegal to vent either R12 or R134a, if you identify the source of a leak in a charged system, and if this requires you to open the system back up to repair the leak, you need to take the car somewhere to have the refrigerant recovered. I thought about buying recovery equipment to cover this possibility, but it's expensive, and by pressure-testing with nitrogen and letting it sit overnight, I've almost always been able to verify that a system is tight before I charge it up.

Chapter 23

Other Things That
Heat Up the Interior

Overview

I've already had some snickers at "other things that heat up the interior." Get your mind out of the gutter. What are you, sixteen? Crikey. This is a serious book. Except for the part about the pyloric sphincter.

In addition to improving the efficacy of the air conditioning system itself, there are several other things that can affect passenger cabin temperature, sometimes dramatically.

Sunshade

Very few things heat up the interior more than direct sun. I used to razz folks who put sunshades on their dashboard, classifying them along with fuzzy dice and dashboard hula girls. Now, I realize how smart this is. Why not knock 20 degrees off the amount of heat your a/c needs to cool?

Figure 243: Don't poo-poo the classic dashboard sunshade.

Degraded foam on heater box flaps

On most vintage cars, the heater box is mounted against the firewall of the car, in front of the evaporator assembly, and provides the path for both fresh air and heated air to enter the car. Most heater boxes have metal flaps lined with foam. A lever or knob on the dashboard opens and closes the flaps. The problem is that, with age, the foam deteriorates, making it so the flaps are never really closed. If the foam on the fresh air flap is degraded, it can allow warm or hot outside air to enter the car, sometimes in very substantial quantities. A separate flap is usually employed to

close off the flow of hot air from the heater core into the passenger compartment. Degraded foam on this flap can cause not warm ambient air but actually *heated air* to enter the passenger compartment. In either case, obviously this influx of hot air can reduce a/c efficacy.

If the evaporator assembly needs to be removed for repair, or if a from-scratch a/c retrofit is being performed and an evaporator assembly has not yet been installed, it is a good time to examine whether the heater box is passing hot ambient air or heated air into the cabin, as without the evaporator assembly in the way, heater box removal is easier.

Figure 244: The foam on these heater box flaps is badly degraded, allowing hot outside air to get into the cabin even when the flaps are closed.

Degraded or missing firewall grommets

As is the case with degraded heater box flaps, degraded or missing rubber grommets on the firewall for the wiring harness, speedometer cable, pedals, and other things, can allow not only out outside air, but hot engine compartment air into the passenger cabin.

Always-on heater boxes

On most vintage cars, the heat is primarily controlled by a lever that opens and closes a valve controlling the flow of hot antifreeze from the engine into the heater core inside the heater box. This heats the air inside the heater box. As stated, there is usually a second lever that moves a flap that controls the amount of hot air that passes into the interior.

However, on some vintage cars, there is no shut-off valve for the hot antifreeze entering the heater box, making the heater box like a second radiator that's always on, right next to the a/c evaporator assembly. On this design, the amount of heat into the passenger compartment is supposed to be controlled by the heater flap, but if the heater core remains on, large amounts of heat typically bleed in, even when the flap is closed. Obviously this decreases the effectiveness of the a/c. It's literally fighting against a little radiator right next door to it.

It may be possible to, as I've done on my BMW 3.0CSi, install a shut-off valve to stop the flow of hot coolant into the heater box so the a/c isn't fighting against a heater.

Figure 245: Heater bypass valve installed on my BMW 3.0CSi.

Floor and firewall insulation

It's very common for the insulation on the firewall of a vintage car to be degraded, causing engine heat to radiate into the interior of the car. Unfortunately, the firewall insulation is usually well-integrated into the firewall, and replacing it may well be a task not easily tackled until an engine compartment restoration.

Transmission tunnel, footwell, and floor insulation, however, is usually readily accessed from inside the car. Certain cars radiate a ton of heat off the transmission tunnel or through the floors due to proximity of the

drivetrain and exhaust (my Triumph GT6 was like a little sauna inside). It may be possible to knock that down using either the fancy sound-deadening stuff like Dynamat, or the inexpensive foil-backed sheet stuff readily available at big box hardware stores.

Tinted windows

One of the reasons I love my 1970s-era BMWs is their high-visibility design with the "greenhouse of windows." However, when talking about air conditioning, a greenhouse is a bad thing; all that window area provides opportunity for the sun to stream in and heat up the interior. If you've done a/c rejuvenation and still aren't happy with the result, you might consider tinting the windows. There are a variety of tinting products and technologies.

After I first drove my a/c-retrofitted '73 BMW 3.0CSi 800 miles to a vintage BMW event and was unhappy with the way the R134a-based air conditioning bogged down in 95° temperatures and high humidity, I began to think what else I could do to help a/c performance. When I arrived at the event, I mentioned this to another owner, and he asked me if I'd thought about tinting the windows. I said that I didn't want to change the look of the car (which is old, European, and has lightly factory-tinted glass). He advised that there were new band-pass ceramic tints that were nearly clear and blocked 99% of the UV and 70% of the heat. He mentioned some German-sounding name, but I forgot what it was.

When I got back home, I did some searching online and found many references to Huper Optik band-pass ceramic tints. I figured this was probably the product that the other fellow had mentioned. I then found a reputable well-reviewed tinting shop in my area. I called and the vendor said he installed Huper Optik and a number of other high quality films. I scheduled an appointment to come in.

At the appointment, the installer showed me the Huper Optik film and noted its shiny appearance. I was surprised at this because online I read that HO wasn't shiny. He said that there were differences between the HO residential film and automotive film, and probably much of what I'd read online was regarding the residential film. The installer then looked carefully at the large curved rear window of my 3.0CSi. He explained to me that to get the tinted sheet to fit curved glass, you have to heat-shrink it, but he determined that the curvature was so great that he wouldn't be able to use the Huper Optik ceramic automotive film because he couldn't shrink and install a single piece. He'd either need to install multiple pieces, which would likely leave a small visible seam, or would need to use a different film. He recommended Geoshield DMC40 ceramic/dye film. He cut a piece and laid it on one of the door windows. It certainly was a visible (not clear) tint, but I thought it looked acceptably light.

It took him about three hours to do the car. Multiple attempts were made to get the rear window done because of its size and curvature. Clearly he put a lot of time and care into it.

When he was done, the first thing I noticed was that, with the tint on all the windows, the car was darker than I'd expected. The installer agreed with this assessment.

But the second thing was that, around the inside of the rubber rear windshield seal, was a border of black tape between 1/4" and 1/2" wide. The installer said that this kind of old windshield had "no room for error" and that, try as he might, he couldn't get his fingers in place to stretch the tint perfectly down to the edge of the rubber window gasket, and the tape ("pinstriping" he called it) was an accepted method of hiding the gap that would otherwise show between the tint and the rubber. He showed me a rear windshield with a dotted black border on a more modern car, and explained how this provided "room for error." I said that I didn't like the look of the black tape, and he agreed, and said that if I could have the windshield removed, he could tint right to the edge.

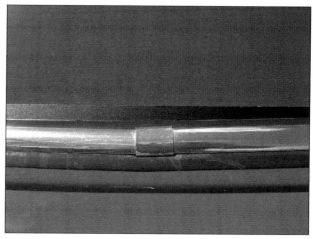

Figure 246: Black tape used as buffer between tint and windshield gasket.

Unfortunately when I looked into it, I found that while the gasket is available and not unreasonably priced, the rear windshield on my 3.0CSi and the two chrome strips that hold it in the gasket appear to be NLA. I've pulled these chrome strips out of parts cars, and they tend to bend up and never lie flat after that. In other words, the risk in pulling the rear windshield out is pretty high.

The installer charged me $280, which I considered a very reasonable sum for a substantial amount of work. He offered to redo anything I was unhappy with, but other than removing the rear windshield, he didn't have an option for making the rear window film installation better (getting rid of the tape).

Although the windows are noticeably darker than I wanted, I decided to live with it, especially since the only choice seemed to be taking the film off. I felt that I should've bailed on the tinting after finding that I'd misinterpreted what I'd read online about Huper Optik film and learned that I couldn't get a nearly clear film that would be effective.

I posted this story to a professional tinting site, and nearly every response said that the tinter knew what he was doing, that it would be nearly impossible to shrink Huper Optik film around the E9's curved rear window, that the ceramic film he recommended was appropriate to the task, and that in order to fit the film to the rear windshield without the use of tape, the glass would have to come out or the gasket would need to be notched.

Over time, I've grown accustomed to the tint of the windows, and I haven't given the border of black tape around the rear window a second look in years.

Figure 247: My 3.0CSi with the factory window tint, before additional window tinting…

Figure 248: …and after window tinting.

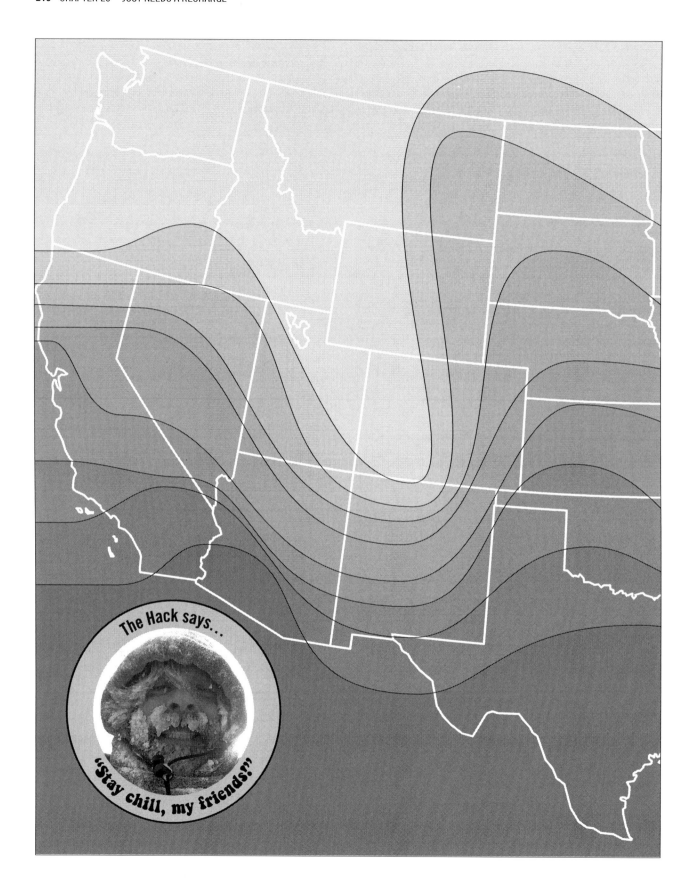

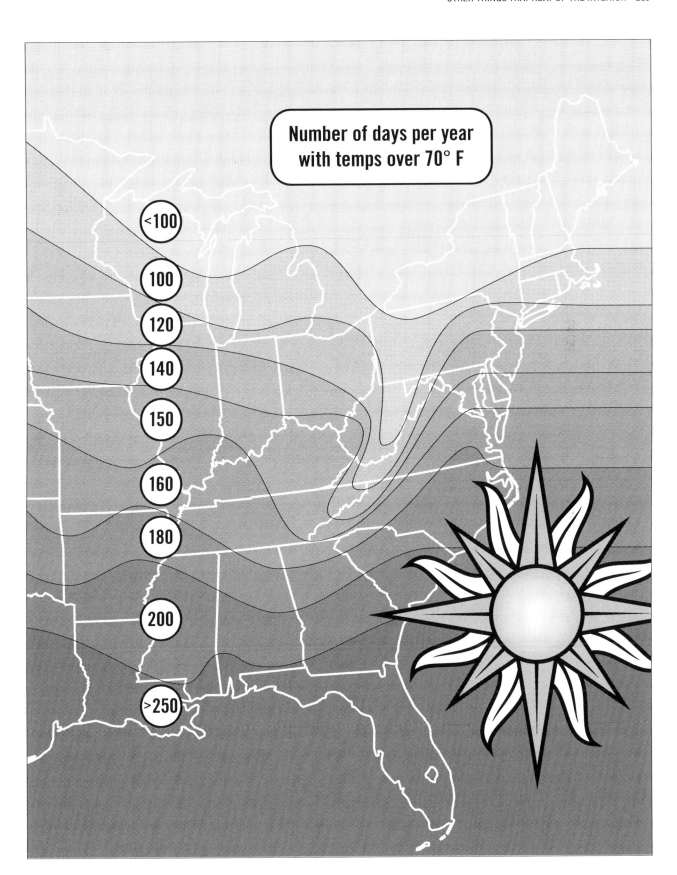

Number of days per year with temps over 70° F

<100
100
120
140
150
160
180
200
>250

Chapter 24

Troubleshooting

Low Side	High Side	Vent Temp	Potential Problem
Low	Low	Warm	Low refrigerant
Very low	High	Warm	Expansion valve clogged or stuck closed, or orifice tube clogged, or moisture in the system freezing expansion valve or orifice tube shut
High	Slightly high	Warm	Expansion valve stuck open

Overview

The bulk of this book has been devoted to a/c rejuvenation and retrofit, since a) that's the bulk of the a/c work I do, and b) in truth, that's what's usually required if the goal is getting the a/c running and performing well in a vintage car. But not every a/c problem requires that big a hammer. Sometimes you *do* have a car with an intact a/c system that requires basic troubleshooting and repair. So here's a basic a/c troubleshooting guide. I'm putting it here, at the very end of the book, for a reason.

First, as I said earlier, if an air conditioning system isn't functioning at all, once you've checked the belt, fuses, and pressure switches, it could be because gaseous refrigerant isn't being compressed, or it is but then it isn't expanding, but the vast majority of the time it's because the refrigerant has leaked out and there's not enough gas there to compress and expand in the first place. There really aren't too many other things it can be, and those aren't all that common.

Second, when you approach a/c from the standpoint of systematic rejuvenation or retrofit, and you flush the system, fabricate new hoses, install new upgraded components, add the correct amount of oil, and then then pressure-test, evacuate, and recharge, you are ensuring that the system is clean, moisture-free, and tight. This further reduces the odds of a problem being due to something uncommon.

Many a/c books and websites show a spread of ten or twenty little thumbnail illustrations of the high and low pressure gauges, and attempt to encapsulate individual diagnoses for each so you can match your pressures to the thumbnails and look up the most likely cause as if you were looking at mugshots to find the perp responsible for your a/c crime. I've never found much value in these, and I doubt that they're terribly helpful to most novices. Low and high side pressures vary too much car-to-car and by temperature and humidity. If you start with a clean tight system, you're unlikely to encounter many of the problems described in those little thumbnails. And if some oddball problem arises, if you understand the basics, you're more likely to be able to correctly diagnose it by thinking it through than by thumbing

through a bunch of postage stamp-sized drawings of manifold gauges as if they were dating profiles.

Figure 249: I hate having to pull newly-installed evaporator assemblies back out, but you have to go where the problem leads you.

Below, I include a table of potential problems and their likely low and high-side pressures. But I draw the line at little pictures :^)

Table or no, to me, fundamentally there are four types of a/c problems.

1. The system is incomplete (e.g., compressor and/ or hoses missing). If that's the case, it's not a troubleshooting issue. Consult the Rejuvenation chapter and get it to the point where it's a complete, clean, tight system.

2. The system does not have refrigerant in it. If that's the case, either the system was just assembled and hasn't had refrigerant added, or refrigerant was in it and it leaked out. If it's the former, consult the Evacuation and Charging chapters. If it's the latter, consult the Pressure Testing chapter.

3. The system has refrigerant in it but is not operational. We have a few suggestions for that below.

4. The system has refrigerant in it and is operational, but does not get cold, or cold enough. That is the bulk of this chapter.

Does the system have refrigerant in it?

Consult the "Test if the system has refrigerant in it" section of the Rejuvenation chapter. The static pressure in psi should be approximately equal to the ambient temperature in °F. So if it's 80° outside, the static pressure should be about 80 psi. If the static pressure is zero, all of the refrigerant has leaked out, which means that you need to find and fix the leak. Pressure-test the system to find the leak as per the sections in that same chapter.

Is the system operational?

When you turn on the a/c, three things must happen in order for the system to be operational.

1. You should hear the compressor click as the clutch engages, and hear the engine bog down slightly under the load (below).

2. The blower fan inside the evaporator housing should turn on.

3. The auxiliary fan on the condenser should turn on.

If none of these three things happen, the problem could be as simple as a blown fuse or fuses, or a connector or connectors have been dislodged. I have seen these three failures caused by three different things on the same car. It is also possible that the actual blower fan motors themselves have gone bad. I test the fan motors by wiring them directly to the battery and making sure they spin. It also is possible for the fan and temperature control switches to fail. Consult the Electrical chapter and, if required, a wiring diagram for your car. Remedy as necessary.

Is the compressor engaging and functioning?

If, when you turn the a/c on, the compressor is not engaging (if the magnetic clutch isn't actuating and causing the hub in the front of the compressor to rotate, and yes I am assuming that there is a belt properly connecting the compressor to the engine), it could be a wiring problem or failed clutch. You can test the compressor by temporarily wiring it directly to the battery as per the section in the Rejuvenation chapter. When you do, there are three possible outcomes.

1. If hot-wiring the compressor engages it and causes the needles on the manifold gauges to swing (high side goes high, low side goes low), then the compressor is working, but if it doesn't engage when you turn on the a/c system normally, something in the standard wiring is preventing voltage from reaching it. You'll need to check the electrical path from the fuse box to the temperature switch to the compressor. It could simply be a blown fuse, or that the system has a bypass switch on the drier or the accumulator that has failed. Use a multimeter to test for voltage going into that switch. If voltage is there but there's no voltage on the output side of the switch, test the switch for continuity and try jumpering over the switch. Consult the Electrical chapter and, if necessary, a wiring diagram for your car. Remedy as necessary.

2. If nothing happens, either the engine isn't grounded so there's no ground path for the compressor (unlikely), or the compressor has a bad clutch.

3. If the compressor clicks and then there's a hellacious squeal, the clutch is working but the compressor is seized.

In both cases 2 and 3, the compressor will need to be replaced, but if it's seized, the entire system should be flushed to remove any contamination it may have thrown.

Clues from the sight glass

If your car has a drier with a sight glass, it can afford some level of diagnosis. The drier is on the liquid line between the condenser output and the evaporator input, so clear liquid refrigerant should be visible through the sight glass. As stated in the Charging chapter, on R12 systems, one indication of correct charging is when the sight glass is free of bubbles, indicating that the drier and the liquid line are both full of liquid, but this is not a reliable charging metric on R134a systems. What you can say, though, is that:

• Seeing a *lot* of bubbles in the sight glass may indicate that the system is undercharged.

• Seeing streaks in the sight glass may mean that you're seeing primarily oil circulating, which may indicate that the system is badly undercharged.

- Seeing dark cloudy liquid may indicate system contamination, such as the desiccant pack in the drier having ruptured.

Calculating superheat and subcooling

Back in the Theory chapter, in the expert-level 4th tier of understanding, I described "superheat," the amount of extra heat absorbed in the evaporator in a system with an expansion valve to ensure that the exiting refrigerant is gaseous so no liquid refrigerant will hit the compressor (liquid is incompressible, so liquid flowing into the compressor could damage it). In contrast, on a system with an accumulator instead of an expansion valve, there is no superheating, because, instead, liquid refrigerant spills into the accumulator, so the measured superheat will be zero or negative.

I also described "subcooling," the amount of extra heat removed by the condenser after the gaseous refrigerant has already been condensed into a liquid to ensure that there is a good supply of liquid refrigerant to the evaporator.

Then, in the chapter on the Manifold Gauge Set, I described the pressure-temperature chart that's typically folded into the back of the gauges, and the concentric pressure/temperature scales on the gauge's dials, but basically blew them both off, saying that pros may use them but DIY-ers rarely do.

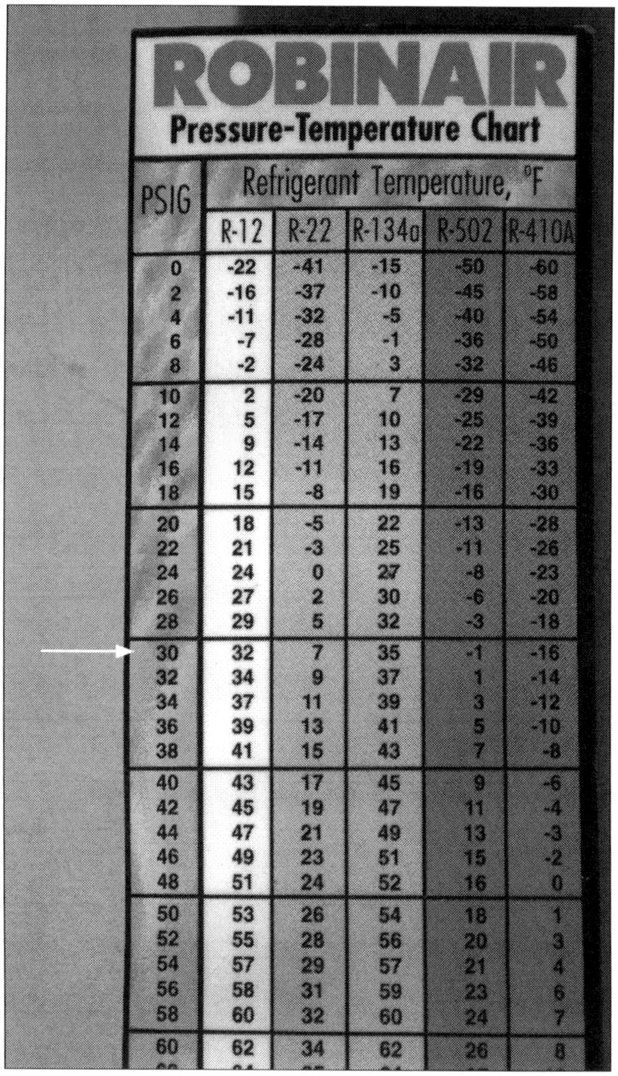

ROBINAIR
Pressure-Temperature Chart

PSIG	Refrigerant Temperature, °F				
	R-12	R-22	R-134a	R-502	R-410A
0	-22	-41	-15	-50	-60
2	-16	-37	-10	-45	-58
4	-11	-32	-5	-40	-54
6	-7	-28	-1	-36	-50
8	-2	-24	3	-32	-46
10	2	-20	7	-29	-42
12	5	-17	10	-25	-39
14	9	-14	13	-22	-36
16	12	-11	16	-19	-33
18	15	-8	19	-16	-30
20	18	-5	22	-13	-28
22	21	-3	25	-11	-26
24	24	0	27	-8	-23
26	27	2	30	-6	-20
28	29	5	32	-3	-18
30	32	7	35	-1	-16
32	34	9	37	1	-14
34	37	11	39	3	-12
36	39	13	41	5	-10
38	41	15	43	7	-8
40	43	17	45	9	-6
42	45	19	47	11	-4
44	47	21	49	13	-3
46	49	23	51	15	-2
48	51	24	52	16	0
50	53	26	54	18	1
52	55	28	56	20	3
54	57	29	57	21	4
56	58	31	59	23	6
58	60	32	60	24	7
60	62	34	62	26	8

Figure 250: Pressure-temperature chart. Note that, for R134a, 30psi maps to 35 °F.

Here's where those things can come together. Those pressure-temperature relationships are used in a method for calculating the superheat and subcooling.

You calculate the superheat as follows:

1. Connect the gauges, run the a/c on high, look at the low-side pressure, and either read on the concentric dial on the gauge what the corresponding temperature should be for your refrigerant, or look it up in the table that comes with the gauge. For example, if you're running R134a, and the low-side pressure is 30 psi, that corresponds to a vapor saturation temperature of 35°F—the temperature at which the liquid is evaporating into a gas.

2. Then directly measure the temperature at the pipe coming out of the evaporator using an infrared thermometer or a multimeter that has a temperature probe attachment. Let's say that that temperature is 55 °F.

3. To get the superheat, subtract the two readings. For this example, the calculation of the amount of superheat is 55° − 35° = 20 °F.

If the superheat is low, the evaporator may be flooded with too much refrigerant, indicating overcharge. If the superheat is very high, the evaporator may be starved for refrigerant, indicating undercharge or a too-restrictive expansion valve.

You calculate the subcooling analogously; you just do it on the high side:

1. Look at the high-side pressure on the gauge, and either read on the gauge what the corresponding temperature is, or look it up in the table that comes with the gauge. For example, if you're running R134a, and the high-side pressure is 200 psi, that corresponds to a saturation temperature of 131 °F—the temperature at which the vapor is condensing back into a liquid.

2. Then directly measure the temperature at the line coming out of the bottom of the condenser using an infrared thermometer or a multimeter with a temperature probe attachment. Let's say that that temperature is 120 °F.

3. To get the subcooling, subtract the two readings.

For this example, the calculation of the amount of subcooling is 131° − 120° = 11 °F.

The superheat and subcooling values can be used as follows:

- If the superheat and subcooling values are both too low, it could mean that the expansion valve is stuck open (or, if it's an orifice tube system, it has an orifice tube that's too big).

- If the superheat and subcooling values are both too high, there could be a restriction in the expansion valve or orifice tube, or elsewhere in the system.

- If the superheat value is low and the subcooling value is high (or, as it's sometimes phrased, if the subcooling is higher than the superheat), it is an indication that the system may be overcharged.

- Conversely, if the superheat value is high and the subcooling value is low (or, as it's sometimes phrased, if the subcooling is lower than the superheat), it is an indication that the system may be undercharged.

- One rule of thumb is that, if the subcooling and superheat are within about two degrees of each other, the system is properly charged. However, I believe that there's too much variance between systems to use this as a reliable charging method, which is why it's here and not in the charging section. In our example, the subcooling is 11° and the superheat is 22°, so that would imply that we're undercharged and should add more refrigerant.

Part of the problem is that there are very few specifications on what superheat and subcooling values should be. An MVAC system is not an HVAC system. Unlike in a residential system, where subcooling and superheat values are used extensively, in a car, the compressor speed and the heat load on the evaporator vary substantially, causing the superheat and subcooling values to change. That having been said, for a newly-installed big parallel-flow condenser and fan, I'd certainly expect to see 20° of subcooling. And, for both subcooling and superheating, small single digit values (less than five) would certainly constitute "low" to me.

Diagnostic table

Below is the obligatory table of potential problems and their likely low and high-side pressures and vent temperatures. It assumes that the compressor is engaging and the evaporator blower fan and the condenser fan are both working correctly. For this table, assume that a normal low-side reading is about 30 psi, and a normal high-side reading is about 250 psi, but these can vary substantially with model, temperature, and humidity. I'll step through the potential problems in the sections following the table.

A/C Diagnostic Table of Potential Problems			
Low Side	**High Side**	**Vent Temp**	**Potential Problem**
Low	Low	Warm	Low refrigerant
Very low	High	Warm	Expansion valve clogged or stuck closed, or orifice tube clogged, or moisture in the system freezing expansion valve or orifice tube shut
High	Slightly high	Warm	Expansion valve stuck open
Low	High	Warm	High side restriction
Normal	Normal	Warm	Moisture in the system
High	Low	Warm	Compressor or accumulator control valve failed
High	High	Some cool	Overcharge
Slightly high	High	Some cool	Air in the system

Clogged expansion valve or orifice tube

As per the chapter on the Expansion Valve, it is possible for the expansion valve to be stuck open, stuck closed, or stuck somewhere in between, but the most common failure mode is for it to be clogged with debris, which is, effectively, stuck closed. If the system was rejuvenated and the evaporator assembly was removed, the expansion valve should have been replaced prophylactically. At a minimum, the expansion valve should've been blown through while the hoses were disconnected to verify it was neither clogged nor closed. As per the table, symptoms of a clogged expansion valve or orifice tube are very low low-side pressure (for example, 10 psi, possibly even going into vacuum as the compressor cycles on), and high high-side pressure (for example, 350 when you're expecting 250). Clogging may also cause the low-side pressure to be sluggish, taking a long time to equalize with the high-side pressure when the system cycles or is shut off.

Expansion valve stuck open

If the expansion valve is stuck open, you should see a bleed-through of pressure from the high side back to the low side, resulting in an elevated low-side pressure (for example, 125 low, 250 high).

Moisture in the system

Moisture in the system should be avoided at all costs, as it reacts with R134a refrigerant to create hydrofluoric acid, which degrades the system from the inside out. It also can cause the oil to turn to sludge, reducing compressor lubrication.

If the system was rejuvenated, the drier replaced with a new one, and the system properly pressure-tested and evacuated, there shouldn't be any moisture in it, but it is possible for moisture to be drawn in if the gauge hoses aren't bled during charging. If moisture is there, it can freeze at the expansion valve or orifice tube. Thus the symptom of moisture in the system can be the same as a blocked expansion valve or orifice tube (low low-side pressure, very high high-side pressure), except that the pressures should start off okay, then get worse as the freezing blocks the valve, and then recover once the system is shut off for a while.

If moisture persists in the system, the formation of acids can and will degrade the performance of the compressor, in which case the symptoms can begin to look like a bad compressor. Moisture in large quantities also can "slug" the compressor, ruining it by causing it to try and compress a liquid that it can't compress.

System is freezing (icing) up

The term "freezing up" or "icing up" is confusingly used for two different situations. The first is moisture inside the system (in the refrigerant), which is described above. The second is when cold fog starts to blow out of the evaporator. This means that the evaporator temperature is below freezing, and humidity that naturally condenses on the outside of the evaporator and should be dripping down and running out the drain hole is freezing instead. The temperature switch should be causing the compressor to cycle off before the evaporator gets that cold. The problem could be that the switch is bad, or that the little bulb at the end of the capillary tube connected to the switch isn't placed where it's supposed to be in the evaporator core and isn't correctly relaying the freezing temperature to the switch. It also is possible that the evaporator isn't draining correctly, allowing moisture to pool and freeze.

Of course, there's also the possibility that you own a '63 Rambler and have the "Desert Only" setting on somewhere other than the desert. Thank you! You've been a great audience!

Air in the system

Air is a "non-condensable" gas. It occupies space in the condenser that would normally be used to condense refrigerant. In theory, if the system was properly pressure-tested and evacuated, there shouldn't be any air in it, but air can get in if someone hooks a set of gauges to a system that already has a charge, and the lines on the gauge set haven't been bled. Air in the system can cause the high-side pressure to be higher than expected.

High-side restriction

If there is a restriction somewhere in the high side (between the compressor discharge and the evaporator inlet), the result is unusually high high-side pressure (say, 350 psi when you're expecting 250). The location of the restriction should be discernable because the temperature will drop on the far side of the restriction. Sometimes this will be visible due to the line sweating or frost forming after the restriction. An infrared thermometer can also be used to find the location. If a restriction is found in a parallel flow condenser, the condenser should be replaced, as the myriad of little tubes can't reliably be flushed out.

System is overcharged

A system that is overcharged has more refrigerant in it than can efficiently boil, evaporate, and expand in the evaporator. As such, it won't cool well, has both low-side and high-side pressures that are too high, and the compressor may sound unusually noisy. If the system is so overcharged that liquid refrigerant reaches the compressor, the compressor can be permanently damaged, as liquid is not compressible.

The best way to avoid overcharging is to start with an empty system, follow the guidelines in the Charging chapter on paying attention to multiple factors (refrigerant weight, volume, rules of thumb, vent temperature, the evaporator output line sweating, the temperature-pressure chart), and stop as soon as the system appears to be working nominally. If you suspect the system is overcharged, keep in mind that it is illegal to vent refrigerant. R12 is an ozone-depleting agent. R134a is not, but it's a potent greenhouse gas, and is still illegal to vent. You'll need to take it in to a shop to have the refrigerant recovered. As part of that, they can weigh what they've recovered and you can judge how far off you were from the recommended weight, if you know it.

System is undercharged

If the system is simply a little low on refrigerant, both the low-side and the high-side gauges will be reading low. In addition, if the system is a Clutch Cycling Orifice Tube (CCOT) system, it may short-cycle (turn the compressor on and off every few seconds) if it's low on refrigerant, but expansion valve systems typically don't exhibit this behavior (see the chapter on Compressor Cycling). If the symptoms point to the system being undercharged, you could take it to a service station, pay them to recover the refrigerant, take it home, pressure-test it, find the leak, fix it, evacuate it, and recharge it with the correct amount of refrigerant, or you could try topping it up as discussed in the "Charging" chapter.

Sheesh. I've made it all sound pretty easy. But most of the time, it actually is.

Oh my god. I've just described a situation where it "just needs a recharge!"

End notes

Rob Siegel has been writing the monthly column *The Hack Mechanic*™ for BMW CCA *Roundel* magazine for over 30 years. He is the author of the books *Memoirs of a Hack Mechanic, The Hack Mechanic*™ *Guide to European Automotive Electrical Systems*, and *Mechanical Ignition Handbook: The Hack Mechanic*™ *Guide to Vintage Ignition Systems*, all from Bentley Publishers, and *Ran When Parked: How I Resurrected a Decade-Dead 1972 BMW 2002tii a Thousand Miles Back Home, and How You Can, Too,* from Hack Mechanic Press.

Rob lives in West Newton, Massachusetts with his saint-like wife Maire Anne Diamond, three black cats, one black dog, a roomful of his wife's insects (don't ask; okay, ask, then go to www.bugworks.net), and as many cars and guitars as he can get away with. Given his druthers, he'd rather be a full-time singer/songwriter, but as his singer/songwriter friend Sam Bayer says, "I ain't in it for the money because there ain't no money in it."

Other books by Rob Siegel

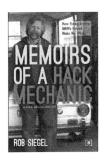

Memoirs of a Hack Mechanic: How Fixing Broken BMWs Helped Make Me Whole (a memoir with actual useful stuff)

Bentley Publishers, 2013
ISBN 978-0837617206

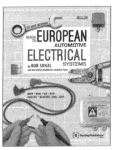

The Hack Mechanic™ Guide to European Automotive Electrical Systems

Bentley Publishers, 2016
ISBN 978-0837617510

Mechanical Ignition Handbook: The Hack Mechanic™ Guide to Vintage Ignition Systems

Bentley Publishers, 2017
ISBN 978-0837617671

Ran When Parked: How I Resurrected a Decade-Dead 1972 BMW 2002tii and Road-Tripped it a Thousand Miles Back Home, and How You Can, Too

Hack Mechanic Press, 2017
ISBN 978-0998950709

Made in the USA
San Bernardino, CA
08 June 2018